# Instructor's Manual

TO ACCOMPANY

# Physics

BY PAUL A. TIPLER





Granvil C. Kyker, Jr.
ROSE-HULMAN INSTITUTE OF TECHNOLOGY
D. Rae Carpenter, Jr.
VIRGINIA MILITARY INSTITUTE
Richard B. Minnix
VIRGINIA MILITARY INSTITUTE
William R. Riley
OHIO STATE UNIVERSITY
Stanley Williams
IOWA STATE UNIVERSITY



WORTH PUBLISHERS, INC.

Instructor's Manual
to accompany
Physics by Paul A. Tipler


Printed in the United States of America.



Worth Publishers, Inc.
444 Park Avenue South
New York, New York 10016

## PREFACE

This is a reference manual for instructors teaching elementary physics to science and engineering students, using Paul A. Tipler's Physics. In it, we have put together resources of several different kinds which may be useful to you in organizing and enriching your course.

The essential resource, obviously, is the textbook itself, and a few words about using Tipler's text may be in order. It is designed for the standard two-semester survey course, with a first course in calculus as a prerequisite (or corequisite). There is more physics in it, however, than can be treated adequately in two semesters (if you are so fortunate as to have the time, it should be adequate for a three-semester sequence) and some selection and omission will be necessary. How you choose material depends on your own students' abilities and backgrounds, on the curriculum into which the course fits, and on your own preferences. It is important, I think, to make some selection and not to try to cover everything; my own experience suggests that the equivalent of approximately a chapter of the text per week is right for students.

Some guideposts for making your selection: a number of sections of the text are marked as "optional"; also, the preface to Tipler's book lists many sections and whole chapters which can be skimmed or skipped without loss of continuity; and, as an illustration, there is a quite specific description of one possible two-semester course treatment in the "Sample Examinations" section of this manual. Some chapters which seem to me likely to be left out of many two-semester courses are Chapters 15, 24, 27, 28, 31, 40, 41, and 42.

If you are organized on a quarter, rather than a semester, basis, about the same amount of cutting will be necessary for a course that lasts three quarters. Notice that Tipler's text lends itself quite naturally to a course in which one quarter is spent on mechanics, one on thermodynamics and wave motion, and a third on electricity and magnetism.

The first section of this manual contains "teaching objectives" for each chapter of the text. These simply list, in the form of five or six questions for each chapter, the central physical ideas that one wants to get across to students. In the next section, there is an assortment of ideas for lecture and discussion topics which apply, illustrate, or amplify the physical concepts being studied, but which are not themselves treated in the text: room acoustics, steam engines, musical instruments, stars, and what not. My feeling is that a little lecture time spent on such things adds considerable interest to the course, and I quite intentionally let myself get sidetracked every now and then.

Lecture demonstration experiments and visual materials such as films are important ways to give an extra dimension to the course. The third and fourth parts of this manual contain, respectively, descriptions of demonstrations and available films suited for use with each chapter of Tipler. (Another very useful visual tool is the overhead projector; I use this a good deal for diagrams and illustrations that I can't manage on a blackboard. You can make your own transparencies on many standard copying machines.)

Answers to the even-numbered exercises and problems, with solutions to some of the problems, are given in the fifth section; answers to the odd-numbered ones are in the text. As an illustration of one of the many ways in which one might organize and write examinations for a two-semester course using Tipler, a set of six sample tests is given in the next section. Finally, in the last part, there is a collection of suggested reading materials, both for your own use and for that of your students, as supplementary reading.

Granvil C. Kyker, Jr.
Terre Haute, Indiana

CONTENTS

TEACHING OBJECTIVES

Granvil C. Kyker, Jr.

Within the scope of each chapter of Tipler's Physics, what are the fundamental ideas and techniques the student should master?

## Chapter 1. Introduction

In general, what kinds of things about nature do we study in physics, and how do we go about it?

Laws of physics are often best expressed as a mathematical relationship between physical quantities. Why? What do we mean by the dimensions of a quantity? What do the units of a physical quantity express, and how do we cope with them in mathematical calculations?

What basic mathematical equipment do we require to approach the study of physics?

## Chapter 2. Motion in One Dimension

What quantities are useful in describing analytically a motion in one dimension? How is velocity defined? Acceleration? What is the distinction between average and instantaneous velocity or acceleration?

The velocity of a particle is the time derivative of its position. What does it mean to take a derivative? What does this process mean graphically? What is the inverse process?

What description can we infer for the special case of motion with a uniform acceleration? In what kinds of real situations does this occur?

## Chapter 3. Motion in Two and Three Dimensions

How do we extend our formal description of motion to a motion in more than one dimension? What kind of mathematical entities do we introduce in order to simplify this extension? What rules of arithmetic do these vector quantities obey?

What does it mean to analyze a motion in terms of its components? How is the motion of a projectile described?

How do we analyze the case of circular motion? In a circular motion at uniform speed, what is the acceleration: If the speed is not uniform, what are its components?

## Chapter 4. Newton's Laws

What are Newton's laws of motion? In the context of them, how are mass and force defined?

If a number of different forces act on a given body, how do Newton's laws apply to it - that is, what is the net effect of the combination of different forces?

What is momentum? In terms of momentum, what does Newton's third law say? How is the third law affected by the concept of action at a distance?

How do Newton's laws apply in different frames of reference?

## Chapter 5. Applications of Newton's Laws

Newton's laws relate the net resultant force on a body to its motion. In specific simple situations, what are the convenient techniques for applying them?

What is the acceleration of, and net force on, an object moving in a circle at a uniform speed?

What is pressure in a fluid? A body submerged in a fluid experiences a "buoyant" force. How does this arise? What kind of drag force acts on a body moving in a fluid, and what kind of motion results?

## Chapter 6. Forces in Nature

There are four basic forces known to act in nature. What are they? How do they behave? On what do they act?

Except for gravity, the forces that act between macroscopic objects are electromagnetic in origin. How are contact forces understood as electromagnetic? How about elastic forces in springs, strings, and such? What is the nature of interatomic and intermolecular forces?

How do frictional forces come about? How do they act?

What are pseudoforces, and how do they arise in noninertial frames of reference?

## Chapter 7. Work and Energy

In many situations the force on a particle is known as a function of its position. How can such problems be treated?

How do we define work? Kinetic energy? What is the work-energy theorem, and in what circumstances does it apply? Does it constitute a complete solution to the problem of the motion of a particle?

What is potential energy, and why is it introduced? What is power?

## Chapter 8. Potential Energy and Conservative Forces

What is a conservative force? What mathematical criteria can be developed to determine whether or not a given force, in one dimension, is conservative? In three dimensions?

Under what circumstances can a potential energy be defined, corresponding to a particular force? How is it defined? What is the potential energy of a uniform force? Of a central force?

How do we define the potential energy of a <u>system</u> of particles?

## Chapter 9. Conservation of Energy

Under what circumstances can the total mechanical energy of a particle be defined so that it is a conserved quantity? How is it so defined? This is the first example of a <u>conservation law</u> that has been encountered. What is special about this kind of theorem?

What can and cannot be determined about the motion of a particle directly from knowledge of its potential energy?

If nonconservative forces act on a particle, what form does the work-energy theorem take?

Conservation of energy applied to fluid flow gives us Bernoulli's equation. What does this say? When is it valid?

## Chapter 10. Many-Particle Systems

How is the center of mass of an arbitrary system of particles defined? How is it located? What about for a continuous body? What determines the motion of the center of mass of a system?

Under what circumstances is the total <u>momentum</u> of a system of particles conserved?

What are the special characteristics of the motion of a system of particles, in a frame of reference in which the center of mass is at rest? What is the total kinetic energy of the system in this frame?

## Chapter 11. Collisions and Reactions

What is a "collision"? A "reaction"? What typically are the characteristics of collision forces? In situations where many successive collisions occur, what average force is exerted?

What tools do we have available to treat collision problems? What is the impulse approximation? Collision problems are most simply analyzed in the center-of-mass frame. Why? In this frame, what happens in an elastic collision? An inelastic collision? How are the results transformed to a more natural frame?

What is a reaction threshold, and why does it arise?

## Chapter 12. Rotation of a Rigid Body about a Fixed Axis

We define kinematic quantities in angular terms for the analysis of rotational motion. How are these defined? Can they be treated as vector quantities?

What is the kinetic energy of a rotating rigid body? What is its moment of inertia? How is this calculated? The quantity of dynamic importance in rotational motion is not the net force on it, but the torque. Why? How is the torque calculated?

Under what conditions is a rigid body in static equilibrium?

## Chapter 13. Rotation in Space and Angular Momentum

In general, how are the torque on, and angular momentum of, a particle defined? What are the properties of the vector product?

For an arbitrary system of particles, how can the motion be related to the torques that act? Under what conditions is the <u>angular</u> momentum of a system conserved?

What analytical tools can we develop to treat the general motion of a rigid body? What sorts of motion occur in particular cases - a rolling body, a gyroscope?

What are the conditions for dynamic balance of a rotating body?

## Chapter 14. Oscillations

What is simple harmonic motion? What is the volocity of a particle undergoing simple harmonic motion? Its acceleration?

What is the dynamic condition under which motion is simple harmonic? In what sorts of real situations does it occur? What sort of potential energy gives rise to simple harmonic motion? On what does the total energy depend?

An arbitrary oscillation can be approximated as a simple harmonic motion. Under what circumstances?

What sorts of motion result from combinations of simple harmonic motions? What is the relation to circular motion at uniform speed?

## Chapter 15. Damped and Forced Oscillations

What physical situations give rise to damped oscillations? Under what assumptions can we analyze such situations? What sort of motion results? What do the results look like for very weak damping? Very strong?

If an oscillator is <u>driven</u> by a sinusoidally varying force, on what does its steady-state motion depend?

What is resonance, and how does the phenomenon arise?

## Chapter 16. Gravity

Newton's law of gravitation summarizes the properties of the gravitational force. What are its properties? On what observations did Newton base this generalization? What kinds of motion are possible for a particle moving under the gravitational force of another body?

How is the gravitational constant determined?

How is the gravitational field defined? The gravitational potential? To what purpose are these quantities introduced? How may the gravitational field be visualized?

How is the gravitational force due to a system of particles calculated?

## Chapter 17. Temperature

What does it mean to say that macroscopic systems are in thermal equilibrium? What property of systems in equilibrium makes it possible to define temperature?

How are various temperature scales defined, and what special properties does the ideal-gas scale possess?

What is the equation of state of an ideal gas? What insight does it yield into the microscopic nature of temperature?

How is the expansion of materials with increasing temperature described?

## Chapter 18. Heat, Work, and the First Law of Thermodynamics

What is heat? How is it quantified, and what is the relation of the temperature change of an object to the amount of heat transferred to or from it? What is specific heat? Latent heat?

What do we mean by internal energy? How is conservation of energy, as an idea, expanded to allow for situations in which the internal energy of a system changes? What is a state function, and why is the distinction an important one?

What work is done in an isothermal change of state of an ideal gas? An adiabatic change? How does the internal energy change?

What is the equipartition theorem, and how does it relate the macroscopic and microscopic properties of a system? Where does it fail, and why?

## Chapter 19. The Availability of Energy

What various statements of the second law of thermodynamics are there, and what kind of statement does the law make about natural processes? What does it mean to call a process thermodynamically irreversible?

What properties must a heat engine have in order to be a reversible engine? How does a reversible engine allow an "absolute" definition of temperature? How is entropy defined, and how does its definition relate to the properties of a reversible heat engine?

What is the significance of the entropy change of the universe? How does it relate to the availablility of energy for macroscopic work? What is our microscopic concept of the nature of entropy?

## Chapter 20. Wave Pulses

What do we mean by a wave pulse? In what sorts of real systems do they occur? How do we construct a mathematical description of a disturbance propagating as a wave?

How do more than one wave pulse, in the same medium, combine? What sorts of phenomena result from the superposition of waves?

What determines the velocity at which waves propagate? How does it depend on the medium in which they propagate? What kinds of phenomena occur at a boundary between different media?

## Chapter 21. Harmonic Waves in One Dimension

What is the particular physical importance of a sinusoidal wave function? How are sinusoidal waves related to simple harmonic motion? How are the frequency and wavelength of harmonic waves defined, and how related?

What are constructive and destructive interference, and how do they come about? What do we mean by the polarization of a wave? What determines the intensity of a harmonic wave, and how does this relate to energy transport?

What is the form of a wave equation? How is its form related to the superposition property?

## Chapter 22. Standing Waves

What are standing waves? How do they come about in simple one-dimensional systems? In what kinds of simple systems do they occur?

On a given system, why can standing waves occur at only certain characteristic frequencies? What properties determine these frequencies? How is this question related to the reflection of waves at a boundary? What do we mean by a "harmonic series" of frequencies?

What is the form of a wave function describing standing waves?

## Chapter 23. The Superposition of Waves of Different Frequency

What wave form results from the superposition of waves of nearly equal frequency? In what kinds of system does this occur?

How are complex wave forms represented in terms of superpositions of harmonic waves? How can this analysis be extended to finite wave packets? What is the relation, and what is its significance, between the spatial size of a wave packet and the range of its component frequencies?

What is the distinction between group velocity and phase velocity of a complex wave? On what property of the medium does this depend?

How can we treat complex vibrations of finite systems as superpositions of standing waves of different frequencies?

## Chapter 24. Spherical and Circular Waves

What kinds of wave functions describe waves propagating outward from a source in two or three dimensions? What is meant by "wavefronts?" By "rays?"

How is the frequency of a wave affected if the source moves relative to the medium in which waves propagate? If the observer moves? What if the source moves faster than the wave speed in the medium?

What is the interference? What determines the interference pattern of two wave sources of the same frequency? How is this affected if several sources interfere? What is meant by "coherence" of wave sources?

## Chapter 25. Wave Propagation

What is diffraction? How is the diffraction of waves analyzed using Huygens' principle? We say that reflection and refraction form "virtual images." What does this mean? Under what conditions does total internal reflection occur?

What are the conditions for reflection from a regular array of scatterers? How does this relate to the reflection of light from a solid?

## Chapter 26. Light

What is the nature of light? From what kinds of phenomena do we infer that light is a wave? What different manifestations of electromagnetic waves are there? How can the speed of light waves be measured?

What laws govern the reflection and refraction of light at a boundary between transparent media? Upon what properties of light does this depend? Material media are dispersive. What are the practical consequences?

In what circumstances do interference and diffraction of light occur? What is the condition for constructive interference in Young's experiment? In reflection from parallel surfaces? For a diffraction grating?

What phenomena result from the polarization of light waves?

## Chapter 27. Geometric Optics

How are images formed by reflection and refraction of light? What do we mean by focal length? On what does the focal length of a curved mirror depend? Of a lens?

What analytic methods can we use to locate the image formed by a given system? What geometric methods? What aberrations occur in spherical mirrors and lenses, and why?

What is the optical structure of the eye? Of simple optical instruments?

## Chapter 28. Special Relativity

What inconsistencies in classical ideas led to the theory of relativity? How do we argue from statements about light propagation to fundamental space and time measurements, and what kind of phenomena follow?

What general transformation can we deduce between the measurements made by inertial observers in relative motion?

How - and why - is the Doppler effect different for light than for other kinds of waves?

What definitions of momentum and energy are consistent with the theory of relativity? How are these related to their original definitions? From what do we infer the interchangeability of mass and energy?

## Chapter 29. The Electric Field

What is electric charge? What are the properties of the forces that electric charges exert on one another?

How is the electric field defined? To what purpose is it introduced? What is the force on a charge in an electric field? We can visualize the field by a lines-of-force map. What are the properties of such a map? How is the flux of the electric field calculated?

What force acts on an electric dipole in an electric field?

## Chapter 30. Calculation of the Electric Field

How is the electric field due to an arbitrary charge distribution calculated? In what circumstances is direct use of Coulomb's law the appropriate method? When is Gauss's law more convenient?

What is the electric field set up by each of the simple symmetric charge distributions?

## Chapter 31. Conductors in Electrostatic Equilibrium

What is the distinction between conductors and insulators? The electric field within a conductor in static equilibrium must be zero. Why? How does this come about?

If there is excess charge on a conductor, where does it reside? Why? What is the electric field at the surface of a conductor?

## Chapter 32. Electric Potential

How is the electrostatic potential defined? How is it calculated? What is the potential due to a point charge?

What is the mathematical relationship between the electric field and the potential? Given either, how can the other be calculated? What is the potential in some of the important simple cases? What is an equipotential surface?

How is excess charge shared between conductors in contact?

## Chapter 33. Capacitance, Electrostatic Energy, and Dielectrics

What is the character of the relationship between the amount of charge on an isolated conductor and its electric potential? How is capacitance defined? What is a capacitor?

How is the capacitance of a given system calculated? For the simple geometries, what are the results? What is the effective capacitance of capacitors in series and parallel combination?

What work must be done to charge a capacitor, and what energy do we consequently associate with the electric field?

What is the effect of a dielectric material between the elements of a capacitor? How does this happen? On what properties of the material does it depend?

## Chapter 34. Electric Current

What is electric current? What is the physical mechanism of current flow in a conductor? What is electrical resistance, and to what properties of the conducting material is it related? How does it depend on temperature?

At what rate is energy dissipated by a current flowing in an ohmic material? Where does it go?

What is the physical basis for the distinction between conductors, insulators, and semiconductors? On what kinds of properties does the behavior of a semiconductor depend?

## Chapter 35. Direct-Current Circuits

What are Kirchhoff's rules? What are the techniques for using them to analyze DC circuits? From what fundamental physical laws do they derive? What is the effective resistance of resistors in series combination? In parallel?

What is the characteristic behavior of circuits containing both resistance and capacitance? What is the time constant?

What sorts of devices, and what kinds of circuits employing them, do we use to measure electrical quantities?

## Chapter 36. The Magnetic Field

How do the forces that magnetic poles exert on each other act? What are the properties of the magnetic force on a current? How do we construct a definition of the magnetic field from these phenomena? What is the relationship of the field to the force on a moving charge? On a current?

The fundamentally important magnetic entity is not the magnetic pole but the dipole. Why? What is the effect of a magnetic field on a dipole? How is a magnetic dipole akin to a current loop?

What kind of motion is characteristic of a charged particle moving in a magnetic field? What sorts of devices are based on this motion?

What causes the Hall effect, and what applications has it?

Chapter 37. Sources of the Magnetic Field

What is the source of the magnetic field? What tools do we have for calculating the magnetic field of a given current configuration? When is Ampère's law a more convenient approach than the Biot-Savart law? Under what conditions do they give different results? Why?

What magnetic field is produced by a straight wire? By a current loop? What is the field inside a solenoid?

What force is exerted by one current on another? What difficulties does this raise with Newton's third law?

How is the idea of current as the source of the magnetic field related to the existence of magnetic materials? What is the magnetization? The pole strength of a magnet?

What are the properties of a lines-of-force map of the magnetic field?

Chapter 38. Faraday's Law

How do we calculate the electromotive force induced in a circuit by a changing magnetic flux? In what circumstances can this be related directly to the magnetic force on charge carriers in the circuit? What is Lenz's law?

What sorts of practical devices are based on Faraday's law?

What does the inductance of a circuit measure? How is it calculated? What are the results for important simple geometries?

How do we calculate the energy associated with the magnetic field in an inductor? What is the characteristic behavior of circuits containing both resistance and inductance? Both inductance and capacitance?

Chapter 39. Magnetism in Matter

What sorts of microscopic effects are produced in matter by magnetic fields? What is the distinction between paramagnetic and diamagnetic materials? What is ferromagnetism, and what causes it?

What is the distinction between the magnetic induction and the magnetic field intensity? To what purpose is the distinction made? To what properties of the material is it related?

What is hysteresis, and what is its significance?

Chapter 40. Alternating-Current Circuits

What kind of source generates an electromotive force varying sinusoidally with time? What current flows in a resistor in response to a sinusoidal EMF? In a capacitor? In an inductor? What is the phase relationship between voltage and current in each case?

How do we determine the effective impedance of a circuit containing resistance, capacitance, and inductance? How does it depend on the frequency? What are the conditions for resonance? On what does the power dissipated in such a circuit depend?

What is a transformer, and how does it work?

Chapter 41. Maxwell's Equations and Electromagnetic Waves

What empirical laws about the behavior of electric and magnetic fields are summarized in Maxwell's equations? What form do they take in free space? How do we deduce a wave equation from them?

What is the speed of electromagnetic waves? What is the relation of the electric and magnetic field vectors? How do we calculate the energy flux?

## Chapter 42. Quantization

What observed phenomena led to the introduction of the idea of quantization of light energy? What are the energy and momentum of a photon?

What assumptions are made in the Bohr model of the hydrogen atom, and how do they depart from classical ideas? What observed properties of hydrogen did the Bohr treatment explain?

How did the de Broglie concept of electrons as waves furnish a rationalization of the Bohr treatment? What is the uncertainty principle? In what way is it necessitated by de Broglie wave-particle duality?

## SIDELINES AND APPLICATIONS

Granvil C. Kyker, Jr.

In this section, there is gathered an assortment of topics within physics, applications to other fields, and related subjects, which may be useful to you as lecture illustrations, subjects for student projects, or whatever. Most of these are not treated, or are mentioned only in passing, in Tipler's text; but all are, I believe, appropriate for discussion and illustration during an introductory physics course.

Of course, this is an open-ended category: quite literally, everything is an application of physics. Obviously, I haven't made any attempt to be exhaustive. This is just a list of things that it has occurred to me to use (or to think, later, that I ought to have used) in my own experience of teaching undergraduate physics. Probably the things I've listed will, themselves, suggest some others to you. Or, if you want to look further for ideas, a number of general references are cited in the "Suggestions for Further Reading" elsewhere in this Guide, as are, in each of the major sections, several more specific articles and books under the heading "Sidelines and Applications".

This list is divided into seven subject headings, corresponding to the order of subjects in Tipler. Within each section there is no strict ordering, although I've made an effort to group related ideas together. A number of suggestions could reasonably be used under more than one subject heading - for instance, it would make sense to talk about "winds" under either mechanics or thermodynamics - and these are cross-referenced.

Many teachers enjoy pitching a physics course, as far as it fits, toward a particular direction or theme. For easier reference, in case your tendency is in this direction, I've coded items that relate especially to astronomy or astrophysics (AA), energy and environmental topics (EE), geology and the earth sciences (GE), or medicine and biology (MB). Introductory books in each of these areas will no doubt suggest other illustrative ideas to you; an especially useful reference on medical-biological applications is Benedek and Villars (see section A.4 in the reading list).

My comments, under specific entries, aren't meant to be any kind of thorough treatment of the topic, but just a notion of where it fits and what it relates to. I haven't included references except in a few cases where it seemed necessary; references to items included in the reading list elsewhere in this guide are just noted, as, for example, "The Feynman Lectures (A.1), vol. 3." In this case, the full citation would be in section A.1 of the "Suggestions for Further Reading."

### A. Physics in General

Chapter 1 of Tipler is a general introduction, but these are just things that didn't seem to fit under any one subject heading.

Instruments. Specific apparatus is mentioned under the appropriate section, but there are a number of things of interest to be said about scientific instruments in general. The most basic instruments simply add precision to our sense observations - using a ruler to measure length, for instance. Most modern instruments, however, extend our senses to quantities to which they don't directly respond: a magnetic field, an electric charge, the surface temperature of a distant star, are tied to the position of a pointer against a dial. Give some illustrations of how this conversion is accomplished.

Every instrument has intrinsic limitations (the input noise of an amplifier, the diffraction limit of an optical system, the spacing of divisions on a ruler); a large part of instrument design consists of making the limitations and precision of the instrument appropriate to the job at hand. Many types of instruments try to get around noise by comparing two measurements, identical in everything except the effect under examination. Examples are the difference amplifier, and the bolometer. Any measurement affects the system under observation - the ultimate limitation is the Heisenberg principle - but good instrument design must also aim at minimizing this interaction.

Transducers. Almost every instrument begins with a transducer of some sort: a galvanometer's moving coil, a phonograph needle, a thermistor, a photoelectric cell. The transducer is the element that transforms the "signal" from one physical form to another, more easily manipulated. In most cases the transformation should be linear. Are there other general characteristics a transducer needs to have? Most transducers convert signals of some sort into electrical outputs, because electrical signals can be amplified, analyzed, and manipulated almost without limit.

Energy Resources (EE). One way or another, almost all the environmental issues now receiving so much attention are rooted in the question of global energy resources. All human activity requires energy expenditure, all energy expenditure "pollutes" (even if only thermally) and, because of the second law of thermodynamics, energy is the one resource that is not even potentially recyclable. The energy we use is either solar or nuclear. Right now we are based on solar energy, but we're spending capital: using solar energy, and indirect use by means of winds, the water cycle, the tides, etc. would constitute living on interest - using a renewing resource as it comes in. At some point it can be interesting to talk about all the different sorts of resources together: their potential size, their environmental consequences, the means and feasibility of exploiting them.

Specific topics are discussed in other entries below.

Dating Methods (GE) (AA). Today we probably think immediately of radioactive dating techniques. You don't have much opportunity to talk about radioactivity in this course, but the fixed time-pattern of decay, and the intrinsic lifetime, can be sold to students very easily. Besides, most of them have heard of carbon dating. Radioactive dating methods also apply to geochronology, of course, but good estimates of the age of the earth were made before radioactivity was ever heard of, by assuming observed geologic processes to have proceeded uniformly. Still other sorts of inference go into dating the solar system and the universe at large. In any case, at some point one wants to talk about the measurement of time; and this kind of thing puts a somewhat different perspective on the subject.

Communications. Various specific aspects are mentioned below, mostly in sections D and F, but there are a number of points about the communication process in general to be made: the properties of transmitter and receiver, noise, the relation between bandwidth (or its equivalent) and information content, the distinction between digital (e.g. Morse code) and analogue (e.g. voice) transmission, the specific requirements for telemetry of instrument readings, etc.

History of Physics. We don't teach physics chronologically, by tracing its history systematically, and it probably wouldn't make much sense to do so. But to let yourself get sidetracked occasionally into the way in which a key concept developed - energy, for instance - or onto the context and the personality of one of the Founding Fathers, provides, I think, a beneficial perspective for the student. If nothing else, it may alleviate his feeling of watching Moses bring down the tablets. Besides, a lot of the great physicists of the past were fascinating characters in their own right:

Faraday, Rumford, Fermi. Rather than suggesting specific instances I will refer you to part 3 of each major heading in the reading list that appears elsewhere in this Guide.

Science Fiction. I imagine the probability is at least 50% that I have lost you just by mentioning this one. Some of the standard science-fiction themes, however - time travel, faster-than-light travel, "terraforming" - make good case studies of what "possible" and "impossible" mean in modern science. Besides, the best of the science-fiction writers working today understand physics and manage to get a lot of it into their stories - in this regard, one thinks of Heinlein, Arthur Clarke, Asimov, and most especially Larry Niven. (If I had to pick one science-fiction story to recommend to physics students, it would be either Heinlein's "The Moon is a Harsh Mistress" or Niven's "Neutron Star"; I can't decide which.)

## B. Mechanics (Chaps. 2 to 16)

Measurements. The fundamental mechanical quantities - mass, length, time - we ordinarily measure by comparison, direct or indirect, with standards. The nature of the standards has changed drastically in the last generation; today they are atomic processes. The reasons for this have to do with the properties that a satisfactory standard should have. What are these properties? How do we go about connecting a ruler or a wristwatch to atomic standards? Measurements on very different scales - astronomical or microscopic - require substantially different approaches. The "derived" quantities (angle, area, volume, velocity, acceleration, flow rate of a fluid) can be measured by making mass, length, and time measurements and combining them. All of them, however, can be measured "directly" in various situations (the goniometer, the planimeter, fluid displacement for volume measurements, the ballistic pendulum, the accelerometer, flow meters).

See also comments under "Instruments" in part A.

Surveying (GE) (AA). Traditional ground surveying is based on triangulation - combining known distances and line-of-sight angle measurements to yield unknown distances, both vertical and horizontal. The fundamental instrumentation includes the fluid level, the transit for precise angle measurements, and length standards. In the last generation aerial surveying has become an important auxiliary approach.

Astronomical distance measurements are also based on triangulation; the parallax of a star, using the earth's orbital diameter as baseline, measures its distance. This method is directly accurate to a distance of perhaps 25 parsecs; systematics of the properties of stars within this range - for example, the color-brightness relationship - are then used to infer the distance to farther stars, and so on outwards.

Ballistocardiograph (MB). This medical research device is an accelerometer, essentially, applied to observation of the heart action. The subject is immobilized on a free table of some sort, and the recoil of the table with each surge of blood through the body (on the order of one ounce) is monitored; blood flow volume, and information on the heart action comparable to an EKG, can be inferred.

Lighter-than-air Flight (MB). There are a number of applications of Archimedes' principle in the manipulation of a system's altitude, in a fluid environment, by control of its density. Balloons (free and dirigible) are the obvious case, although you may want to postpone this until the section on heat if you want to get into hot-air balloons. Submarines take in water, increasing their mean density, to dive, and expel it to surface. Most fishes can do the same trick: they have isolated "swim bladders" full of gas in their bodies (from which land-animals' lungs are thought to have evolved), whose size can be manipulated to raise or sink them in the water.

Boats. Anything that floats is an application of Archimedes' principle; if you want to expand on this you can get into the design features of boats and ships. Stability of flotation is a key feature of hull design; in this regard, the position of the center of buoyancy (the center of gravity of the displaced water) is crucial. The other key consideration is streamlining the shape to minimize hull drag forces. Hull drag goes roughly as the second or higher power of the speed, so the power required to drive a given shape increases very sharply with speed. A sailboat makes a particularly interesting resolution-of-forces problem; a surprising proportion of students haven't any idea how a sailboat can make progress upwind. Note that a sail is more an aerodynamic (i.e., a vertical airfoil) than a reaction device.

Winds (GE) (EE). This is another balance-of-forces problem that is a touch out of the ordinary. The basic driving force, of course, is the pressure gradient in the atmosphere; since the pressure differences are of thermal origin, use of winds as a power source is an exploitation of solar energy. Away from the earth's surface, however, winds tend to blow along, rather than across, isobars, because the Coriolis force of the earth's rotation is always perpendicular to the direction of the motion. This is the geostrophic wind. This tendency is modified by the centrifugal force, if isobars are curved as around a high or low cell, and, near the ground, by the viscous drag due to the ground. Various sorts of local winds arise from characteristic geographical and thermal situations. (You might prefer to talk about winds later, in the section on heat; however, all you really have to sell students on is that hot air rises, and cool air settles.) These include the morning sea breeze (and nighttime land breeze), valley winds, drainage winds and foehns, and so on.

Icostasy (GE). This is the idea that, over broad regions, the crust of the earth is in approximate hydrostatic balance. Mountains can be viewed as blocks of lighter rock "floating" in the denser crustal rock, with correspondingly deep roots below to buoy them up - rather like icebergs floating in water; the ocean basins have a thinner crust than continental slabs, and so forth. The rock is not "fluid" in the ordinary sense, but slow plastic flow does take place over a geologic time scale.

Water Beds (MB). A direct application of Pascal's principle - that added pressure is transmitted unchanged to every point in a confined fluid - the water bed was developed by hospitals, to alleviate bed-sores (at pressure points) for patients confined to bed for long periods. Other applications will occur to you.

Pumps. A pump is a gadget for increasing the potential or kinetic energy of a fluid. There are innumerable varieties, based on several different operating principles. Both rotary and reciprocating pumps move fluid mechanically by taking it in and squeezing it out of a working volume; the animal heart is a two-stage reciprocating pump. Centrifugal pumps work by setting the fluid rotating, the centrifugal force causing it to flow outward. Several sorts of pump have no moving parts in the ordinary mechanical sense - the simple aspirator, the oil-diffusion and ion-getter vacuum pumps, and so forth.

Electromagnetic Pumping and Flow Metering. See item in part F.

Friction at Body Joints (MB). Friction in ordinary mechanical situations are well covered in Tipler, but this is a different kind of illustrative situation. Quite large normal forces exist in the long-bone joints due to muscular tension; in the leg joints these can reach values like 1000 pounds. The lubrication of joints is surprisingly effective, the frictional coefficient typically being less than 0.01.

Roads. The design considerations involved in road layout and surfacing constitute an interesting force problem, because of the range of parameters - vehicle speed and concentration, frictional coefficient under different weather conditions - that must be taken into account. The road-banking problem itself is discussed in Tipler. I once made a very productive in-class problem session out of giving some assumed parameters and having the class design a freeway cloverleaf.

Energy Resources (EE). See item in part A.

Elasticity. The treatment of linear elastic deformations is one of those "properties of matter" topics that was a standard part of the introductory physics course when I went to school, and has since been just about squeezed out. All that usually survives is Hooke's law. A slightly more detailed discussion of the elastic properties of solids - the different sorts of strains, the corresponding elastic moduli and the relations between them - can make an interesting side trip if you have time. When I talk about these things it is usually in connection with static equilibrium problems, because the obvious engineering illustrations overlap so well. Strain gauges - elastic deformation transducers of various sorts - are a related topic; they can be enormously precise.

Seismometers and Earthquakes (GE). See item in part D.

Real Fluids. Fluid-flow situations are treated in Tipler only to the point of getting Bernoulli's principle for a nonviscous flow, as an instance of conservation of energy. Introducing the idea of viscosity leads to a variety of other illustrations - if you've talked about the factors governing flow in pipes, for instance, it makes later analogies with DC circuits and Ohm's law a lot more convincing, as well as applications to things like blood circulation. One can take this to the point of a qualitative discussion of turbulence, the Reynolds number, and the effects on aerodynamic and hydrodynamic systems.

Aerodynamic Flight. The basic forces important in powered flight are thrust, drag, and lift. Thrust is developed by an engine of some sort, but the other two are messy fluid-dynamic problems, although perfectly accessible to qualitative discussion. Drag forces are of essentially the same nature as for boats, although in a different quantitative domain. Lift is produced by the downward deflection of air, and depends in a complicated way on airfoil shape, angle of attack, and several other parameters. The Bernoulli's principle argument that is often used to explain airfoil lift is just plain wrong.

Hydraulic Machinery. Hydraulic presses, hydraulic control of automobile brakes or aircraft parts, and other instances that will occur to you are essentially hydrostatic devices - direct applications of Pascal's principle.

Fluid Metering. Velocity of fluid flow is measured by several techniques. Some devices - the Venturi, the Pitot tube - are based on pressure-difference measurements, via Bernoulli's principle. Others - anemometers - are variations on the theme of putting a propellor in the fluid stream and letting it come to equilibrium with the flow speed.

The Atmosphere and Weather. See item in part C.

Blood Circulation (MB). This is the obvious illustration of things like pumps, hydrostatic pressure differences, viscous flow in pipes, and such in the medical domain. One can think of a number of kindred topics: blood-pressure measurement, the body's modulation of blood flow, the effects of constrictions in major vessels, etc.

Rocket Flight. This is heavier-than-air flight without aerodynamic lift - flight by reaction. Rockets constitute a very direct illustration of momentum conservation in a non-collision situation. Given the basic equation for the velocity, a number of related points can be discussed: the dependence of the attainable velocity on propellant specific impulse, its dependence on mass fraction and the point of staging, the $\Delta v$ required for a given application (e.g. trans-lunar orbit insertion) and its attainment, and so on.

Turbines. Turbines are fluid-driven devices for producing mechanical energy in the form of a rotating shaft. The old grain-mill water wheel is a turbine. Today they are used in engines, in power generation, and so on; a propellor is a turbine-in-reverse. There is an important design distinction between turbines designed to move with the driving fluid, and those ("reaction" turbines) that deflect the fluid to a different direction.

Firearms. A firearm is an external-combustion rocket; some of the basic considerations are the same, except that a bullet doesn't carry its fuel along with it. Points to be made would include the pressure that the propellant must generate, the corresponding strength requirements of the firing chamber, the importance of the rate at which the propellant burns, the difference that the desired use and trajectory make in design, and such.

High and Low Pressures. One of the most familiar sounds around a working physics lab is the gurgling vacuum pump. The reasons that so many physical phenomena are best studied at low pressures, and some of the techniques for obtaining high vacuum, bear talking about at some point. Another whole set of phenomena is characteristic of very high pressures - different phases of familiar materials (there are five kinds of ice), different behavior of phase changes, etc. Steady-state high pressures are limited by strength of materials; higher pressure transients can be produced explosively. And, of course, nature outdoes any attainable laboratory pressures by far, in stellar interiors.

Engines

Perpetual Motion Machines. See items in part C.

Centrifuge (MB). This is a device for producing pseudoforces by rotation; a centrifugal pump, and the spin-cycle of your washing machine, are examples. In biological and medical applications, enormous centrifugal forces can be produced; these are used to separate liquids from solids or from other, immiscible, liquids, in a variety of applications. Yet another application is the standard science-fiction dodge of producing artificial gravity in a space station by spinning it; in this case, though, the Coriolis force produces some unexpected effects.

Helicopters. Helicopters achieve aerodynamic flight by spinning the airfoil, so decoupling lift from forward speed. Conservation of angular momentum, of course, says that the spinning blades must produce a torque on the fuselage; the little tail propellor on almost all helicopters is there to yield a counter-torque. Unbalancing these torques is one of the ways helicopters are controlled.

Inertial Navigation. In general, this means on-board course determination by computer integration of the output of an accelerometer of some sort; it is used in aircraft, missiles, and submarines. A simple instance is the gyrostatic compass, in which the spin direction of a balanced gyroscope is used as a reference.

Simple Machines. The fundamental concepts of machinery: the lever, the pulley, the wheel and axle, and the incline. The concept of mechanical advantage follows from conservation of energy, and the pulley and incline have probably been discussed earlier; but if I talk at all about all these together, it is usually in connection with static equilibrium problems, because you need the idea of torque.

Statics and Architecture. Basic architectural usage provides an endless variety of examples of static equilibrium problems: the arch, the elements of the truss, cantilevered structures, the various sorts of bridge design, and so on.

Statics and the Skeleton (MB). Another whole set of statics examples can be found in the engineering of the human skeleton: the forces involved, and the jointing, in picking up something with your hand, or why leg muscles must be capable of forces up to nearly a ton. The limbs are designed as levers with a mechanical advantage less than 1; mechanical advantage is sacrificed for mobility. Bones are hollow, for greater stiffness per unit weight. Another topic to touch on in the same connection is that of scaling - the "square-cube law" and why King Kong couldn't stand up.

Automobile Suspensions. This is a good practical illustration of the damped harmonic oscillator: given reasonable design goals, what should be the force constant and damping?

Musical Instruments. See item in part D.

Illustrations of SHM. Several rather out-of-the-ordinary examples are suggested in the article by Maor (B.2 in the reading list).

Tides (GE). The patterns of tides were an important evidentiary item for Newton in developing the theory of gravitation - for example, the reason for their occurring twice daily. This can also be discussed advantageously in terms of motion in a noninertial frame of reference. Tidal friction is an important factor in the evolution of the earth-moon system, as well as explaining why high tides lag behind the moon. Resonance effects occur in the tides in partially enclosed basins - the Bay of Fundy is a well-known example.

Orbits (AA)(GE). The orbits of planets and of artificial satellites are the laboratory for gravitational interactions. Gravitational perturbations were responsible for the discovery of Neptune, and apparently are the cause of the divisions in Saturn's rings. Basic orbital problems, such as the Hohmann ellipse for a trip between planets, are perfectly accessible, as are the perturbations of earth satellite orbits - the reason why, for instance, the primary effect of atmospheric drag is to circularize a satellite orbit.

Satellite Measurements (GE) (AA) (EE). A variety of kinds of measurements can be carried out using earth satellites that would be far more difficult - if possible at all - without them. The first things that come to my mind are details of the earth's gravitational field, atmospheric research and weather mapping, resources mapping such as the infrared false-color land-use pictures, and above-the-atmosphere astronomy (especially solar). Others will occur to you.

Stellar Eschatology (AA). The end of the life-cycle of a star occurs when gravity takes over; when there are no longer internal combustion sources to provide sustaining pressure, some form of gravitational collapse occurs. The various forms depend on the mass of the star, and on the assumptions you make - it may end up as a white dwarf (electron-degenerate), as a neutron star (essentially solid nuclear matter) or perhaps a "black hole," collapsed past its own Schwarzchild radius and immune from any interaction with the rest of the universe.

## C. Thermodynamics (Chaps. 17 to 19)

Thermometry. The definition of temperature and of temperature scales is very thoroughly treated in Tipler. A great variety of systems are used as thermometers in appropriate applications. A random selection includes: the ordinary mercury- or alcohol-in-glass thermometer; the constant-volume gas thermometer; a bimetallic strip expanding, as in a household thermostat; the thermistor (at very low temperatures, commonly an ordinary carbon resistor); the thermocouple; and, at high temperatures, the color and/or intensity of radiated light.

Calorimetry (MB). The measurement of temperatures, heat capacities, etc. by measurement of heat transfers within an isolated system is calorimetry. Measurement of the specific heats of materials is probably the most common application, as in Tipler. Other applications would include the measurement of the heat of combustion of fuels, of the energy content of foods, etc. The basal metabolism rate measures the overall rate of combustion, or energy generation, in the body in a quiescent state. This has actually been done with a whole-body calorimeter, although much more commonly - and less cumbersome - by measuring the rate of oxygen consumption. An adult human is a heat source of the order of 100 watts.

Thermography (MB). Infrared detectors are capable of registering temperature differences substantially less than 0.1°C. Coupled with scanning techniques, they can be used to build up a temperature "picture" in various situations. A military use is the detection of hostile troops, machinery, etc. under cover or at night. The techniques has found a variety of medical applications; small anomalies in skin temperature, detected thermographically, can be interpreted to detect cancers or pregnancy, to indicate vascular disorders, and for many other purposes.

Low Temperatures (MB) (EE). Various techniques can be applied to reach very low temperatures. Evaporating liquified gases, especially helium, under reduced vapor pressure, can yield temperatures below 1°K; and values below 0.01°K can be reached by demagnetizing paramagnetic salts. Of the many fascinating phenomena observed only at very low temperatures, the one of the greatest practical importance is superconductivity. Superconducting high-field magnets are already in common use, superconducting computer elements are becoming important, and the phenomenon is likely to have a future role in power transmission. Superconducting magnets will be an important component in thermonuclear reactors.

Medical applications include cryosurgery - the selective freezing and destruction of tissues by low (usually liquid-nitrogen) temperatures, and hypothermia, the retarding of deleterious effects during surgery by lowering the body temperature somewhat.

Heat Transfer (EE) (GE) (AA). The whole subject is open - it is little discussed in Tipler. The thermal conductivity is easily defined, and a number of applications will come to mind - in living quarters, for instance, the order of magnitude of heat loss, the effect of windows and insulation, double-paning of windows, and so forth. The conduction loss through a thin glass window will come out unreasonably large, which is as good a way as any to introduce convection (convection in the air spreads the temperature drop out over a stagnant air space on either side of the window) - the transfer of heat by mass motion of the medium, as distinct from conduction. It is convection that is primarily responsible for establishing the temperature gradient in the atmosphere, while the overall heat balance of the earth is governed primarily by thermal radiation, as this is the only way to transfer heat to empty space. A little qualitative talk about heat transfer in the interiors of stars, and the relative importance of convection and radiation, puts the subject into quite a different context.

Heat Regulation in Animals (MB). Mammals and birds maintain a rather constant body temperature, roughly independent of - and typically higher than - that of their surroundings. Temperature control is accomplished by manipulating the rate of heat loss at the body surface, both by evaporating water from the skin and by regulating the blood flow to the body surface. The regulating element in the feedback loop is an organ in the brain called the hypothalamus.

Heat Balance of the Earth (GE) (EE). The equilibrium between incoming solar radiation and the earth's reradiation to space is a complex of several processes, delicately balanced. The processes are radiative in nature, but need not wait on a full discussion of electromagnetic radiation; just to state the $T^4$ law is enough to go on with. The planetary albedo (about 35% overall, a little over 50% for clouds) is an important parameter. The unreflected radiation is absorbed, mostly in the atmosphere, and reradiated to space; constituents of the atmosphere that are opaque to the infrared reradiation, such as $CO^2$ and $H_2O$, play an important role. The radiation reaching the earth's surface is nonuniform in space and time, while the radiation of the earth is reasonably uniform; thus different parts of the earth have an excess or a deficit in the balance, causing the temperature variations that drive wind and weather systems.

Several of the parameters - $CO_2$ concentration, the effect of average cloudiness on the albedo, and such - are of concern in terms of the long-term effects of human activities, and it is interesting to look quantitatively at the effects of a variation in one of them. The results should be looked at very cautiously, however, as both positive and negative feedback mechanisms exist in the system.

Winds (GE) (EE). See item in part B.

The Atmosphere (GE) (EE). The atmosphere is the biggest and most interesting ideal-gas system on earth, and a number of its properties illustrate the gas laws, heat transfer, and fluid mechanics. The isothermal pressure variation is easily calculated; somewhat more fun is to assume convective equilibrium and calculate the adiabatic lapse rate. Warm air rises, cool air settles, and the rotating earth is unequally heated at equator and poles; these effects, together, give rise to the general circulation of the atmosphere, responsible, for instance, for the prevailing westerlies in mid-latitudes and the easterly trade winds near the equator. The atmosphere is layered vertically into several divisions with quite different properties, with relatively slow mixing between them. Under normal conditions the bottom layer (the troposphere) is quite active, and any mad-made contaminants injected into it are mixed and dispersed relatively rapidly; under special weather conditions, the development of an inversion layer (temperature increasing with altitude) can essentially destroy vertical mixing, trapping pollutants near the ground in a haze or smog layer.

Clouds (GE). Typically the temperature of the atmosphere decreases with increasing altitude at a rate of around 10°C per kilometer. At some point, the "dew point" is reached - that is, the relative humidity at the local temperature reaches 100% - and the moisture content of the air condenses into clouds of water droplets. Specific type, shape, structure, and altitude of different sorts of clouds are a function of the details of local atmospheric conditions.

High and Low Pressures

Lighter-than-air Flight. See items under part B.

Stellar Interiors (AA). The solid-like average densities of stars make it difficult to grasp that the ideal-gas law offers a good description of stellar interiors. It does, however; and a crude approximation of the pressure and temperature in the interior can be made quite simply, starting with an estimate of the pressure needed to bear the weight of the outer parts of the star.

Stellar Energy (AA). Another relatively simple calculation, starting with the rate of energy output of the sun and the estimates of its age, quickly convinces one that nuclear reactions are the only possible energy source. Neither chemical combustion nor gravitational contraction can expend energy, even at the sun's relatively slow rate, for nearly long enough.

Thermal Pollution (EE). Every form of human activity, every means of energy expenditure or production, produces waste heat. "Thermal pollution" most often refers to the ecological effects of waste heat rejected, from a factory or a power plant or some such, in a fairly concentrated way to a body of water. The biological effects are outside our scope, but simple models giving the extent, size, dissipation, and such of the temperature increase are fun to play with numerically. The parameters of alternative heat dissipation practices - cooling ponds, cooling towers, and such - are also worth discussing.

Heat Radiation (GE) (AA)

Microwave Heating (MB). See items under part F.

Solar Energy (EE). Usually this is taken to mean direct exploitation of the energy delivered to the earth in sunlight; almost all the energy we use is solar in origin. There are a variety of interesting techniques for conversion: focusing the sun's light using huge concave mirrors, exploiting the greenhouse effect, laying out acres of photovoltaic cells, and so on. The central feasibility problems in all methods are the very diffuse delivery of the sun's radiation and the need for large-scale energy storage means because of the daily (and other) intensity variations.

Geothermal Energy (EE). This means, by various means, exploiting the temperature gradient in the earth's interior as a source of energy. There are local concentrations of the interior heat near the surface, as in geysers and hot springs; but these are not a potentially very large resource in world-wide terms. The essential problem, as for solar energy, in using the bulk of the geothermal energy available is one of concentrating it.

Engines. We talk about idealized heat engines, mostly, in discussing the second law; in this context, it can be entertaining to talk about some of the varieties of the real thing. The large stationary steam-turbine engines of electric generating plants are quite recognizable in terms of the simple heat engine cycle. With the passing of the steam locomotive, the mobile external-combustion engine has just about disappeared, at least in land applications. Most of today's work is done by internal-combustion engines, based on either the four-stroke (Otto) or the two-stroke (Diesel) reciprocating cycle. It takes a little more thought to relate these to a

Carnot cycle, but they are of course subject to the same thermodynamic and practical limitations. The Wankel engine is a rotary engine currently arousing a good deal of interest; jet and rocket engines are reaction propulsion devices. Many engines are based on the turbine principle, discussed elsewhere.

Perpetual Motion Machines. When I was young and dewy-eyed, someone tried to teach me the first and second laws of thermodynamics as "it is impossible to construct a perpetuum mobile of the first kind" and "it is impossible to construct a perpetuum mobile of the second kind." It had an engaging symmetry about it, but didn't convey much. Nevertheless, the distinction is a real one, and there is a lot of fun to be had by looking at some of the (quite serious, some of them) tries that people have had in the past at making a perpetual motion machine. See especially the article by Angrist (section C.4 in the reading list).

## D. Waves and Optics (Chaps. 20 to 27)

Ultrasound (MB). Any mechanical wave above the frequency range of human hearing is ultrasonic, the usable range now extending into the gigahertz. At the very high frequencies, where ultrasound is an important research tool in the structure of solids, transduction is usually based on the piezoelectric effect in, say, quartz. The ultrasonics used in fluid cavitation cleaners, homogenizers, and the like are usually of the order of $10^5$ hz. Ultrasonography is the construction of a picture of some object from the delay and intensity of echoes; in medicine it is used to visualize internal structures in the body, analogous to radiography. The Doppler effect allows the examination of the motion of internal organs, as, for instance, the inspection of the early fetal heart.

Sonar (MB) (GE). Sonar is echo-ranging using sound waves - the sonic analogue of radar. In its basic meaning it refers to sonic or ultrasonic waves in water. The original development was military - for submarines and their detection - but it can be used quite generally for underwater exploration, measuring water depth and ice thickness, and so on. Porpoises, seals, and other aquatic mammals are sonar-equipped by nature; the most familiar instance of animal sonar is that of bats. Bats' chirps, in the neighborhood of $10^5$ hz, enable them to detect objects the size of small insects in complete darkness.

Room Acoustics. The basic ideas of room acoustics can be communicated in about five minutes, and make an excellent illustration of the reflection and absorption of waves at boundaries. A microphone and an oscilloscope are enough for a crude measurement of your lecture room's reverberation time; with the aid of a Polaroid camera, an instructive comparison can be made of the results with and without students in the room.

Musical Instruments. These are the obvious illustrative material when you are talking about standing waves and resonance, and they can be taken however far you have time for. The basic systems are a stretched string and an air column, although others such as membranes and solid rods are present in the percussion section. The harmonic series is available from any confined air column; if you have a good horn player available, an entertaining demonstration is to have him play a tune on a trumpet mouthpiece stuck into a length of garden hose. Most stringed instruments require a sounding board and/or cavity as an acoustic coupling device. Tone is a function of harmonic content (but note that attempts at reconstruction can be confusing, because waveform shape depends on the phase relation of the components, while the ear is phase-insensitive), and the low-register flute (an open pipe) and the oboe (a half-open pipe) make an interesting comparison.

The Ear (MB). In vertebrate animals, the ear is the transducer that converts acoustical vibrations of the air to nervous impulses. It is a complex structure which serves, as well, as the body's accelerometer. Sound waves funneled into the auditory canal by the outer structure of the ear set up vibrations in the membrane (the eardrum) which are mechanically coupled by a linkage of small bones (the anvil, hammer, and stirrup) to the cochlea, a fluid-filled organ containing nerve cells that sense the vibrations of the fluid. See also van Bergeijk et al. (in part D.2 of the reading list).

Shock Waves. A shock wave is a sharply defined, non-periodic, high-intensity wave. In practice they arise from wave sources moving faster than the wave velocity in the medium. Because of the intensity of the disturbance, the reflection and transmission of shock waves at boundaries departs from the linear behavior of ordinary waves. The most familiar example is the sonic "boom" produced by aircraft exceeding the speed of sound in air; Cerenkov radiation is an optical shock wave.

Seismometry and Earthquakes (GE). A seismometer is a sensitive accelerometer applied to detection of local mechanical vibrations of the earth. A variety of detection and transduction mechanisms can be used - a massive pendulum, strain gauges, magnetic and capacitative transducers, and so forth. The fundamental application is to the observation of seismic waves produced by earthquakes; investigation of their delays, internal reflections, etc. has yielded much of our picture of the earth's interior structure. Similar investigations of the moon have been undertaken, observing the seismic waves from impacts on the surface, and the technique is also applied to the detection of underground explosions on earth.

Water Waves. Waves on the surface of water are a little more complicated than some other kinds of mechanical waves because two distinct mechanisms (gravity and surface tension) operate. At long wavelengths - above a few centimeters - gravity dominates. Such waves are dispersive, the wave velocity being a function of wavelength and water depth; the behavior characteristic of ocean waves moving onto a shore - increasing in amplitude and breaking over - is a dispersion effect. Waves on natural bodies of water are wind-generated; the exception is the tidal wave (which has nothing much to do with tides), an intense wave pulse generated by sea-floor earthquake activity.

Tides (GE). See item in part B.

Superheterodyning. This is the trick, based on beat frequencies, that is used in nearly all commercial radio and television receivers. A local oscillator signal, which tracks the receiver tuning, is mixed with the received signal to produce a constant beat frequency. The stages of amplification can then work on a fixed, lower, frequency, eliminating the need for variable tuning of each stage.

Stellar Interferometry (AA). The diameters of stars can be inferred approximately from their luminosity, color, and distance. Direct observational measurement is limited by the practical size of telescopes: the diffraction limit depends directly on the diameter of the instrument. An array of telescopes, however, has the diffraction limit characteristic of the whole array size; combined interferometrically, the array can resolve the sizes of some of the larger stars. The same technique is commonly used in radio astronomy.

Optical Instruments. The basic ideas of image formation, and the structure of the compound microscope and the telescope, are thoroughly discussed in

Tipler. If you want to pursue this further, there are obviously an unlimited number of things to talk about. A random sample: practical astronomical telescopes (reflectors vs. reflactors, mountings, Newtonian, Cassegrain, and other configurations); terrestrial telescopes (uses, Galilean telescope, binoculars); eyepiece design (the eyepiece is a highly corrected compound magnifier used to view the objective image in a telescope or microscope - it usually has a short focal length); apertures, shutters, and stops; cameras and projectors; and on and on.

The Eye (MB). The vertebrate eye is a box camera whose image plane is occupied by a complex array of photosensitive organs which transduce the image light into nerve signals. Its basic structure is described in Tipler. Variable focusing is accomplished by altering the shape of the single lens; variable sensitization is accomplished both by a variable stop (the iris) in front of the lens, and by biochemical adaptations in the retina. Certain of the retinal organs (in man and a few other species) are color-sensitive. The resolution limit of the human eye - due both to the spacing of the receptors on the retina, and to diffraction - is of the order of half a minute of arc. The most common defects of the eye are accommodation failures of the lens - which can be corrected by supplementary lenses - and clouding of the cornea and aqueous humor.

Color. Color is the physiological perception of the spectral distribution of light within the visible range. There are enough interesting things to talk about to fill a book - see, for instance, the Optical Society of America volume (in part D.2 of the reading list). The perception, recording, and description of colors seems to require, in general, three degrees of freedom: standard color comparison is in terms of hue, brightness, and saturation; color photography is accomplished by using three emulsions, sensitive in different spectral bands, which print as red, green, and blue, and color printing is done in an analogous way; and there are apparently three varieties of color-sensitive cones in the retina of the eye. On the other hand, see the article by Land (D.4).

Atmospheric Refraction (GE). Refraction arises from a change in refractive index; there is no particular need for a sharp boundary. The temperature and pressure of the atmosphere, and thus its refractive index, change with altitude, and over long distances substantial refraction can occur. One result is that the sun has already set, geometrically at least, when you watch it go down. The common mirage is a refracted image of part of the sky, seen below the horizon and shimmering like the surface of a pond; an inverted temperature gradient near the ground - as on a hot day over a cooler body of water - can give rise to images of terrestrial objects "looming" above the horizon.

Rainbows (GE). The rainbow is also an atmospheric refraction phenomenon, but due to refraction in spherical water droplets rather than in the air itself. The geometry of the main rainbow is a simple and excellent illustration of both refraction and dispersion; and a surprising number of students have never seen the secondary rainbow or, if they have, have never noticed that the colors are in inverse order.

Fiber Optics (MB). Fiber optics, and light-piping in general, are most directly illustrative of total internal reflection. It is easy enough to treat quantitatively such things as the maximum curvature for total reflection in a Lucite fiber. Image transmission by bundles of thin fibers can be considerably more efficient than by ordinary optical systems; this is especially true in medical applications, where fiber optics has made it possible to peer into most of the nooks and crannies of the living body. Examples are the hypodermic microscope - which is just what it sounds like - and the illuminating and viewing of obscure surgical fields.

Radar (AA) ( GE). Radar is the detection, ranging, and inspection of distant objects by means of reflection of radio waves (or microwaves). Originally developed for military purposes - the detection and navigation of aircraft at night - radar has now an enormous variety of uses, from air traffic control to weather scanning. The motion of the object observed can be inferred from the Doppler shift of the echo wave; this is how the highway cop catches you speeding now. Radar astronomy is the inspection of celestial objects by echoes of radar waves from high-powered transmitters on the earth; the distance, motion, and something of the surface character can be inferred. Radar astronomy yielded the first reliable information about the rotation of Mercury and Venus.

Lidar (GE) (EE). Lidar is the same process as radar, but in the visible region. Its primary applications are in investigations of the atmosphere; a whole spectrum of atmospheric information is available: the formation and structure of clouds, the concentration and (with resonance techniques based on tunable-dye lasers) nature of atmospheric pollutants, and so forth.

Photometry. Photometry is the measurement of the intensity of light. A basic technique is optical comparison with the light of a standard source (Lummer photometer); the same sort of comparator, but measuring calorimetrically the heating effect of the absorbed light, is the bolometer. Practical measurements rely heavily on the photoelectric effect; see the item under part G.

Photoelectric Effect

Photochemistry. See items in part G.

Polarized Light. A number of phenomena related to the polarization of light are discussed in Tipler; for much more discussion see Shurcliff and Ballard (in D.1 of the reading list), and especially the list of suggested classroom demonstrations elsewhere in this Guide. In a few other contexts: the Kerr effect is the induction of birefringence of materials by applying an electric field, used especially to make very high-speed photographic shutters; the vision of some insects and crustaceans is polarization-sensitive, so that they can orient themselves by the polarization of sky light even without the sun being visible; polarization of starlight, and its correlation with reddening, yields information on interstellar dust.

Spectroscopy. See item in part G below.

Holography. Lasers, as strong coherent light sources, have made holography - visual reconstruction of an interferogram - practical in recent years, but there are many students who will never have seen, or even heard of, a hologram. Setting up to view holograms takes only a laser and an optical bench, and a qualitative discussion of the process goes down easily after you have discussed interference. It is not that hard, in fact, to set up to make your own with a small group of students.

Laser Surgery (MB). The power density in a laser beam is huge compared to any conventional light source - large enough to fuse and vaporize materials in the very small region exposed to the beam. The laser has already become a standard surgical tool, as a result, being applied to very small or otherwise inaccessible sites. Surgery within the eye, on the retina, is possible without opening the eye, and destruction of cancerous tissue can be accomplished with minimum trauma to surrounding tissues.

## E. Relativity (Chapter 28)

Relativistic Travel. Even within the ultimate limitation of the velocity of light, the parameters of travel at relativistic speeds bear looking at. It is perfectly possible for a man to travel to a star 150 light years away in his lifetime, if he goes fast enough; if he travels at .99 c, the distance is Lorentz-contracted to 21 light years. According to clocks on the earth, though, he made it only because his clocks were running slow; and if he ever turns around and comes home he will find that upwards of 300 years have gone by there.

Another mode of travel that is fun to look into is constant acceleration. Deriving this is probably beyond what you want to get into, but you can set up the problem and quote the result. Numbers come easily because one g-year is almost exactly equal to c. A good practical point can be made by figuring the energy requirements of some of these expeditions.

Paradoxes. The apparent paradoxes of relativity mostly boil down to questions of simultaneity; a few of these, as illustrations, help bring home the idea of its breakdown. The discussion in Taylor & Wheeler (E.1) is excellent. A unique one is a meter stick sliding across a hole in a table; in the table's frame, the stick sort of snakes through the hole. Is the rigidity of a body a kinematic property?

Tachyons. In the past few years it has been suggested that particles may exist that can only move faster than light, without violation of special relativity. There seems to be little reason to believe that they do exist, other than that they can. There are obvious causality problems to be dealt with if tachyons can interact at all with ordinary matter; yet if they cannot, are they in principle undetectable? If so, why talk about them? See the Feinberg article (E.4 in the reading list).

Mass and Energy (EE). The interconversion of mass and energy isn't specific to nuclear reactions, of course, but it's only there that a measurable fraction of the mass is converted. I sometimes illustrate this with a few macroscopic numbers on nuclear fission and fusion reactions as energy resources; the whole bit can be done in terms of atomic masses, without any need to go into atomic structure.

General Relativity (AA). Any analytical treatment is far beyond our scope; a central point in the predicted effects, however, is just that light has "mass" in the sense that a gravitational field acts on it. Two of the classical confirmations - the deflection of starlight, and the gravitational red shift (which, using the Mossbauer effect, can now be demonstrated on the earth) - require no more foundation than this. You may prefer to wait until the idea of the photon has been introduced.

## F. Electricity and Magnetism (Chaps. 29 to 41)

Atmospheric Electricity (GE) (EE). The earth's magnetic field is very familiar; that it also has an electric field is somewhat less so. You can imagine the surface as one element of a spherical capacitor, the ionosphere as the other, with a few hundred kilovolts across it; the field is typically 100 V/m near the ground in fair weather. The field is very strongly dependent on atmospheric conditions, with intense fields and accompanying lightning discharges occurring in thunderstorm conditions. It is also modulated locally by air pollution conditions and by the ionization density in the atmosphere. Auroras are electrical discharges in the ionosphere, apparently instigated by events on the solar surface.

Ionization Detectors. All radiation detectors respond, in various ways, to the ionization produced by subatomic particles; particles with no charge are detected by the ionization due to secondary charged particles that they produce. The basic form is the ionization chamber and its variations (proportional counter, Geiger tube). Cloud and bubble chambers operate on the wake of ions left along the track of the particle, which act as centers for condensation or cavitation in fluids; scintillation detectors on the visible light produced by ion recombination; surface-barrier detectors by collecting the ionization produced in the depletion layer around a pn junction. Cumulative detectors include photographic emulsions and thermoluminescent dosimeters. If you want to get into the ionization process a bit, the energy transfer to a free electron is a nice impulse-approximation calculation.

Piezoelectric Effect. The production of an electric field in a crystalline material under stress, and the inverse effect, are both referred to as the piezoelectric effect. The effect finds its main application as an electromechanical transducer - in phonograph pickups, microphones, and very high frequency ultrasonics.

Electric Effects in Bone (MB). An electric field has been found to stimulate growth in living bone. (See, e.g., Liboff et al., Clinical Orthopaedics 106 (1975), 330 and other papers cited there.) Bone also is piezoelectric, and it may be that this provides the feedback mechanism whereby the long bones of the body grow in such a direction as to support the stress applied to them.

Xerography. This now-standard dry copying process is based on a photoconductive material such as selenium. The light in the bright parts of the image cast on a charge's selenium plate render it conductive, and the charge leaks away; this leaves a charge image on the plate, which is used to attract charged powder particles into a corresponding image on paper. The same technique, used as an alternative to film for recording X-ray images, is xeroradiography.

Ionic Conduction. We think of conduction in terms of electrons - or maybe electrons and holes - but there are important processes in which electrical conduction is by positive and negative ions. The obvious case is electrolysis in ionic solutions, with its applications in electroplating and in refining of metals such as copper. The migration along the electric field of complex molecules in solution is electrophoresis, which is an important biochemical analytic tool.

Electrochemical Cells. The original source of electromotive force, the voltaic cell, consists of two dissimilar metals immersed in an electrolytic solution. Oxidation and reduction reactions at the electrodes have the net effect of transferring charge between them by migration of ions through the electrolyte; the result is a seat of EMF whose operation is limited only by chemical deterioration of the electrodes. Volta's original cell consisted of zinc and copper in a sulfuric acid bath; the most common modern varieties today are the zinc-ammonium chloride "dry" cell and the lead-sulfuric acid storage battery, but a great variety of reactions may be used. The open-circuit EMF of a single cell is a thermodynamic property of the electrode reactions.

Skin Conduction (MB). Body tissues, including the skin and structures near the surface, are sopping with electrolytes and are fair conductors of electricity. Conduction between electrodes on the skin is referred to as the galvanic skin response (GSR), although conduction proceeds by internal tissues as well as over the skin surface; changes in the GSR because of perspiration, vascular changes, etc. are the basis of the polygraph. A related technique is "neurodermometry," in which the skin surface is scanned with an electrode to inspect nervous or peripheral vascular damage.

Nerve Conduction (MB). The propagation of a nerve impulse along a nerve fiber is electrical in character, but proceeds by a complex physiological sequence. Typical speeds of propagation are on the order of meters per second. The stimulation of a nerve fiber causes a change in the electrochemical properties of the membrane surrounding the fiber, which allows an exchange of sodium and potassium ions through it. The result is a temporary reversal of the potential difference across the membrane; this in turn stimulates neighboring parts of the nerve fiber, and the impulse propagates along it rather as a wave.

EKG and EEG (MB). Most processes of the body are electrically stimulated, and corresponding potential differences detected on the body surface offer a means of inspecting these processes. The electrocardiogram (EKG - don't ask) is a recording of electrical impulses, measured over the torso, associated with the heart action. Indications of various heart disorders are readily inferrable. The signals observed on the skin are on the order of $10^{-4}$ volt. Electrodes on the head register characteristic rhythmic patterns associated (in not very clearly understood ways) with brain function; this is the electroencephalogram.

The pn Junction. The distinction between p-type and n-type semiconductors is made in Tipler; an obvious next step is to take up the properties of the pn junction. The rectifying action of a single junction is quite easy to get across, and it is the only nonlinear circuit element students are likely to see at this level. If you want to describe amplifying devices, I believe either the vacuum triode (though the device, in practice, is about obsolete) or the field-effect transistor is easier to get students to believe in than is the junction transistor.

Amplification. You can do a great deal of talking about electronic devices - sound reproduction systems, etc. - if you just sell the idea of amplification. The most I have ever tried to do is to describe some amplifying device qualitatively, draw the simplest possible equivalent circuit (floating input, Thèvenin output), and apply it in a few simple cases such as getting the gain into a simple load resistance.

Oscilloscope. The most basic electrical-measurement device, after the galvanometer applications treated in Tipler, is the cathode-ray oscilloscope. Its operation should probably be discussed in any case, because by now it has probably been used in several classroom demonstrations. Electric and magnetic deflection of charged particles have been discussed, and the oscilloscope's kinship to the TV tube makes its operation plausible.

Radio and TV. About all that is needed to talk about the operation of radio and television receivers are the ideas of amplification and the tuned circuit. The various ways of coding signals - modulating a carrier - will bear talking about. Diode demodulation is easy to get across, and yet is a revelation to a lot of students; the ideas you need to have for this are rectification and the RC circuit. Yet another topic which can take a fair amount of discussion is the encoding of a television picture. It is probably best to treat all of these at the block-diagram level. The superheterodyning trick is mentioned in an item in part D above.

Analogue-Digital Conversion. Students by now have very likely seen some devices that use ADC's, and they afford a good illustration of some basic circuit ideas. A standard way to do this trick is to charge a capacitor a little way up (stay in the linear region) while a multivibrator clock ticks. When the capacitor voltage matches the (analogue) input, the number of clock ticks is the (digital) output.

Particle Accelerators. All particle accelerators use the charge of the particle as their handle on it. There are two basic kinds: the DC accelerator typified by the Van de Graaff, and the "reciprocating" types based on the cyclotron. Both the Van de Graaff and the cyclotron are mentioned in Tipler. The relative merits of the two approaches, their limitations, and the techniques required for producing very high energies can be discussed. Note the distinction is not just one of geometry: a linear accelerator is a stretched-out cyclotron.

Ion Propulsion. This is a method of rocket propulsion that amounts to using the beam from a high-current heavy-ion accelerator as a reaction mass. Because the impulse available per unit "engine" mass is low, ion rockets are potentially most useful in applications requiring a low but precisely controllable thrust.

Magnetic Poles. All our experience is that electric current is the sole source of the magnetic field, that the magnetic "pole" is an artifact. Is it in fact impossible for isolated magnetic poles to exist? No one knows for sure, and the elegant near-symmetry of Maxwell's equations makes the idea tempting enough that quite subtle experiments have been devised to search for them; see the article by Ford (in part F.2 in the reading list). Presumably if such an object did exist, it would behave in analogy with electric charge: there would be a net force on it in a uniform magnetic field, a flow of "magnetic charge" would be a source of the electric field, and so on.

Terrestrial Magnetism (GE). The earth's magnetic field is roughly that of a dipole inclined at about $10^{o}$ to its rotation axis, although there is a complex pattern of departures in both space and time from a pure dipole field. Among the time variations is a small diurnal variation due to tidal drag of the sun on the ionosphere. The field apparently is generated by circulating convection currents in the earth's molten core, although the mechanism by which the currents are maintained is not entirely clear. The magnetic moment is on the order $10^{22}$ $A \cdot m^2$.

Paleomagnetism is the study of magnetism of the earth in past ages, by the remanent magnetization of rocks of various ages. The most striking finding is that the earth's field has reversed itself at irregular intervals - intervals of millions of years - many times in the past. Magnetic reversal data provide the most important evidence for sea-floor spreading and continental drift. On this latter subject, the delightful book by Hallam, "Revolution in the Earth Sciences" (Oxford, 1973) is highly recommended.

Magnetometers. Almost any physical phenomenon that responds linearly to a magnetic field can be exploited as a magnetometer. A few examples are the rotating-coil magnetometer (a small-scale AC generator), the Hall effect, and the very sensitive NMR gaussmeter.

Magnetic Memory. The characteristic of ferromagnetic materials of retaining their magneticization more or less permanently after the magnetizing field is removed is the basis for the most common sorts of computer memory. Tiny "cores" of iron-oxide ceramic materials (ferrites) which can be magnetized in either direction (representing the two states of a binary bit) are the most common "live" memory element; other configurations include magnetic tapes and magnetic disc storage.

Electromagnetic Pumping and Flow Metering (MB). If a current is set up transversely across a conducting fluid, which flows through a magnetic field, there is a magnetic force along the direction of flow; this trick can be exploited as a pump without moving parts. Applications occur in the handling of molten metals - as in foundries, or in cooling liquid-metal nuclear reactors. Electromagnetic pumping has also been used in heart and kidney machines, where the absence of mechanical parts greatly simplifies sterilization. The inverse process can be applied to measure a fluid flow rate.

Plasmas. A plasma is a fluid in which a large proportion of atoms are ionized, as at extremely high temperatures. Matter in the stars is in the plasma state, as it is at the temperatures required for thermonuclear reactor operation. The latter is the basis for the largest part of current plasma research, although there are many other applications, potentially, in space propulsion and in high-temperature technology in general. The motion of plasmas is substantially complicated, as compared to ordinary fluid dynamics, by the magnetic forces of the plasma on itself. One instance is the pinch effect - the self-induced constriction of a plasma flow due to magnetic attraction - which provides one possible approach to confinement and heating of plasmas in thermonuclear reactors.

Microwaves. Electromagnetic radiation in the centimeter wavelength range, in common usage, is neither radio nor infrared light. These microwaves are gaining a wide range of applications. Because of the wavelength, it is practical to build highly directional antennas for microwaves, leading to their use for relaying television and telephone messages. High-resolution radar employs microwaves for the same reason. Absorption of microwaves in organic matter occurs typically over a range comparable to the sizes of everyday objects; a result is that they can be used for heating organic materials, as in the microwave oven or - at somewhat lower intensity - in medical diathermy treatment.

AC Measurements. If you take up AC circuits (Chapter 40 in Tipler), the AC bridge circuits provide a convenient set of illustrations. AC bridges operate just like Wheatstone bridges, except that there are two balance conditions in general: the signals at the detector points must be equal in magnitude and phase. An interesting result is that some bridge circuits are unbalanceable. Various AC bridge circuits exist; they can be used to measure inductance, capacitance, or frequency. About the only interesting feature of voltage and current measurements - beyond the analogous DC measurements - is the clip-on (Faraday's law) AC ammeter.

Electric Power Generation (EE). The basic idea of the AC generator is treated in Tipler. Some auxiliary practical points can be made; for instance, the economics of high-voltage transmission. In broader terms of energy resources and consumption, the increasing reliance we place on electrical energy poses a dilemma because of its relative inefficiency. Electric generators are driven by heat engines of one or another sort, which places an absolute limit on their efficiency; in practice, and allowing for transmission losses, somewhere around a third or a half of the ideal thermodynamic efficiency is achieved. Overall perhaps 15% efficiency is achieved in energy delivery by the electrical route. The problem this poses is compounded because most foreseeable alternative energy sources - solar power, nuclear power - will be exploited most easily via electric power generation.

Electron Optics. Properly shaped nonuniform electric and magnetic fields have a focusing effect on a beam of charged particles. This property is easy to illustrate for the case of a simple electric gap lens or a magnetic quadrupole pair. One application is in transport and focusing of accelerator beams. Whole optical systems, analogous to ordinary optical instruments, can be built up of such focusing elements; the most important is the electron microscope, which exploits the shorter wavelength of fast electrons to yield much higher resolution than optical microscopes are capable of.

G. Quantization (Chapter 42)

Photoelectric Effect. In addition to being a foundation stone of the quantum theory, the photoelectric effect has practical applications of its own, among them the photoelectric cell; the photomultiplier tube (a device for detecting very faint light signals by generating photoelectrons, then amplifying their number by successive secondary-electron productions); and the television camera.

Photochemistry (EE). Reactions caused by, or enhanced by, the presence of visible light on the reactants are referred to as photochemical. The most important photochemical reaction, certainly, is photosynthesis in green plants - the main source of oxygen in our atmosphere. Other photochemical reactions - the photo-induced reduction of silver halide salts - are of fundamental importance in photography. Photochemical reactions in the atmosphere are of central importance in the formation of smogs.

Spectra (AA). The numerical regularities in the hydrogen emission spectrum were basic to the development of Bohr's model. Less simple but comparable regularities exist in the spectra of other elements; these can be illustrated if not justified. The spectral lines of any element are characteristic of the element, and of its state of ionization; this fact allows qualitative and quantitative spectral analysis of trace components of materials. The analogous case in nuclear gamma-ray spectra, instigated by neutron absorption, is neutron activation analysis. Our analysis of the properties of distant stars - their temperature and composition - is based on spectroscopic information.

The Uncertainty Principle. This is hardly an application; but the gedanken experiments having to do with the operation of the Heisenberg principle in very simple measurements are very instructive. Much of this arises out of arguments between Einstein and Bohr. There is an absolutely beautiful discussion of the two-slit interference experiment for water waves, bullets, and electrons in The Feynman Lectures (A.1), vol. 3. I never miss an opportunity to steal it.

X Rays (MB). X rays are electromagnetic radiation with wavelength shorter than ultraviolet - on the order of an Angstrom; they are produced by bremsstrahlung of a beam of electrons, electron transitions in the inner levels of heavy atoms, and so forth. Moseley's theory of characteristic X-ray lines, besides being a very direct application of Bohr's ideas, provided the first definite means of determining atomic number. The wavelength of X rays is of the right order to display marked interference effects from adjacent atoms in a solid, and X-ray diffraction has become a fundamental crystallographic tool. The medical use of X rays for radiography exploits their penetrating power.

CLASSROOM DEMONSTRATIONS

D. Rae Carpenter, Jr., and Richard B. Minnix

The demonstrations suggested herein are not meant to be an exhaustive listing but rather a group of suggested demonstrations which have been used by the authors over a number of years for the topics in this text. We have tried to select those which have appealed to students as opposed to those that produce little class reaction. For the most part, emphasis has been placed on those requiring very simple apparatus, often available in toy, hardware, or building-supply stores.

Demonstrations require time to set up and try prior to the lecture. Many institutions cannot afford the expense of a technician for setup so lecturers frequently avoid demonstrations either because of the time they require or because of unfamiliarity with the technique. An effort has been made to include here those which are quick to set up and require little or no delicate adjustments.

No claim of originality is made for the demonstrations presented here. They have been collected from many sources, but particular acknowledgment is due to the United States Naval Academy which held short courses on lecture demonstrations sponsored by the National Science Foundation in 1970, 1971, and 1972. Since our participation in these courses, a continued exchange with other participants has resulted in many additional ideas.

Various publications featuring demonstrations have appeared through the years and there is considerable duplication of basic ideas with variations of technique or application. The following have been found extremely useful:


Demonstration Experiments in Physics, Richard M. Sutton, McGraw-Hill Book Company, New York, 1938.

A Demonstration Handbook for Physics, G. D. Frier and F. J. Anderson, Professors of Physics, University of Minnesota, Minneapolis, Minn., 1972.

Demonstrations in Physics, Julius Sumner Miller, Ure Smith, London, 1969.

Physics Demonstration Experiments, Harry F. Meiners, The Ronald Press Company, New York, 1970.

Physics Demonstration Experiments at William Jewell College, Wallace A. Hilton, Professor of Physics, William Jewell College, Liberty, Mo., 1971.

# 1
# INTRODUCTION

CLASSROOM DEMONSTRATIONS

1. UNITS

A) "BODY" UNITS - Assist students in becoming familiar with metric units by identifying various units with parts of human body. Approximately 1 cm is width of small fingernail, 1 decameter is breadth of hand at thumb joint, and 1 m is "reach" from tip of chin to tip of outstretched hand (drygoods store clerks used this as yard in bygone days).

B) PAINTED METER STICK - To show decameter and as aid in making measurements visible to large class in subsequent demonstrations, paint each 10 cm segment on meter stick alternately in contrasting colors (e.g., red and white). If painted on English side, metric markings remain clear for demonstrator to read lengths accurately.

C) DISSECTIBLE LITER BLOCK - Cube 10 cm on side with removable 1 cm cube is available commercially.

D) LIQUID MEASURE - Show glass beakers of various sizes up to 1 liter.

E) PONDER MASS - Ponder is old term used in dictionary in sense of "weigh". Use beam balance to ponder, as distinguished from weigh, several different masses.

# 2
# MOTION IN ONE DIMENSION

CLASSROOM DEMONSTRATIONS

1. CONSTANT VELOCITY AND ACCELERATION Use air track both level and inclined.

2. CONSTANT ACCELERATION Roll glass or steel marble down inclined aluminum track made of right angle stock (rotational energy affects results slightly). Strobe light of sufficient intensity may be used to locate position of marble at equal time intervals.

3. FREE-FALL ACCELERATION OF GRAVITY

A) COIN AND FEATHERS - Connect Lucite tube (∿ 5 cm dia. x 120 cm long) to mechanical vacuum pump. Place coin and feather, smaller than tube diameter, inside. Compare rates of fall when tube at atmospheric pressure and when evacuated.

B) DOLLAR BILL - Drop flat and crumpled bills simultaneously. Crumpled bill has acceleration close to "g" but flat bill has large air drag.

C) GRID WITH CAMERA - Drop golf ball in front of grid made from white string passing through holes on pegboard as background for strobe time exposure photo with Polaroid camera. Use steel ball for nearly pinpoint reflection for quantitative data. Transparency type film may be projected for class if high intensity strobe is used.

D) NUTS ON PAN - Crimp lead sinkers to fishline. Space at intervals measured from end as S, 4S, 9S, 16S, etc. Attach that end to cookie pan to produce audible sound as nuts fall. Though distance intervals are unequal, time intervals between impacts are equal. S = 10 cm is convenient.

E) REACTION TIME

a) Quantitative - Hold meter stick vertically by one end. Have student place thumb and forefinger opposite 50 cm mark ready to catch stick in flight after someone else releases it. Calculate reaction time from distance of fall before being caught. Can be used to study statistics for various trials on one individual or for various individuals.

b) Qualitative - Offer to give dollar bill to student who can catch it in free fall. Teacher releases bill held vertically at end while student prepares to grasp with thumb and forefinger, starting opposite Washington's picture. Beware of student anticipating release!

# 3
# MOTION IN TWO AND THREE DIMENSIONS

## CLASSROOM DEMONSTRATIONS

1. VECTOR NATURE OF FORCE Use force table to show $\vec{3} + \vec{4} = \vec{5}$.

2. "g" SIN θ  Arrange a right triangle of wire or thin rod mounted to a vertical board (hypotenuse must be vertical). Place nut on each wire. Observe equal times of fall for nuts along sides A, B, and C. Motion along C is more sensitive to friction.

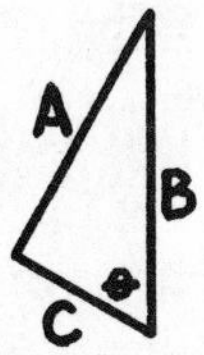


3. PROJECTILE MOTION

A) SPRING GUN - Use spring gun to compare independence of vertical and horizontal motion. Alternatively, this may be done with card and paper clip for projecting one penny while another falls vertically. Pivot card at "x" by holding lightly between thumb and forefinger. Flick with one finger of other hand at arrow to propel coin "B" horizontally while coin "A" falls vertically.

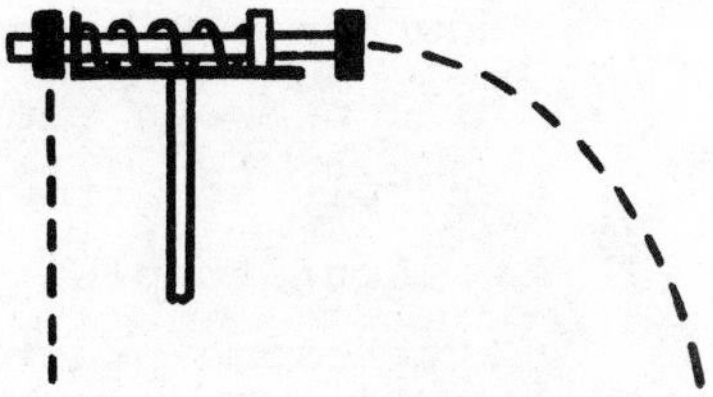

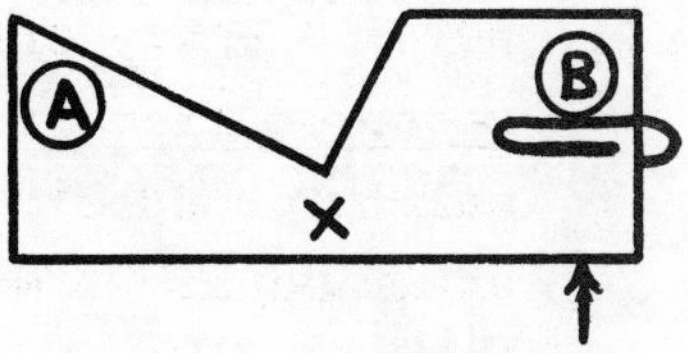


B) STROBE PHOTO - Use grid in Demonstration 3C, Chap. 2, to take strobe time exposure photo of golf ball leaving an inclined track. Steel ball gives nearly pinpoint reflection for quantitative data.

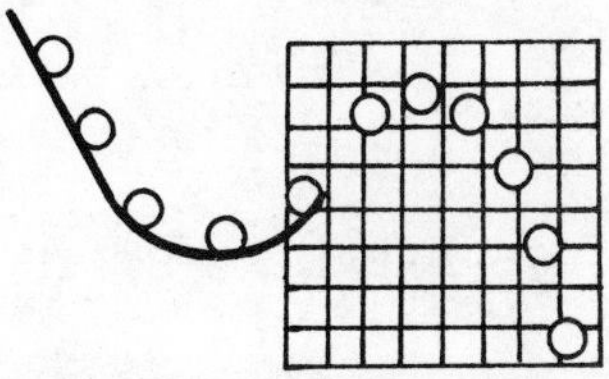

C) STROBE PHOTO ANALOG - At about 10 cm intervals on meter stick, suspend small cylinders on strings of appropriate length, $s = \frac{1}{2} at^2$, to simulate successive positions in projectile motion. Angle between stick and horizontal represents gun elevation angle.

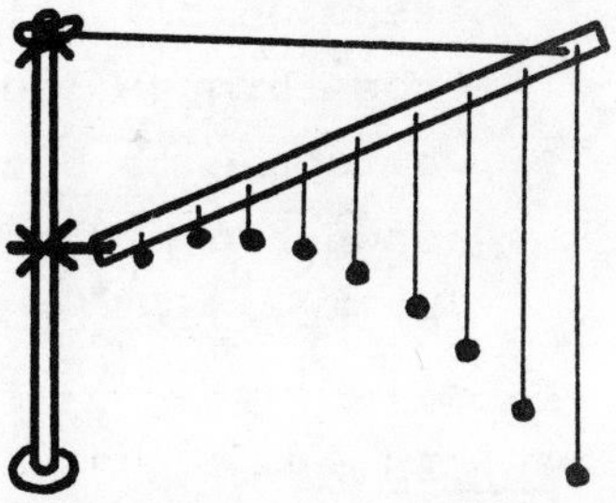

D) MONKEY GUN - Outfit small toy monkey with iron plate to suspend from electromagnet. Aim "gun" consisting of tube with steel ball at suspended monkey. Trip wire at muzzle of gun opens electromagnet circuit to drop monkey as ball emerges. Apparatus available commercially but replace can by toy monkey to add realism. When demonstrator exclaims that monkey is still alive, have assistant ready with cap pistol or hatchet to rush out and finish job. See text example 3-4.

4. CIRCULAR MOTION  Show vectors for tangential velocity and radial acceleration by mounting arrow at circumference of disk placed on variable speed rotator. Use single arrow which can be changed from tangential to radial direction. (Also used for Chap. 14 with shadow projection for simple harmonic motion.)

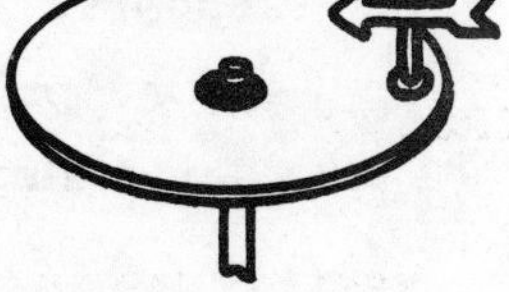

# 4
# NEWTON'S LAWS

CLASSROOM DEMONSTRATIONS

1. INERTIA

A) COKE BOTTLE AND BILL - Place one Coke bottle upside down on top of another (mouth to mouth) with dollar bill between them. Hold bill at end and strike sharply at arrow with one finger to remove bill without toppling bottles. Use 10 or 16 oz size after some practice!

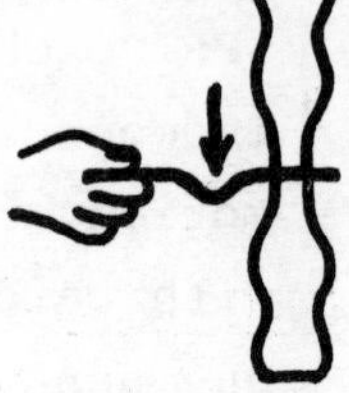

B) HAMMER AND PLATE - Place hand on table underneath 1/4" thick heavy plate. Pound on plate with hammer without hurting hand.

C) HANGING MASS AND BOARD - Suspend 20-30 kg object with rope ∿ 2 m long. Strike sharply with old baseball bat (a broken one works nicely) or "bat" made of 3/4" soft pine board. For harder woods, bat cannot be quite so thick. Take off watch and wear athletic supporter!

D) BREAKING STRING WITH LARGE MASS - Suspend Mass of 10-30 kg with single strand of string with breaking tension slightly greater than weight of mass. Place rod through loop (double string of same material) attached to bottom of mass. Snatching rod quickly downward breaks lower, double string whereas slow, steady pull breaks upper, single string.

2. FORCES

A) FORCE TABLE - See Demonstration 1, Chap. 3.

B) TENSION IN ROPE - Hang weight from spring scale, preferably reading Newtons, to determine its value, W. Attach two strings, one to each side of scale, and tie weight to end of one. With pulley, arrange strings and scale horizontally with other string end tied to rigid support. Read tension (=W). Use second pulley and add identical weight to other end of string. Show that tension still equals W.

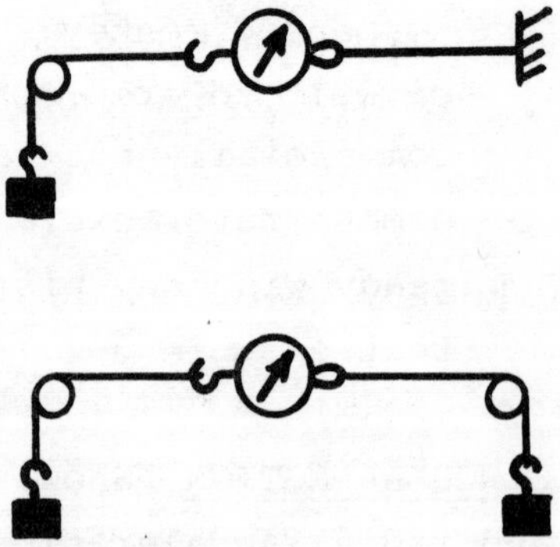

C) TUG OF WAR - Get two husky students to pull against one another at opposite ends of a rope. Have coed use one finger to deflect rope. Discuss application to automobile mired in mud. Alternative is to use 2 B above with another spring scale to read deflecting force vs. tension.

3. MASS If using engineering units, show "slug" of lead. Lead brick used for nuclear shielding approximately one slug. See Question 22.

4. NEWTON'S SECOND LAW - QUANTITATIVE Use air track and air bearing pulley.

5. NEWTON'S LAWS - QUALITATIVE The following group of demonstrations utilize one or two low flat wooden carts made of 3/4" plywood about 60 x 100 cm with hard, ball-bearing wheels (skate wheels are satisfactory). They should be sturdy enough to hold up to three students each.

A) ACTION/REACTION - With demonstrator on one cart and student on another, they push on one another with flat outstretched palms to illustrate Third Law.

B) CHANGE OF MASS AND ACCELERATION - Arrange as in A but place two persons on one cart (or one heavy and one light person). Try three persons on one cart against one on the other.

C) EXCHANGING MOMENTUM - Student standing on floor throws gallon plastic jug of sand (or medicine ball) to demonstrator standing on cart. Sand provides the momentum exchange or "action-at-a-distance".

D) ISOLATED SYSTEM - Repeat C except have student stand on second cart locked rigidly to demonstrator's cart to form "isolated system".

E) FIRE EXTINGUISHER ROCKET - Sit on cart and discharge large $CO_2$ extinguisher held between knees and braced firmly against chest or shoulder. Prepare short cassette tape of Apollo-type countdown including a "hold" for safety officer (assistant) to fit crash helmet on demonstrator's head. Extinguisher should have horn or nozzle removed. Necessary to cut off orifice tip or make screw-on attachment to get unidirectional flow.

6. CONSERVATION OF MOMENTUM

A) RECOIL - Suspend test tube horizontally by two strings or wires. Rinse tube with water to leave small amount inside. Plug tube with stopper and heat with burner until stopper blows out.

B) TOY BALLOON ROCKET - Blow up toy balloon and release to form rocket.

C) TOY WATER ROCKET - Available in toy stores with rocket, funnel and air pump. Designed to soar several hundred feet into air when loaded with several hundred grams of water. Adapt to run on wire angled upward to lecture room ceiling by epoxying wood block and screw eyes to rocket. Pump up first with ∿ 20 strokes without water and show short flight with air as "fuel". Use about 50 gm water and repeat using same number of strokes to show effect of heavier "fuel". Remember to clear table beneath rocket and don't use full charge!

# 5
# APPLICATIONS OF NEWTON'S LAWS

## CLASSROOM DEMONSTRATIONS

1. $\vec{F} = m\vec{a}$ ATWOOD'S MACHINE For quantitative results, use ball bearing pulley of Lucite with holes drilled in interior to reduce inertia as well as friction. Diameter of 10-15 cm allows masses on either side to pass without bumping. Compare theoretical and experimental values of acceleration. Large discrepancy in values due to friction when two weights on ends almost equal. Using weights of larger difference gives better result but shortens time interval requiring greater effort to measure. Good example of compromise often necessary in experimental work.

2. EQUILIBRIUM Form right triangle of narrow shelving board with side lengths in ratio 3:4:5. Paint sides in strips of contrasting colors to show number of length units. Hang block over plane by means of weights supplying proper force components through strings parallel and perpendicular to plane. Remove plane to show it exerts no forces.

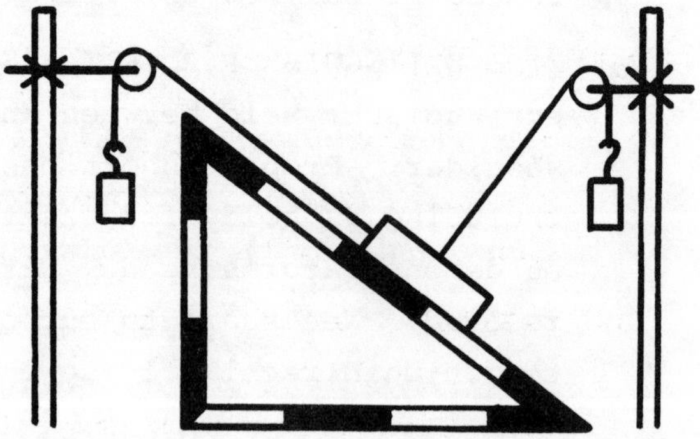

3. CENTRIPETAL FORCE

   A) BALL ON STRING THROUGH GLASS TUBE - Use short length of glass tube with fire polished ends to spin ball at various speeds and various radii for different weights.

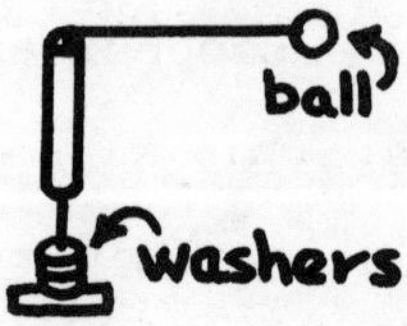

B) CHAIN ON DISK - Fit a loop of metal window sash chain (∿ 25 cm dia.) loosely over a wooden disk. By means of metal shaft in center of disk, use electric hand drill to spin disk in vertical plane. Push loop of spinning chain off disk with screwdriver blade and note rigidity of loop as long as it spins. Very effective on slick board or floor since loop slips in place with little forward motion.

C) PLANTS IN CENTRIPETAL FIELD - Grow a few simple plants on a table continuously rotating at 60-180 rpm for several weeks. Plants align with total acceleration.

4. <u>GOLF BALLS IN JAR</u> Secure two identical glass jars (∿ 2 liters) with identical lids. Epoxy ordinary golf ball to string and attach to lid so as to hang at about center of jar. Epoxy <u>hollow practice</u> golf ball to string and attach to <u>bottom</u> of other jar. Use practice ball without holes to look like real one. Paint both balls red for visibility and fill both jars with water.

A) LINEAR ACCELERATION - Accelerate jar with solid ball by sliding rapidly along table or held in hand.

B) CENTRIPETAL ACCELERATION - Place jar with solid ball on board clamped on turntable. Use short dowel rods to hold jar on board. Spin to show effects of acceleration.

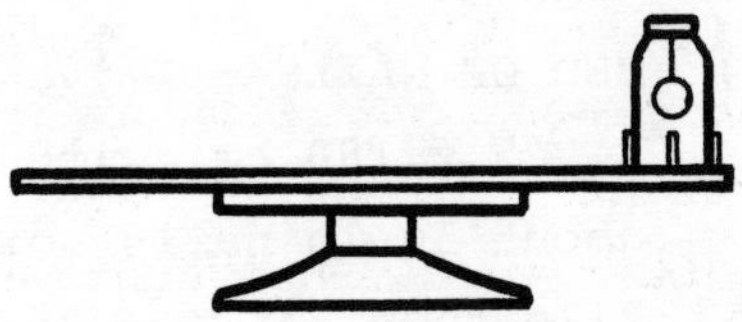

C) BUOYANT FORCE - Repeat A and B using the jar with the plastic ball which floats up from bottom string. See Exercise 31.

5. <u>BUOYANT FORCE</u>

A) BAG OF GAS - Fill a small plastic kitchen bag ("Baggie") with natural gas and close with rubber band. Use an analytical balance to compare mass of empty bag and rubber band and apparent mass of filled bag.

B) CARTESIAN DIVER - Available commercially but cheap substitute is medicine dropper. Amount of water inside "body" must be adjusted due to variations in atmospheric pressure.

C) SHIP IN A LITER - Fit a cylindrical wooden block to the inside of a beaker to show that large volume of wood will float in less than 10% that volume of water. Taller, smaller diameter beakers with block custom tapered to fit closely give more pronounced effect.

6. <u>PRESSURE</u>

A) SUCTION CUPS (MAGDEBURG HEMISPHERES) - Place T-shaped handles on pair of suction cups used as replacements on car-top carriers. Push cups together and then attempt to separate. Film of water or glycerine on cup improves seal effectiveness.

B) COLLAPSE A CAN - Bring to a boil about 100 ml of water in gallon metal can ("Ditto" fluid can works well). Remove flame and seal with screw cap or tight stopper. A pedagogically less desirable alternative is to use a plastic gallon milk jug pumped out with a vacuum pump.

C) TORRICELLI'S PRINCIPLE - Cylinders with several orifices at different heights are commercially available but one may be made from Lucite tubing. Seal plate on one end using ethylene dichloride applied by medicine dropper as bonding agent. Thin wall cylinders have less turbulence at orifices.

D) HYDROSTATIC PARADOX - Commercially available apparatus has base containing linkage to detect deflection of diaphragm due to pressure. Vessels of various shapes are connected to base to show dependence on area of base alone.

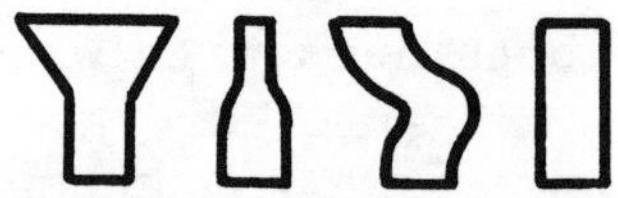

E) BED OF NAILS - Drive ∿ 3100 eight penny nails into 3/4" plywood (∿ 75 x 180 cm) with pre-drilled holes on ∿ 2 cm centers. Requires about 50 lb nails sorted to give 34 lb of nearly same length. Do NOT file down nails. Straddle bed, support body by both hands and feet, and lower body onto nails GENTLY! Reasonably comfortable for clothed demonstrator. Not recommended for bikini-clad coed!

7. <u>VISCOUS FORCES - RAW VS HARD-BOILED EGG</u> Spin raw egg rapidly on its side. Stop it and then quickly release it. It begins to rotate again because its yolk never stopped rotating. Hard-boiled egg will not do this. Excellent alternative uses hollow plastic egg-shaped containers used for panty hose. For "raw egg", epoxy halves together, drill small hole in one end and fill with water using hypodermic springe. Seal hole with epoxy. For "hard-boiled egg", melt paraffin to fill each half almost full. Allow to cool and contract. Complete filling later and press two halves together in vise using moderate pressure while wax still soft. Used also in Demonstration 5, Chap. 13.

# 6
# FORCES IN NATURE

## CLASSROOM DEMONSTRATIONS

1. AIR DRAG Drop flat and crumpled dollar bills simultaneously. See Question 1 and refer to Demonstration 3B, Chap. 2.

2. LARGE EXPONENTS Show 16 mm sound movie Powers of Ten available from Charles Eames Studio, 901 Washington Blvd., Venice, California 90291. Reviewed in AJP 40, 1357 (1972). Also see note in AJP 41, 425 (1973).

3. EXCHANGE FORCE MODEL Refer to Demonstration 5C, Chap. 4.

4. ELASTIC FORCES - LINEAR AND NON-LINEAR Take data on spring, wide rubber band, and shock cord (elastic cord available in camping equipment stores) to show linear and two types of non-linear behavior.

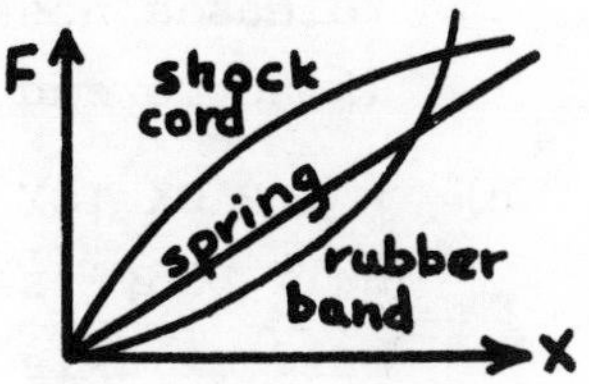


5. FRICTION - AREA AND COEFFICIENT Use a large-dial balance to pull wooden block at uniform speed along lecture table. Add masses to top to increase normal force. Use another block with each of its four sides having different material epoxied to its faces: leather, sandpaper, brass, Teflon, paraffin-coated Masonite, etc.

6. FRICTION - ANGLE OF REPOSE Slowly raise an inclined plane until block resting on it just begins to slide. $\tan\theta = \mu_{static}$. To get sliding coefficient, repeat but gently tap the plane continuously as it is raised. Use block with various face materials in Demonstration 5 to get different $\mu$.

# 7
# WORK AND ENERGY

## CLASSROOM DEMONSTRATIONS

Some of the demonstrations listed in Chaps. 6, 8, and 9 also might be shown with this chapter.

## 8
## POTENTIAL ENERGY

CLASSROOM DEMONSTRATIONS

1. PENDULUM Stored energy depends on height above reference level.

2. TOYS Julius Sumner Miller's Toy Set available from Atomic Laboratories, Inc., has numerous toys which make interesting demonstrations. A few of these are found only in larger toy stores but many are available in dime stores.

   A) FINICKY FIDO - The springy neck of this toy dog is deflected so that nose is stuck into pan of tar. After few seconds, tar suddenly releases nose (stored energy) and dog does backward somersault (kinetic and potential energy change).

   B) ROLLBACK TOY - Animal figure with weighted lower half body is suspended on a twisted rubber band at axis of a rolling frame. When rolled, figure remains upright causing band to twist and store energy. When released, it rolls back and forth.

   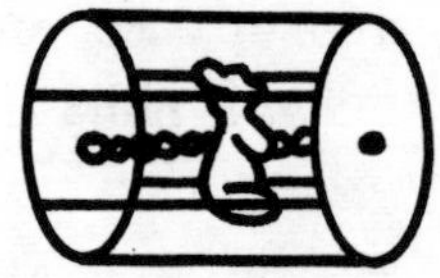

   C) JUMPING JACK - Use toy jumping jack or doll with spring and suction cup. Pushing down on doll compresses spring and seats cup on slick surface. When cup releases, spring energy propels doll upward.

## 9
## CONSERVATION OF ENERGY

CLASSROOM DEMONSTRATIONS

1. CONSERVATION OF MECHANICAL ENERGY

   A) PENDULUM - Suspend large mass (duckpin bowling ball) from ceiling about 3 m from side wall. Place student with back to wall and start pendulum from his chin. Test of faith in conservation law!

B) GALILEO'S PENDULUM - Arrange rod such that free swinging pendulum cord strikes it as it passes through equilibrium position. Although this changes pendulum length and period, bob swings up to original height of release.

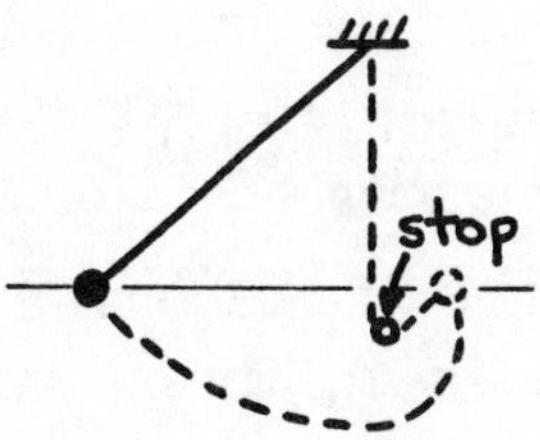


C) HOT WHEELS - Use "Hot Wheels" track and loop available in toy stores to form loop-the-loop. Show that car must be released at vertical distance above table of at least 2.5R to just complete loop. Greater heights required to allow for friction and rotational energy of wheels. Since latter is negligible, hot wheels demonstration is more appropriate here than rolling ball (see Demonstration 3C, Chap. 13).

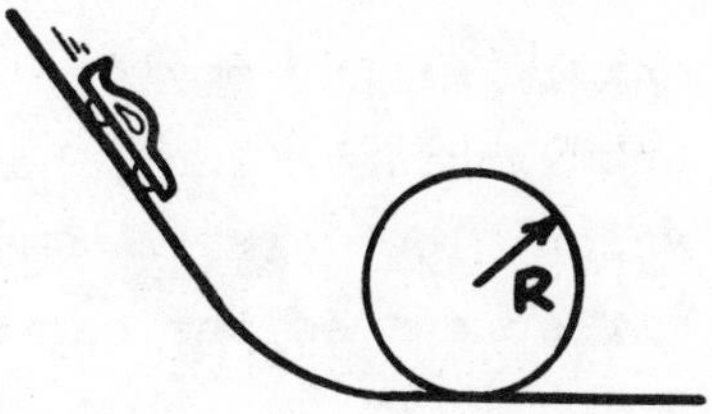


2. ESCAPE VELOCITY Place water in small juice can and whirl in vertical circle on end of string while discussing centripetal force. Now pour water into another larger can (the "space" model having improved "aerodynamic characteristics") which is resting on a wooden box over a hole (unseen by students). Water passes through hole in can bottom and into pan unseen by students. Remove this can from above box and whirl in vertical circle while talking about "escape velocity". Whirl faster and jump up and down for effect! When whirling ceases, turn can upside down to show water has "escaped" by having exceeded "escape velocity".

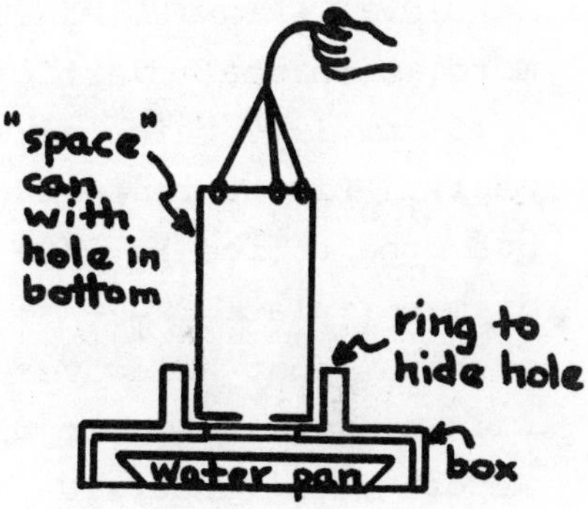


3. BERNOULLI'S EQUATION

A) SPOOL AND CARD - Place a thumb tack through center of 2-3 cm diameter disk made from index card. Place sharp end of tack into hole in spool from sewing thread. Blow through other end of hole to show card cannot be blown off. Turn upside down while blowing for greater effect.

B) BALL IN FUNNEL - Place ping pong ball in small funnel to which hose has been connected. Blow through hose (or use compressed air) while turning funnel to various orientations.

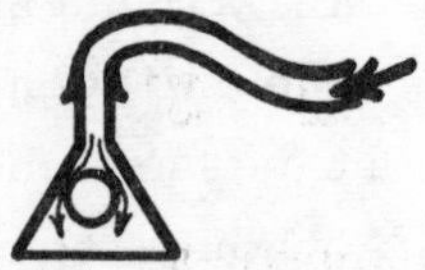

C) BALL IN AIR OR WATER JET - Place air-filled plastic beach ball in air stream from hose attached to output end of vacuum cleaner. Or place ping pong ball in stream from small compressed air jet (hole drilled with #53 drill works well). To use water, make jet hole slightly larger (#27 drill).

D) CAR IN MILLER TOY SET - Julius Sumner Miller's Toy Set by Atomic Laboratories, Inc., has a spring wound toy auto with a "smoke stack" which blows air. A small, light, styrofoam ball is supported in this air stream as the car moves forward.

E) TWO LIGHT BULBS - Suspend two light bulbs from table rod. Blow sharply between bulbs and students can hear them clank together. Suspend in field of overhead projector to produce magnified image on screen.

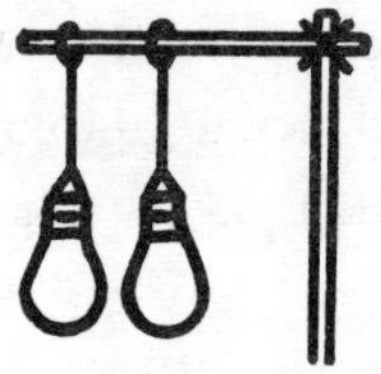

F) CARD OVER SPINNING PLATE - Mount a small motor with shaft vertical and attach 3/16" or 1/4" thick aluminum plate to shaft. Diameter depends on motor speed but good choice is 3500 rpm with 35 cm diameter plate ($V_T$ = 64 m/sec). Strip of thin paper held over spinning disk will stick closely to disk due to high speed air flow beneath strip. Repeat using underside of disk for effect opposing gravity. Use 35 mm projector for shadow projection of image (see Chap. 26).

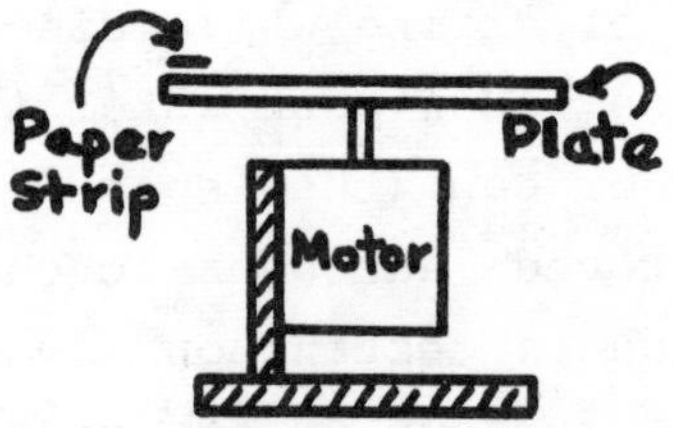


G) CURVING OF SPINNING BASEBALLS - Styrofoam balls used for Christmas and ornamental decorations are light and rough enough to have appreciable air film rotating with them when spun. Diameters of 6-8 cm work well. To provide good spin and distance use a "thrower" made from a 30-40 cm length of mailing tube or plastic pipe of a diameter just larger than ball. Split pipe in half lengthwise and line with sand-paper or emery cloth to provide rough surface. Throw overhand perpendicular to student's view to show balls <u>rising</u> due to spin. Throw some <u>toward</u> students to observe fast "break".

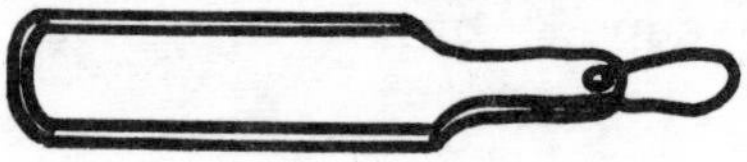

10

# MANY-PARTICLE SYSTEMS

## CLASSROOM DEMONSTRATIONS

1. <u>CENTER OF MASS</u>

A) DOUBLE CONE ON INCLINED PLANE - Commercially available, the plane is slightly inclined so a uniform cylinder rolls downhill. The double cone rolls in opposite direction.

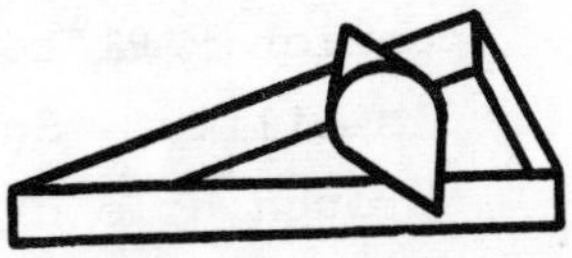

B) SEESAW - Use 2-3 m length of board (2x6 or 4x4) with movable pivot block. Use various numbers of students on one end changing lever arm as necessary to get center of mass over pivot.

C) SWIVEL HIPS AND PENDULUM ON CART - Use cart described in Demonstration 5, Chap. 4. Stand on cart with feet well spread and swing hips from side to side so that cart moves one way while body moves oppositely. Attach table clamp with rod near center of cart. Hang on rod 2-3 kg mass as pendulum with length about half meter. As pendulum oscillates one way, cart moves in opposite direction. Add several kg of mass to cart in steps to show reduction of amplitude of cart motion.

D) HUMAN BEINGS

a) Connect two 1 kg masses by about 40 cm of cord and hang on man's chest around his neck to simulate effect on shoulders and spinal column of large breasted women. Comment on effect on posture.

b) Stand in doorway with nose and toes touching door jamb and try to rise on toes. Impossible because center of mass cannot move forward to position over toes. Repeat with several kg in each hand with arms stretched straight forward on opposite sides of wall to move center of mass over toes.

c) Kneel on lecture table with forearms flat on table and elbows touching knees. Place short object such as cigarette lighter at tips of outstretched fingers. Now place hands behind back and try to tip over object with nose without losing balance. Most women can, most men cannot. RAY! RAY! ERA!

2. CONSERVATION OF MOMENTUM

A) AIR TRACK - Show collisions of various types. Show swinging pendulum attached to single glider.

B) See Demonstrations 5 and 6, Chap. 4.

C) PENDULUM TOY OR BILLIARD BALLS - Pendulation toy available in novelty store has steel balls in contact suspended by bifilar suspension. Place on stage of overhead projector for better class visibility. Snooker or billiard balls held by a horizontal wire through hole drilled through center of each also work well. Use care to drill as close to center as possible.

D) MARBLES ON ALUMINUM TRACK - Place a half dozen marbles on a piece of 1x1 cm aluminum angle held horizontally by two "V" blocks. One or more additional marbles may be carefully pushed (or accelerated using an inclined track resting on the horizontal one) to provide collisions. Advantage of this over B and C is heavier (steel) marble can be inserted so all objects not same mass. Disadvantage is effect of rotational kinetic energy and friction.

E) 3 TO 1 MASS - Commercially available, this consists of two steel balls each on bifilar suspensions adjusted to collide exactly on center. Frequently, one mass is three times the other. This is not necessary but it does result in smaller mass having velocity following first rebound of half the original which makes it easy to see. After second rebound, larger mass, regardless of whether or not it is 3 to 1, will stop, i.e., after every even numbered collision system repeats its initial condition. See AJP 41, 575 (1973) for discussion of time reversal invariance using this demonstration.

3. FINDING CENTER OF MASS - GEOGRAPHIC MAP OF STATE Glue road map of state (or nation) to Masonite backing and cut to shape of map with jig saw. Hang map from holes drilled at various locations along edge and use string and plumb bob technique to locate center of mass. Locates "geographic" center of state (or nation).

11

# COLLISIONS AND REACTIONS

## CLASSROOM DEMONSTRATIONS

1. IMPULSE

A) EGG IN SHEET - Fasten one end of bed sheet (double-bed size) to stick of wood. Have student on each side hold one end of stick high in one hand and grasp free corner of sheet low in other hand. This forms target for demonstrator (or big student) to throw raw egg into. Don't ease up - really fling it. Beware of either missing sheet or letting egg roll out end of sheet after rolling to bottom. Break egg in dish to prove it was not hard boiled!

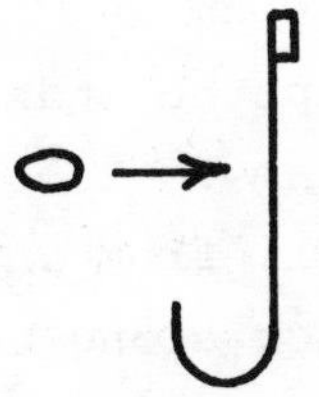

B) CARTS WITH SAND JUG - Refer to Demonstration 5C, Chap. 4.

2. COLLISIONS IN A GAS-MOLECULAR MOTION DEMONSTRATOR A small, adjustable-speed motor vibrates a four-sided frame mounted over a glass plate. When mounted on overhead projector, plastic or metal balls simulate molecular motion. May be used to illustrate concepts of pressure, temperature, and diffusion, Brownian motion, etc. Available commercially from Educational Materials and Equipment Co., P. O. Box 63, Bronxville, N.Y. 10708.

3. ELASTIC-INELASTIC COLLISIONS Show variation between behavior of rubber, silicone putty, superball, and Apiezon putty when dropped from same height onto various surfaces.

4. TWO-DIMENSIONAL COLLISIONS - AIR TABLE Demonstrate rebounds with equal and different masses and with walls. Strobe photos may be taken.

5. Q VALUE ANALOG - MARBLES IN SAUCER Place a half dozen marbles in a shallow saucer. Roll single marble down "V" shaped aluminum track inclined at different angles. Incoming marble must have sufficient energy to knock another marble from saucer. Use steel bearing to simulate more massive incoming particle.

6. COEFFICIENT OF RESTITUTION Measure coefficient by measuring total time for all rebounding to cease. $t = t_o \frac{1+\varepsilon}{1-\varepsilon}$ where $t_o$ is time of first fall gotten from $t_o = (2 h_o/g)^{1/2}$. Use glass marbles, steel, lead, wood, and rubber balls on table, floor, thick glass, steel plates and on flat side of a rectangular metal can to give various combinations of materials.

12

# ROTATION OF A RIGID BODY ABOUT A FIXED AXIS

## CLASSROOM DEMONSTRATIONS

1. ROTATIONAL KINETIC ENERGY - MAGNETIC AXLE ROLLING WHEEL
Commercially available, this toy is a plastic wheel ∿ 6 cm in diameter with magnetic axle having tapered ends. Tipping causes wheel to roll on wire frame. Because of magnetic attraction, axle will roll from on top of wires around ends of wires and back along bottom.

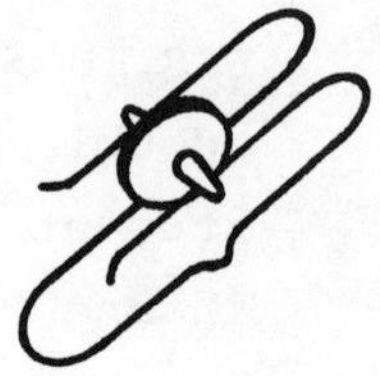

2. TORQUE

A) CROQUET MALLET - Place screw eyes at various places along handle to permit hanging weight holder. Grasp mallet head with both hands. Use various angles, θ, to show change of lever arm without change of force. Have students try it!

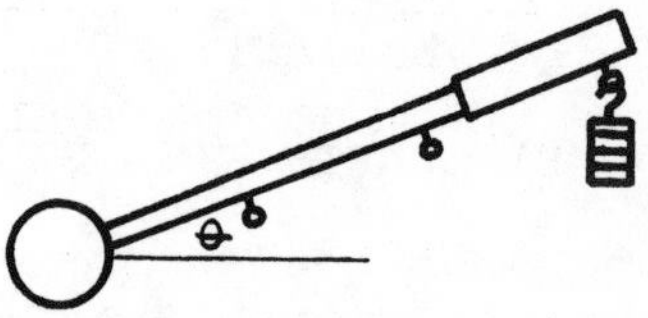


B) LEVER AND FULCRUM - See Demonstration 1B, Chap. 10.

C) ROLLING YO-YO - Construct yo-yo of two thin circular metal plates about 30 cm dia. Mount to "axle" consisting of wooden cylinder about 15 cm dia. and 12 cm long. Fasten string to axle. Nearly horizontal forward pull causes yo-yo to roll forward. If forward pull is nearly vertical, yo-yo rolls backward. For radii with ratio 2:1, equilibrium position is with string 30° to vertical. For oscillatory system, pass string over pulley and hang weight on end.

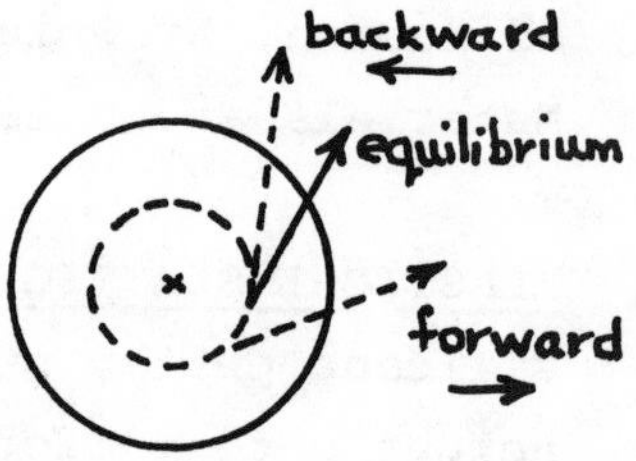


D) CAR WITH LOCKED WHEELS - Take toy plastic car ∿ 20 cm long having wheels rigidly fastened to common axle. Use small alligator clip to lock rear axle and wheels to force skidding. Place car on inclined plane and note that rear end skids sideways. Now lock front wheels and note car continues to track straight down incline with little or no sideways skid. Discuss braking while moving forward or backward on snowy or icy hills.

3. <u>ROTATIONAL DYNAMICS - SPOKED WHEEL</u> Screw six spokes of 8 mm O.D. aluminum tubing into aluminum hub 4-5 cm dia. which has ball bearing mounted horizontal axle. Fasten to hub two Lucite or phenolic pulleys having different diameters on which weight may be hung to produce driving torque. Make six brass (or other high density material) annular cylinders 3-4 cm long with inner diameter to fit over spokes and outer diameter ∿ 4 cm. Fasten with thumbscrew so each can be moved to any desired radius. Show effect of increased inertia with same mass by moving all cylinders out to large radii. For fixed radius, show effect of changing torque by using larger diameter pulley or increasing hanging weight.

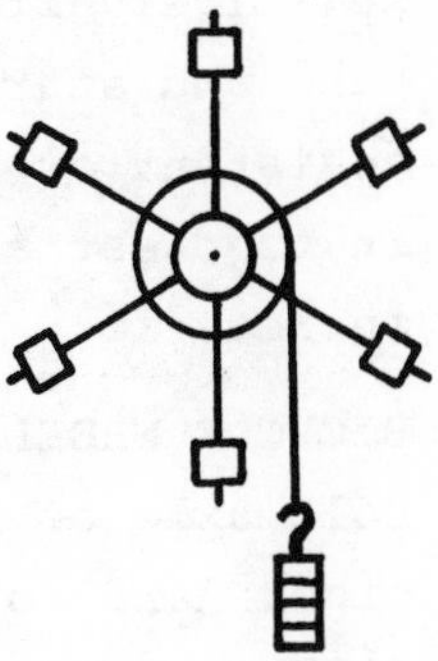

4. <u>STATIC EQUILIBRIUM</u>

A) BODY ON INCLINE - See Demonstration 2, Chap. 5.

B) SEESAW - See Demonstration 1B, Chap. 10.

C) FORCE TABLE - See Demonstration 1, Chap. 3.

# 13
# ROTATION IN SPACE AND ANGULAR MOMENTUM

## CLASSROOM DEMONSTRATIONS

1. <u>TORQUE AND ANGULAR ACCELERATION - STABILITY OF A VERTICAL ROD</u> See Demonstration 3, Chap. 12. Use one of the masses described there on 80-100 cm length of type of tubing described for the spokes. Compare the ease of balancing in two different positions, mass close to and distant from supporting finger.

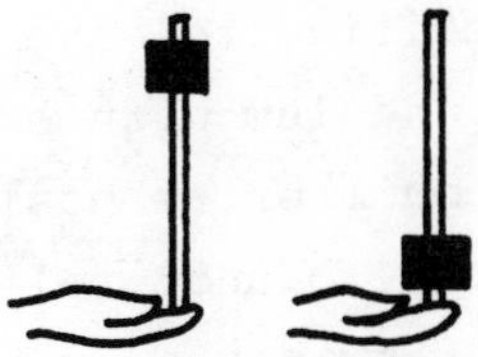

2. <u>CONSERVATION OF ANGULAR MOMENTUM</u>

A) BALL ON STRING WITH GLASS TUBE - See Demonstration 3A, Chap. 5. Pull downward on string to shorten radius and observe change of angular velocity.

B) MASSES IN EXTENDED HANDS - Sit on stool mounted on rotating platform relatively free of friction. Place about 2 kg in each outstretched hand and start rotating body and stool slowly with torque from an assistant or using push with one foot. While rotating, bring masses in to chest and lower elbows to vertical position to reduce I and increase ω.

C) BICYCLE WHEEL - Stand or sit on friction free rotating platform. Hold axle of bicycle wheel vertically above head with one hand. Use other hand to spin wheel. Without waiting too long (else table friction will reduce velocity), grab wheel to stop it thereby restoring the entire system to initial zero angular momentum.

D) WATCH ON WATCH GLASS - Place stopwatch or old style pocket watch with crystal down on watch glass with convex side up to produce friction-free mount. Stick small mirror scrap to watch case with putty to reflect laser beam at grazing incidence on wall. Reaction of case to balance wheel rotation causes reflected beam to oscillate. Arrange for beam to graze wall 6-8 m from watch for large optical lever arm. Remember current students have little knowledge about "old-fashioned" balance wheel so explain operation.

E) ELECTRIC MOTOR ON TURNTABLE - See Demonstration 3F, Chap. 9 for motor details. Place motor on rotating platform. Turn motor on and watch platform rotate in opposite direction. Use "capacitor run" motor which is easily reversed to show reversal of platform motion. Note: Repeat with motor shaft displaced from platform axis nearly to circumference of platform to show angular momentum depends on axis <u>direction</u> but not <u>location</u>.

F) PENDULUM AND BOTTLE - Attach ball to long wire from ceiling to make pendulum. Place stool underneath pendulum with soft drink bottle on stool at equilibrium position of pendulum ball. Bet students they cannot release ball so it will miss bottle as it swings away but will knock it over as ball returns. Old carnival game!

G) APPLICATIONS - Discuss conservation of angular momentum involved in somersaults done by divers and trampoline artists, or when cat thrown upside down lands on feet.

3. TRANSLATION AND ROTATION

A) KICK THE BLOCK - Drill a wooden block (30 cm long 2x4) to receive three broad tip felt pens ($\sim$ 10 cm apart) with tips protruding short distance through bottom. Center pen should be at center of mass. Place block on sheet of white wrapping paper 1.5 - 2.5 m long. Kick block at center of mass to show all three traces are nearly parallel. Kick well off center to show rotation of outer pens but translation of pen at center of mass. Different color pens make traces distinguishable.

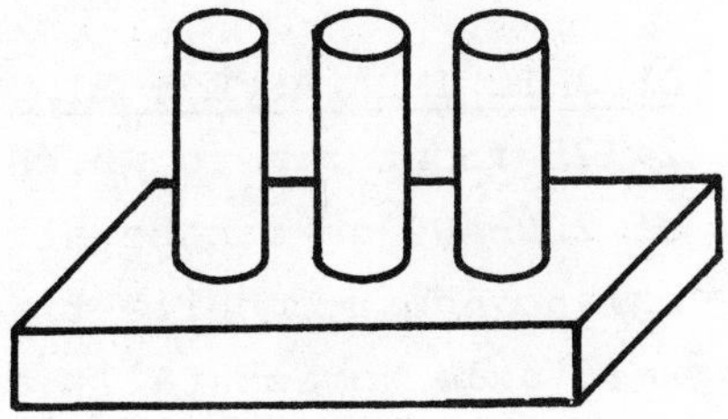

B) ROLLING OBJECTS RACE - To show velocity of objects rolling from rest down inclined plane is independent of both mass and radius, roll several solid spheres down incline. To show dependence on radius of gyration or mass distribution, run the race with a hoop, solid disk, and sphere. Objects of smaller radii exhibit some unwanted energy losses due to friction.

C) LOOP THE LOOP - Commercially available, this consists of inclined track followed by loop. Used with a heavy ball bearing 2-3 cm dia., it shows correction needed for rotational kinetic energy when calculating height, h, from which ball must start to just complete loop. Watch out for slipping of ball. Also see Demonstration 1C, Chap. 9.

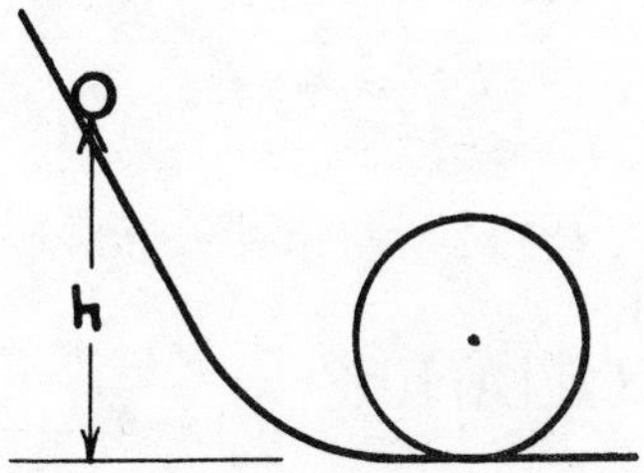


4. GYROSCOPIC PRECESSION - BICYCLE WHEEL Use bicycle wheel in 2C. Hang by string attached to end of axle to show wheel falls when not spinning and precesses when spinning. Reverse spin direction to show vector nature. May also use U-shaped stirrup support on rotating platform to hold wheel. Commercially available alternatives are air supported ball gyro and MITAC continuously-powered gyro. Discuss application to bicycle riding, i.e., explain why rider overbalanced to left can right bicycle by rotating handlebars and front wheel to left.

5. STABILITY OF SPINNING OBJECTS Discuss conservation of angular momentum and mechanical energy with changes in axis of rotation. A regular size or toy size football, when set spinning rapidly on floor about an axis through its small dimension, will flip up to spin about its long axis. Same can be done with hard-boiled egg or panty hose "egg" container (see Demonstration 7, Chap. 5). Tippy tops and heavy class rings will

undergo 180° change of orientation when spun. Note carefully that spin direction as a vector is not changed.

6. DYNAMIC IMBALANCE - BICYCLE RIM Use 26 x 2.125 front rim to which identical masses of 200-400 gm can be attached similar to balancing automobile tires and rims. Hold axle horizontally and attach single mass to produce imbalance. Now use another mass placed diametrically opposite on same face of rim to produce static balance. Hold axle in hand and spin to show little vibration - good dynamic balance. Now shift second mass to opposite face of rim to show static balance remains but axle shakes violently due to dynamic imbalance - principal axis of inertia no longer axis of rotation. Discuss types of balance for auto tires and why "weights" are used on inner and outer sides of rim.

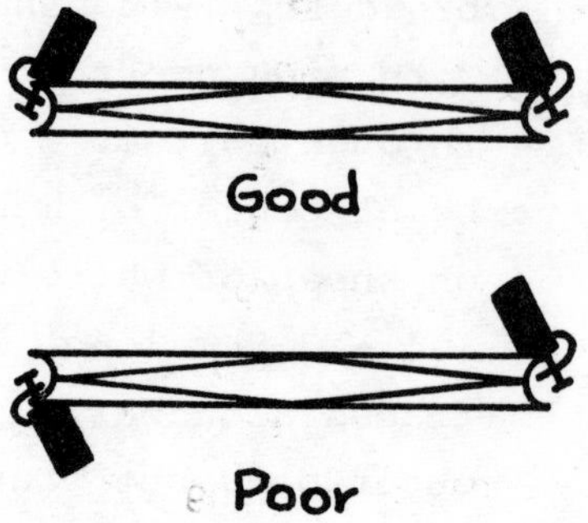


# 14
# OSCILLATIONS

## CLASSROOM DEMONSTRATIONS

1. CIRCLE OF REFERENCE - SHADOW PROJECTION OF ARROWS Use disk with arrows described in Demonstration 4, Chap. 3, with 35 mm projector as light source to project shadow on screen (see note on shadow projection, Chap. 26). Shadows represent velocity and acceleration in simple harmonic motion.

2. SIMPLE HARMONIC MOTION

A) MASS ON SPRING - To "graph" this motion in time, have student hold nozzle of can of spray paint beside mass, following its up and down motion as closely as possible. Have two other students move a 2-3 m length of wrapping paper horizontally at constant speed past the moving vertical nozzle to result in a large scale sine wave.

B) PENDULUM - Remember errors increase significantly for larger amplitudes where sin θ no longer nearly equals θ.

C) HACKSAW BLADE - Attach mass of 100-200 gm to hole on end of hacksaw blade and clamp other end. Good engineering example of fixed-free beam vibration.

D) AUDIO OSCILLATOR WITH OSCILLOSCOPE - Show change of amplitude and frequency visually.

E) WIRE IN MAGNETIC FIELD - Stretch bronze or steel wire ∿ 1 mm dia. between two rigid supports ∿ 1 m apart with suitable tension adjusting mechanism such as that used on stringed musical instruments. Place strong "Magnetron" magnet so wire can be vibrated transverse to field. Attach oscilloscope to ends of wire to detect emf generated. Move magnet to various positions along wire to show different frequencies of vibration. Use old violin bow to excite wire although plucking with finger is satisfactory for fundamental. Weaker magnets will require oscilloscope with higher amplification.

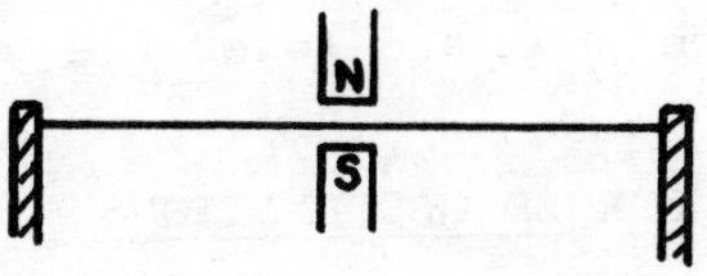


3. LISSAJOUS PATTERNS

A) OSCILLOSCOPE - Use two audio oscillators, one connected to vertical input and other to horizontal. Show change of pattern with amplitude, frequency ratio, and phase.

B) BLACKBURN'S PENDULUM - Commercially available, this conical container is filled with sand which dribbles from apex of cone. Motion in plane of figure has period determined by $L_2$ while that perpendicular to this plane has period determined by $L_1$. Cheap alternative is to use inverted gallon plastic jug with small hole in cap. Cut large hole in jug bottom to facilitate filling with sand.

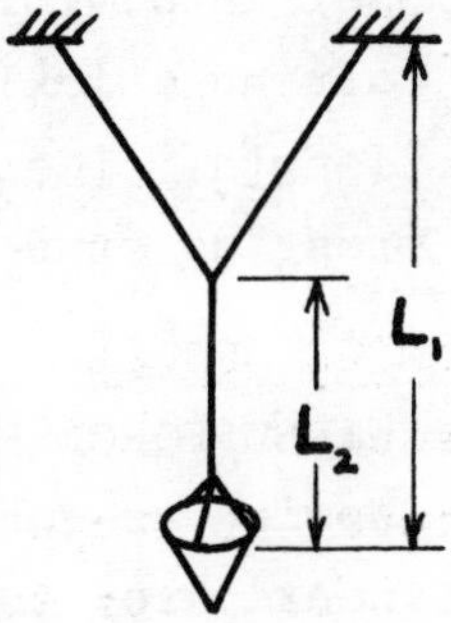

15

# DAMPED AND FORCED OSCILLATIONS

## CLASSROOM DEMONSTRATIONS

1. DAMPING - WIRE IN MAGNETIC FIELD Use Demonstration 2E, Chap. 14 and watch amplitude decay after plucking wire. Note difference in decay of higher and lower frequencies.

2. FORCED OSCILLATIONS

   A) TUNING FORK ON SOUNDING BOARD - Strike fork and place on desk or table to act as sounding board.

   B) DAMPED OSCILLATOR DRIVEN BY PHONO TURNTABLE - Distributed by Macalaster Scientific Company, this apparatus may be used to obtain amplitude vs frequency plots for various degrees of damping.

3. RESONANCE

   A) COUPLED PENDULA - To loosely supported horizontal string, attach several pendula of same length plus one considerably longer and one shorter. When one of the identical pendula is set into vibration, the horizontal string quickly transmits sufficient energy to excite others of same length. Identify one of pendula of same length as instructor and rest as students - some tuned in, some tuned out! Discuss tank circuits.

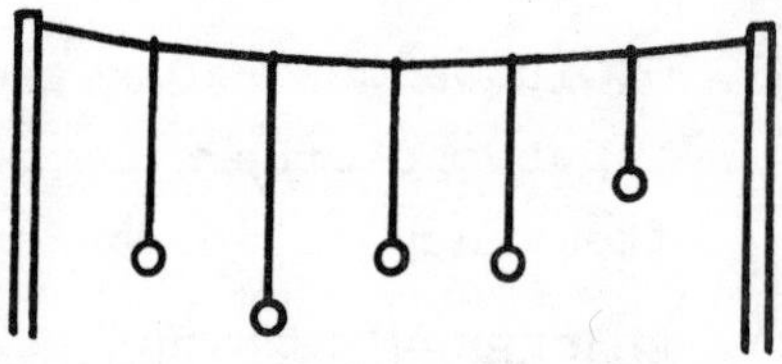

   B) WILBURFORCE PENDULUM - Commercially available, this mass on helical spring is tuned to have vertical translational frequency equal, or nearly so, to the rotational frequency. Tuning is accomplished using machine nuts or threaded masses which may be moved radially from the center.

   C) SCREEN DOOR SPRING - Heavy springs ∿ 1 cm O.D. and 30-40 cm long, sold for screen doors, oscillate well vertically with several kg attached. If mass is about right for vertical translational frequency to equal simple pendulum frequency, strong coupling is observed. Show coupling is eliminated by inserting long loop of string at top of spring to increase "pendulum" length and reduce "pendulum" frequency.

   D) TACOMA NARROWS BRIDGE - Classic case of bridge collapse excellently photographed in film loop number 80-2181 available from Holt, Rinehart and Winston, Inc.

# 16
# GRAVITY

## CLASSROOM DEMONSTRATIONS

1. FILM LOOPS Show following film loops, available from Holt, Rinehart and Winston, Inc.

| | |
|---|---|
| Kepler's Laws | 80-3635 |
| Central Forces, Iterated Blows | 80-3627 |
| Orbiting Bodies in Various Force Fields | |
| Part I Positive Power Laws | 80-4211 |
| Part II Negative Power Laws | 80-4229 |

2. PRINCIPLE OF EQUIVALENCE-INERTIA BALANCE Use inertia balance, available commercially, to determine inertial mass of an unknown and compare with its gravitational mass.

# 17
# TEMPERATURE

## CLASSROOM DEMONSTRATIONS

1. THERMOMETERS

   A) RESISTANCE - Carefully remove envelope from 200 watt incandescent bulb. Digital meter connected to filament shows resistance varies from $\sim 5\ \Omega$ to $\sim 10\ \Omega$ when heated by heat gun (hot air blower) or held high above burner flame. Use CCTV to make digital readout visible to large class.

   B) THERMOCOUPLE - Many thermocouples will produce few mV emf when heated by heat gun or burner. Chromel-alumel gives $\sim$ 10 mv. Use digital meter and CCTV as in A.

   C) THERMAL PAINT - Temperature sensitive paint may be used to show change of color with temperature.

D) GALILEO'S THERMOMETER - Thin spherical glass bulb (∿ 6 cm dia.) is sealed to length of 5 mm I.D. glass tubing. Bulb is coated with mixture of lamp black and shellac and mounted through stopper in flask containing water with food coloring added. Warm bulb with hands to drive out trapped air and draw liquid up into tubing. Use two parabolic reflectors to focus energy from 200 W incandescent bulb or Bunsen flame onto bulb. Changes in atmospheric pressure require adjustment of liquid level in glass tubing. Show on CCTV for large classes.

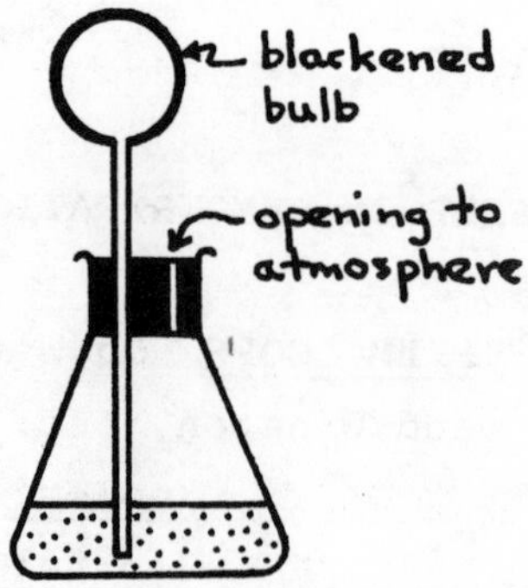


E) LIQUID CRYSTAL - Encapsulated liquid crystals change color as temperature changes. Available along with liquid crystal digital wall thermometers from Edmund Scientific Co.

2. EXPANSION

A) METAL ROD - One end of a metal tube (or rod) is fixed and the other rests on a rotatable shaft which turns in nearly frictionless bearings as tube expands. Readings made from graduated dial over which pointer connected to rotating shaft moves. Use ∿ 1 m tubes of various materials. Discuss automobile thermostats. Suspend thermostat in heated water and measure temperature at which it opens.

B) RUBBER BAND -Hang ∿ 1 kg from rubber band (∿ 6 mm width). Remove lens from 35 mm projector, insert aluminum or cardboard slide with ∿ 10-12 mm dia. hole, and use to shadow project band and weight on screen. Provide reference marker and supply heat from infrared heat lamp. Note that rubber band contracts!

C) BALL AND RING - Metal ball and ring, each mounted on handle, are constructed so that ball will barely pass through ring at room temperature. Ball will not pass when heated but will pass if both ball and ring heated.

D) RUBBER BALLOON - Place inflated toy balloon in liquid nitrogen. Two liter, wide-mouth dewar convenient. Remove balloon and observe as it warms.

E) DIME ON COKE BOTTLE - Place small Coke bottle in large beaker and surround with crushed ice. Remove after cooling, moisten mouth of bottle, and then cover it with dime. Bottle will "burp" as trapped air expands. Speed up by warming bottle with hands. Coke bottle used because dime nicely fits mouth indentation.

F) COLLAPSE A CAN - See Demonstration 6B, Chap. 5.

G) BALLOON INSIDE FLASK - Boil few ml of water in 500 ml flat bottom Florence flask. Remove from heat and quickly apply small, round, toy balloon over mouth. Balloon may be drawn in and out by heating and cooling flask. May be necessary to use rubber band to seal balloon to neck of flask.

3. DIFFERENTIAL EXPANSION

A) BIMETALLIC STRIP - Two dissimilar metal strips are bonded together and fastened to a handle. Strip bends when heated because two metals expand differently.

B) JUMPING DISC - Paper-thin bimetal discs are available from Edmund Scientific Co. Heated dome-shaped disc may be depressed to stable position which becomes unstable upon cooling. Jumps up to 1.5 m.

4. IDEAL GAS LAW

A) "BOYLE" MARSHMALLOW - Place marshmallow in transparent, illuminated vacuum chamber and evacuate with mechanical pump. Most dramatic change occurs when chamber is quickly repressurized to atmospheric pressure. Small Plexiglas chamber works well on overhead projector.

B) MOLECULAR MOTION DEMONSTRATOR - See Demonstration 2, Chap. 11.

C) GRAM-MOLECULAR VOLUME MODEL - Available commercially, this cardboard box has volume 22.4 liters with related data printed on faces.

# 18
# HEAT, WORK, AND THE FIRST LAW OF THERMODYNAMICS

CLASSROOM DEMONSTRATIONS

1. CHANGE OF PHASE

A) MAKE LIQUID NATURAL GAS (LNG) - Feed natural gas through glass tube to bottom of test tube partially immersed in liquid nitrogen ($LN_2$). Collect few ml of liquid, then remove from $LN_2$. Light end of test tube with match to show vaporization. Then pour flaming vapor and liquid on floor.

B) MAKE DRY ICE - Illustrate rapid cooling of gas upon expansion by making dry ice with $CO_2$ fire extinguisher. Dry ice collects on several layers of cloth held over end of nozzle. Discuss operation of refrigerators and air conditioners.

C) DRINKING BIRD - Commercially available in novelty stores, this bird is made by blowing glass tube in shape of bird and adding main bulb to posterior. Bird is filled with liquid of high vapor pressure. Bill and head are covered with fuzz to give large area for evaporation. When head is wet, evaporation cools interior, lowering vapor pressure, drawing liquid into head. This shifts center of gravity toward head and tips it into beaker of water where the fuzz again becomes wet. In this position, fluid flows back into main bulb and bird rights itself again. Process is repeated as long as water is in beaker. Also in Miller's Toy Set mentioned in Demonstration 2, Chap. 8.

2. <u>ADIABATIC COOLING - WILSON CLOUD CHAMBER</u> Attach bicycle pump to tube which passes through rubber stopper placed in mouth of $\sim$ 5-10 liter glass jug. Hold stopper and pressurize jug with pump. Allow stopper to pop out and fog droplets will form as pressure reduces suddenly. Fog forms more readily if smoke, which provides condensation nuclei, is added to jug before pressurization. Discuss application to Wilson Cloud Chamber, smog, etc.

3. <u>HEAT/MECHANICAL ENERGY CONVERTER - RUBBER BAND ENGINE</u> Construct rubber band engine from rim ($\sim$ 50 cm dia.) and hub ($\sim$ 10 cm dia.) made from Plexiglas ($\sim$ 1.27 cm thick) with thick rubber bands as spokes. Support by horizontal axle mounted in ball bearings. Rubber contracts upon heating, so center of gravity of wheel shifts off axle if rubber spokes to one side of axle are irradiated with heat lamp. Resulting torque causes heated, shorter spokes to move out of irradiated region and cool as new spokes move in, producing continuous rotation. Move lamp to opposite side to show reversal. May be necessary to balance wheel prior to each use with small dab of putty. Can also be made using rim and axle from bicycle wheel with good bearings.

4. <u>REGELATION-COMPRESSED ICE</u> Support block of ice so that wire carrying $\sim$ 4 kg on each end can pass over top. Wire will pass through block without cutting it in two. Use smallest diameter wire ($\leqslant$ #22) which will support masses on ends. Different cutting rates of Cu and Fe wire show dependence upon heat transfer between top and bottom of wire.

5. PLASTIC FLOW - COMPRESSED ICE  Make brass cylinder ∿ 15-20 mm I.D. and ∿ 7-8 cm long with loosely fitting cylindrical brass piston. Braze plug to one end and drill ∿ 3 mm dia. hole in side near that end. Fill with crushed ice and apply pressure to piston with very large C-clamp. Ice will be extruded from the hole because of plastic flow under high pressure. Remove piston and warm cylinder with hands to remove solid chunk of ice. Smaller C-clamp may be used if piston size reduced. Discuss glacier flow and why mountains are not higher (see article by Weisskopf, Science, 187, 605 (1975)).

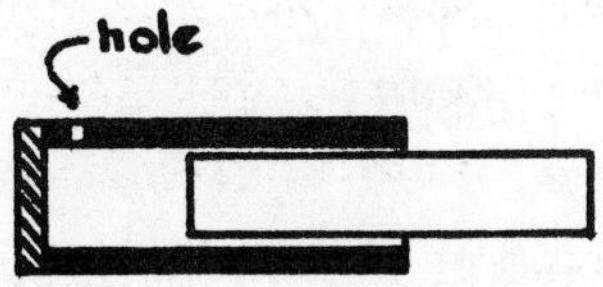


# 19
# THE AVAILABILITY OF ENERGY

CLASSROOM DEMONSTRATIONS

1. REVERSIBILITY-GLYCERINE CYLINDER  Illustrate reversibility with an absolutely amazing unmixing demonstration. The annular region between two concentric Plexiglas cylinders is filled with glycerine. Long needle syringe filled with red dye is inserted to bottom of annulus and slowly raised leaving line of dye. Inner cylinder is then rotated about 10-12 rev. Dye is apparently well mixed with glycerine. Actually, it lies in a fine one-armed spiral. If motion is reversed by exactly same number turns, spiral is unwound and original line of dye is approximately established! Discuss entropy and irreversibility. Also excellent analog of spin echo technique in NMR studies. See article by Heller, AJP, 28, 348 (1960).

2. ENTROPY AND TIME REVERSAL  Show film loop of same title available from AAPT Film Repository.

3. TIME REVERSAL INVARIANCE  See Demonstration 2F, Chap. 10.

# 20
# WAVE PULSES

## CLASSROOM DEMONSTRATIONS

### 1. TRANSMISSION OF ENERGY

A) DOMINOES - Illustrate mechanism of energy transfer with long row of dominoes stacked on edge such that tipping one domino at end causes others to fall in succession.

B) HEAVY ROPE - Use two hands to sharply whip one end of heavy rope ($\sim$ 2 cm dia.) held by student at other end. Almost impossible for student to keep end fixed.

C) BELL IN VACUUM - A small bell (with clapper), mounted in Plexiglas chamber, cannot be heard when chamber evacuated. Use chamber on overhead projector so student can see clapper in motion even when not heard. Shows sound is mechanical wave requiring medium for transmission.

### 2. VELOCITY OF PULSES

A) SPRING, RUBBER HOSE, OR LIGHT ROPE - Variation in tension produces noticeable change in velocity of pulse.

B) WAVE MACHINE - Three rib-like structures, developed by Bell Telephone Laboratories, are distributed by Allegri Tech, Inc., 141 River Road, Nutley, N.J. 07110. One unit has elements 23 cm long, 4 mm dia., connected by elastic wire "spine". Second unit has elements 46 cm long with identical "spine". Third unit has elements of varying length as "impedance matching" section. Longer cross arm quadruples inertia factor with same elastic factor in spine thereby reducing wave velocity. Similarities in Wave Behavior, 16 mm sound movie using this device, is available from Film Library, Bell Telephone Labs, Inc., 600 Mountain Ave., Murray Hill, N.J. 07974.

C) TIME RESOLUTION OF EAR - Attach small funnel to each end of rubber hose $\sim$ 1.5 m long and mark center of hose. Have student hold funnels over ears while seated with back to table. Lay rest of hose flat on table. Send a pulse to each ear by striking hose sharply with edge of meter stick. Students can usually determine which ear receives pulse first if path difference is as large as 3-4 cm. Minimum path difference detectable divided by speed of sound in air is time resolution of ear ($\sim 10^{-4}$ sec). Discuss how relative time of arrival of sound at two ears tells us directions of sources.

3. SUPERPOSITION Show film loops Superposition of Pulses (S-81590) and Superposition of Pulses in a Spring (S-81293) available from Encyclopedia Britannica Educational Corporation.

4. TRANSVERSE AND LONGITUDINAL PULSES Use a long helical-wound spring (∿ 2 cm dia.) to show transverse and longitudinal pulses. Tie small colored strips of cloth to some coils to call attention to their motion. Or show Encyclopedia Britannica film loop (S-81291) Single Pulses in a Spring.

5. REFLECTION AND PHASE CHANGES

A) WAVE MACHINE - Use the device referred to in 2B above to show reflection of pulses from free and fixed ends. Couple two rib-like structures to show reflection from discontinuity.

B) FILM LOOPS - Show Encyclopedia Britannica film loops on Reflection of Waves in a Spring - Free End and Fixed End (S-81295), Reflection of Pulses I - Fixed End (S-81591), and Reflection of Pulses II - Free End (S-81592). Latter two are computer animated.

C) MICROWAVES - See Demonstration 12, Chap. 26.

# 21
# HARMONIC WAVES IN ONE DIMENSION

## CLASSROOM DEMONSTRATIONS

1. HARMONIC WAVE

A) ROTATING SLINKY ON OVERHEAD - Stretch short length of slinky spring and mount so it can turn about horizontal axis. Use on overhead projector. Traveling waves observed when spring is rotated. Change direction of travel by changing direction of rotation.

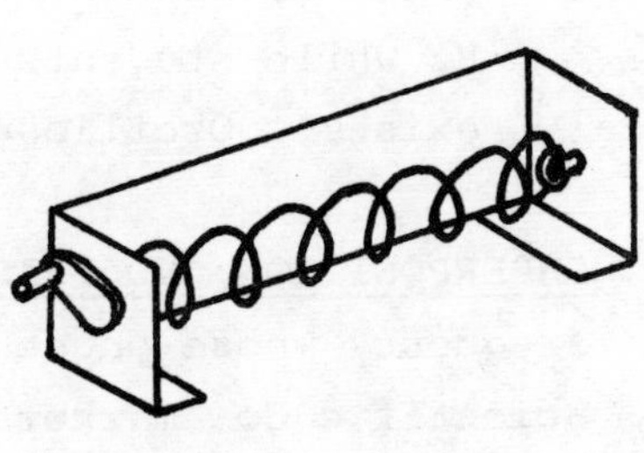

B) SIREN DISK - A disk (25.4 cm dia.), available commercially, is made with four circles of uniformly spaced holes and one circle of randomly spaced holes. Disk is turned by variable speed rotator and jet of air is directed at holes. Different musical notes are heard from different circles of regularly spaced holes but noise is heard from circle of randomly spaced holes. Harmonic sound waves are pleasing to man.

2. POLARIZATION-MECHANICAL ANALOG Use long, helical-wound spring ($\sim$ 2 cm dia.) passing through wooden slot placed vertically and another placed horizontally to show blocking of transverse waves with components in one plane. Show that longitudinal wave is not blocked by either. Do not push "picket fence" analogy too far - see Shurcliff and Ballard, Polarized Light, Van Nostrand (Momentum Book No. 7), 1964.

The remaining demonstrations utilize good oscilloscope, several audio oscillators (20-20,000 Hz), high-fidelity amplifier and microphone, and 8 $\Omega$ speaker so students can hear harmonic waves as well as see them on oscilloscope. Use CCTV to make oscilloscope trace visible to large class.

3. WAVE PARAMETERS

A) OSCILLATOR, OSCILLOSCOPE, AND SPEAKER - Define $\lambda$, f, and amplitude and show on oscilloscope. Discuss relationship of pitch and loudness to f and amplitude.

B) WAVELENGTH OF SOUND IN AIR - Mount two small ($\sim$ 10 cm) speakers on optical bench. Connect output of variable frequency audio oscillator to one speaker, which serves as transmitter, and to horizontal input of good oscilloscope. Connect other speaker, which serves as receiver, to vertical input of scope. Line to voice coil output transformers should be used with both speakers for impedance matching. Lissajous pattern formed on oscilloscope changes as distance between speakers is varied. Separation must be changed by $\lambda$ to make Lissajous pattern repeat. Adjustment easiest for 0° and 180° phase angles. Find velocity of sound in air from f and $\lambda$.

C) RANGE OF HEARING - Vary audio oscillator frequency from 20 to 20,000 Hz while students listen to determine where their cut-off for hearing exists. Oscilloscope shows disturbance still present after cut-off.

4. SUPERPOSITION AND PHASE DIFFERENCE Superpose two harmonic waves of same frequency whose phase difference and amplitude can be varied. Pasco Scientific Co. markets "Fourier Synthesizer" which provides two 500 Hz signals whose phase can be controlled for this purpose.

5. LISSAJOUS PATTERNS See Demonstration 3A, Chap. 14.

6. DEMONSTRATION RECORDS An excellent two record sound demonstration set called The Science of Sound was produced by Bell Telephone Laboratories and was available through Bell System companies in the early 60's. Included 20 demonstrations ranging from "How We Hear", "Loudness", and "Reverberation" to "Music Scales" and "Doppler Effect". Although no longer available from Bell System, sets may be available in some colleges and universities which could be copied on tape.

# 22
# STANDING WAVES

CLASSROOM DEMONSTRATIONS

1. TRANSVERSE STANDING WAVES

   A) COIL SPRING - Produce standing waves manually in helical-wound spring (∿ 2 cm dia. and 4-6 m long) rigidly supported at one end. Stretch spring for best results at higher frequencies and to show increased velocity. Rubber hose, substituted for spring, may be excited by eccentric attached to variable speed rotator. Use strobe light to show "slow motion".

   B) WHIP ANTENNA - Whip antenna or bicycle safety flag, manually excited, produces standing waves with antinode at upper end. Decreasing diameter of antenna toward upper end decreases node to node distance. Bicycle safety flag produces fewer overtones.

   C) ALUMINUM ROD - Mark rod (∿ 1.3 cm dia. x 2 m) at points 0.224 and 0.776 times its length. Hold between thumb and forefinger at one of these points and strike rod sharply at center with edge of hand. Support at other marked point. Standing wave is produced with nodes at marked positions. Al preferred due to high "Q" producing less damping.

   D) MICROWAVES - Produce standing μ waves by placing plane aluminum reflector ∿ 1 m from transmitter. Explore pattern with diode detector connected to audio amplifier and speaker for audible detection.

   E) CIRCULAR STANDING WAVES - Piece of banding material used in shipping, joined to make circle (∿ 65-70 cm dia.), can be excited manually to produce circular standing wave pattern. Works best in horizontal position. Use colored vinyl tape to accent nodal points. Discuss bell modes of gongs.

F) CHLADNI PLATES - Aluminum plate (0.16 cm x 30 cm square preferable), rigidly supported by rod at its center, produces two dimensional standing wave pattern when bowed perpendicular to its plane. Holding edge with finger and bowing at different locations produces varied patterns. For dramatic effect, paint plate flat black, illuminate with UV light, and use fine sand mixed with fluorescent paint. Try plates of different shape.

G) VIBRATIONAL MODES OF THIN FILM - Drive circular soap film (see Demonstration 14, Chap. 26) with loudspeaker placed at opposite end of plastic tube from film. Use amplified audio oscillator signal and increase frequency slowly, observing higher modes. Replace circular film support with square or other shapes. Replace audio oscillator with cassette music for interesting effects.

2. LONGITUDINAL STANDING WAVES

A) SLINKY SPRING - Show film loop, Longitudinal Standing Waves In A Spring from Encyclopedia Britannica (S-81298).

B) SINGING PIPES - Almost any pipe 1-2 m long will resonate when lowered to optimum position over Fisher high temperature (grid top) burner. Stove pipe, conduit, downspout, Plexiglas tubes, and mailing tubes work well; large diameter tubes are easiest to excite. Adjust burner until blue tips are formed a few mm above grid. In lieu of continuous burner excitation, attach several pieces of high temperature gauze to wire frame and insert into tube $\sim$ 16 cm from its bottom. Heat gauze cherry red and tube "sings" when removed from burner. Amaze students by turning pipe horizontal, "pouring sound on floor, and then scooping it up again."

C) SINGING ROD - Hold aluminum rod ($\sim$ 1.3 cm dia. x 2 m) between thumb and forefinger at center and stroke longitudinally with other thumb and forefinger to make it "sing". Spray rod first with "tacky" substance (sometimes called "dry play") sold for athletes by sporting goods stores. May also use rosin. Produce higher harmonics by changing point of support (nodal point).

D) GAS FLAMES - Large burner is constructed from piece of downspout ($\sim$ 10 cm dia. x 1.5-2 m) which has small holes drilled with #54 drill at regular intervals of $\sim$ 2.5 cm along the top. One end is closed by metal plate and other end is fitted with rubber diaphragm and loudspeaker. Two inlets supply gas feed. When gas passes into pipe and out small holes, it may be lighted at each of holes to give line of regularly spaced uniform-sized flames. Audio oscillator driving speaker is tuned to give standing waves in pipe. Presence of pressure maxima and minima is indicated by higher and lower flames. Rapidly vary frequency and then replace oscillator with cassette tape player using fast contemporary music with good bass.

E) RESONANCE TUBE - Adjust length of air column in piece of electrical conduit (∿ 2.5 cm dia.) by lowering into vessel of water. Excite column with tuning fork or by exhaling across top. Scribe dimensions on outside of tube for easy measurement.

F) ORGAN PIPE - Purchase variable pitch whistle with movable slide in variety store. Remove slide and use hand to illustrate effects of closed and open ends.

G) SINGING CORRUGATED PIPE - Corrugated flexible plastic tube (∿ 1 m long x 2.5 cm dia.) found in some variety stores emits loud and clear pure tone when holding one end and swinging tube in circle. Waste line found in marine supply centers will also work but spiral-wound vacuum cleaner hose will not. See article by Crawford, AJP 42, 278 (1974).

# 23
# THE SUPERPOSITION OF WAVES OF DIFFERENT FREQUENCY

## CLASSROOM DEMONSTRATIONS

### 1. BEATS

A) OSCILLATORS, OSCILLOSCOPE, AND SPEAKER - Feed output of each of two audio oscillators through ∿ 100 Ω protective resistors to input of single amplifier. Amplifier output is fed to vertical input of oscilloscope and speaker, connected in parallel. To hear beats well, set oscillators at few hundred Hz with difference of few Hz between them. To "see" beats well, set oscillators at few thousand Hz with difference of few hundred Hz between them.

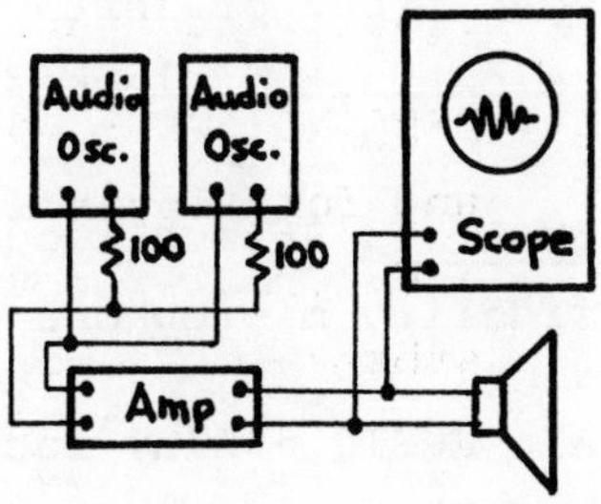


B) TUNING FORK WITH ONE TINE LOADED - Use two identical tuning forks and place rubber band on one tine of one (320 Hz works well). Strike both forks and hold one fork to each ear. Or, use microphone, amplifier, and speaker to make beats audible for large class.

C) DIME STORE WHISTLES - Purchase $\sim$ 6 plastic, police-type whistles. Crush and remove warbler in each with needle-nose pliers. Blow different pairs simultaneously and choose best combination. Use audio oscillator and Lissajous figures on oscilloscope to determine frequency.

D) SPEED OF SOUND IN ALUMINUM ROD - Excite fundamental of rod as in Demonstration 2C, Chap. 22. Then $\lambda$ is twice length of rod. Beat vibrating rod against audio oscillator (with speaker) to determine f.

2. <u>FOURIER SYNTHESIS</u>

A) PASCO SYNTHESIZER - Pasco Scientific Co. markets a "Fourier Synthesizer" which generates two fundamentals of 500 Hz and eight higher harmonics, each with amplitude and phase control. May be used to synthesize square, triangular, and other shape waves and to show effects of phase.

B) MECHANICALLY-GENERATED SQUARE WAVE - Use equipment described in Demonstration 2E, Chap. 14. Locate magnetron magnet at center of wire to give strong field there. Gently bowing wire near one end produces square wave on oscilloscope! Bowing excites all harmonics but, since even ones have node at center, only odd harmonics produce induced emf seen on scope. Requires some bowing practice.

3. <u>PHASE AND GROUP VELOCITY</u> Use the equipment described in Demonstration 1A above to show difference in phase and group velocity. Or, if dual trace oscilloscope available, connect one variable-frequency audio oscillator to each input and lock sweep on one of them. Set oscillators to slightly different frequencies and measure wavelengths. Display group pattern by setting input selector to add two signals. Make group move right or left by adjusting frequency of other oscillator above or below that of locked-in oscillator.

4. <u>QUALITY</u> Attach good oscilloscope and 8 $\Omega$ speaker to output of high-fidelity microphone and amplifier.

A) MUSIC - Play rock, folk, classical, and computer-generated music. Compare waveforms on scope at high and low sweep rates. Pasco Scientific Co. markets cassette tapes which have sustained notes produced by various musical instruments. Computer generated music records are contained in book <u>Music By Computers</u>, eds H. von Foerster and J. W. Beauchamp, John Wiley and Sons (1969).

B) SYNTHESIZER - Use synthesizer in 2A above to add several harmonics with various phases to a fundamental.

C) ALUMINUM ROD - When highly excited, Al rod of 1D above produces overtones which may be seen on oscilloscope if end of rod held near microphone. Overtones may be damped out by grasping rod at center with whole hand.

D) VOICE - Make sustained vowel sounds and show waveforms on oscilloscope. Compare waveforms of vowels spoken by several students. Compare vowels with fundamental and one or two overtones produced by B above. Discuss "voice prints".

# 24
# SPHERICAL AND CIRCULAR WAVES

CLASSROOM DEMONSTRATIONS

1. <u>WAVE FRONTS</u> Show various wavefronts with ripple tank. Or, show film-loops <u>Circular Wave Reflection from Various Barriers</u> (80-2322) and <u>Reflection of Waves from Concave Barriers</u> (80-2330) available from Holt, Rinehart and Winston, Inc.

2. <u>DOPPLER EFFECT</u>

   A) VIBRATING REED - A rod, with reed at one end, is equipped with shaft which fits standard, variable-speed rotator. Reed emits sound when excited by air currents produced by rotation. Pitch is higher as reed approaches observer and lower as it moves away from observer. Operate at low speed. Available commercially.

   B) ALUMINUM ROD - Excite rod as in Demonstration 2C, Chap. 22 and rotate about its center while held overhead.

   C) TUNING FORK ON STRING - Drill small hole in bottom of stem of tuning fork and attach string. Strike fork and swing in horizontal circle overhead.

   D) BELL LABORATORIES RECORD - Play Doppler effect demonstration on <u>The Science of Sound</u> record set. See Demonstration 6, Chap. 21.

3. <u>INTERFERENCE</u>

   A) TWO SPEAKERS - Place two speakers 1.5 - 2 m apart and connect them in parallel to audio oscillator set at $\sim$ 4000 Hz. Have students move their heads back and forth to detect interference maxima and minima. Have small classes explore whole room. Add reversing switch in leads to one speaker to reverse phase. Have students note that, with everything stationary, switching phase changes interference max. to min.

B) ALUMINUM ROD - Excite rod as in Demonstration 2C, Chap. 22, and hold stationary. Ends of rod act as sources. Have students move heads to note interference.

C) MOIRÉ PATTERN - Simulate interference pattern of A above by overlaying on overhead projector two transparencies of concentric rings of regularly increasing radius so that they almost superimpose. Separation of rings corresponds to $\lambda$ and distance mismatch between centers corresponds to separation of speakers. Transparencies available from Edmund Scientific Co.

D) FILM LOOPS - Interference of Waves (80-2405) and Effect of Phase Difference Between Sources (80-241) available from Holt, Rinehart and Winston, Inc.

# 25
# WAVE PROPAGATION

CLASSROOM DEMONSTRATIONS

Many demonstrations appropriate to topics in this chapter may be done with ripple tank. However, in practice, it is much easier and just as effective to use some of the excellent film loops available from Holt, Rinehart and Winston, Inc.

| | |
|---|---|
| Diffraction and Scattering Around Obstacles | 80-244 |
| Single Slit Diffraction | 80-2421 |
| Straight Wave Reflection from Straight Barriers | 80-231 |
| Refraction of Waves | 80-234 |
| Barrier Pentration of Waves | 80-2363 |
| Bragg Reflection of Waves | 80-235 |

Other demonstrations on these topics are suggested in Chap. 26 and Chap. 27 where they are treated in more detail.

1. TOTAL INTERNAL REFLECTION-RAY TRACING Paths of individual rays may be made visible in smoke, chalk dust or water to which eosin (fluorescin) has been added. Sources include laser, projector lamp with lens and slits to produce "rays", or blackboard optics kit (Leybold). These may be used with Lucite or glass prisms, curved or coiled Lucite rods and fiber optics. Hollow or air prism may be used with water tank.

2. SCATTERING

A) CHALK DUST WITH LASER - Beat two erasers together to make laser beam visible. Alternate is to use 35 mm projector beam focused by lens. Beam is made visible by passing it through a box having glass or plastic front and filled with tobacco smoke.

B) LIQUIDS - Place small reflector spotlight bulb (50 W) over battery jar filled with water. Note scattering due to particles found in most city water. Increase scattering by adding eosin (fluorescin) or powdered cream.

C) ARTIFICIAL SUNSET - Pass light from 35 mm projector with "slide" having 12 mm dia. aperture through long axis of water tank 60-80 cm long. Emerging beam is displayed on nearby white screen set at angle for good student viewing. For about 10 liters of water add, by pouring along entire tank length, 100 ml photographic hypo, stirring well from end to end. Then add 25 ml concentrated sulfuric acid, well distributed and well stirred. After about 5 min, formation of precipitate causes previously white "sun" on screen to turn to deeper orange and red of "sunset". Light scattered out sides of tank simulates blue sky. Use Polaroid to show it is partially plane-polarized (see Demonstrations 19B and C, Chap. 26). Also simulates "hazy" day after much precipitate formed.

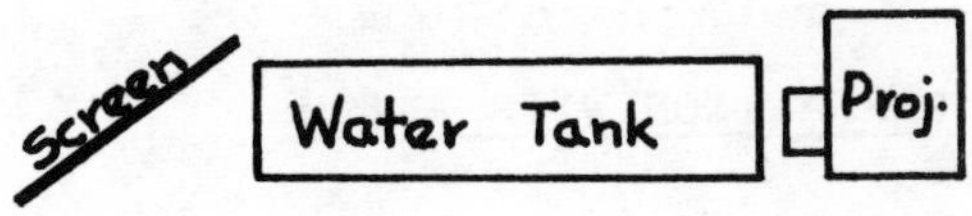


# 26 LIGHT

## CLASSROOM DEMONSTRATIONS

A very convenient light source for optics demonstrations as well as shadow projection is 35 mm projector. Useful additional features are two position switch for 300 W or 500 W operation and zoom lens. Low profile of Kodak Carousel or Ektagraphic is convenient. "Slides" made of 5 cm square aluminum 1 mm thick may be drilled to form apertures of 12, 9, 6 and 3 mm dia. Epoxy double-edge razor blades to one of Al slides with 12 mm aperture to make slit $\sim$ 1 mm wide.

For shadow projection, use 12 mm aperture as "slide" and remove usual projector lens. Sharpness of shadow improves as projector is moved farther from object, however, size of shadow decreases.

1. ELECTROMAGNETIC WAVES-MICROWAVES Use commercially available μ wave transmitter and receiver to show:
   A) RADIATION OF DIPOLE ANTENNA
   B) POLARIZATION
   C) STANDING WAVES
   D) SINGLE SLIT DIFFRACTION
   E) DOUBLE SLIT INTERFERENCE
   F) LLOYD'S MIRROR
   G) MICHELSON INTERFEROMETER

2. RAY OPTICS Reflection and refraction for flat and curved surfaces may be shown with optical disc or blackboard optics kit (Leybold).

3. DIFFERENT INDICES OF REFRACTION Place spoon in glass of water and observe magnifying effect and discontinuity at handle.

4. REFRACTION WITH PRISM

   A) GLASS PRISM - Use narrow slit in Al or cardboard slide in 35 mm projector to produce narrow tall beam. Place tall (5-10 cm) glass prism in beam and observe spectrum on white card or screen. A second glass prism may be added to increase dispersion. A triangular bottle "prism" filled with carbon disulfide or ethyl cinnamate produces large dispersion.

   B) WATER PRISM - Use slide above to produce horizontal beam (axis of slit also horizontal) reflected by plane mirror into rectangular dish ∿ 10 cm deep. Place plane mirror in water at angle of 30-40° to surface to form water prism. Beam returning from mirror in dish is reflected above projector to screen. If observed from side with slightly cloudy water, beam path may be seen as aid to adjusting source and mirror.

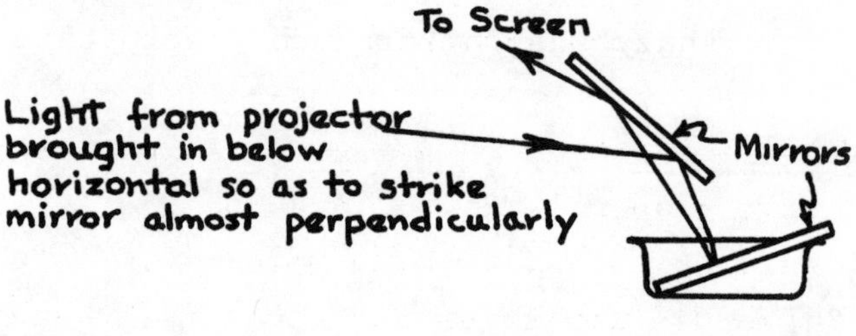


5. REFRACTION - RAINBOW Use 35 mm projector with zoom lens to illuminate round bottom flask filled with water to simulate giant water drop. Rainbow is seen on screen ∿ 1 m behind projector. Light beam should be barely larger than flask. Use slide with ∿ 12 mm aperture.

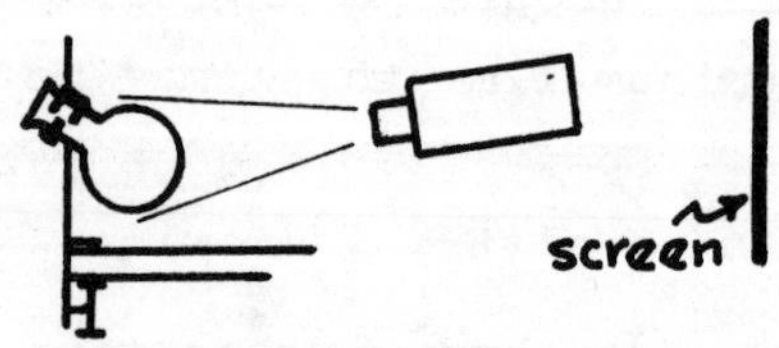

6. EQUAL INDICES OF REFRACTION Place small beaker inside a larger one. Pour into smaller one mixture of 4 parts carbon tetrachloride and 1 part benzene. Allow small one to overflow into larger and observe smaller one "disappear".

7. DIFFRACTION BY OBSTACLES AND SLITS Use film loops of ripple tank referred to in Chap. 25.

8. SINGLE SLIT DIFFRACTION Have students use "slit" between two fingers close to eye to observe line filament of 25 W or 40 W showcase bulb. Students may vary width of "slit" by squeezing fingers together.

9. TWO-DIMENSIONAL DIFFRACTION Observe incandescent bulb about 6 meters away through window screen, ladies' hose, or ladies' neck scarf. Latter two analogous to x-ray powder pattern.

10. DIFFRACTION BY OBSTACLES Use carbon arc to cast shadow of needle and razor blade on screen. Focus arc on slit with condensing lens (f $\sim$ 10 cm). Place needle and blade $\sim$ 4-5 m from slit and screen a similar distance behind. Adjust slit position and width to obtain best bright line down center of shadow of needle. May also be done with laser using needle and blade in lieu of pin in Demonstration 17K.

11. INTERFERENCE ANALOG WITH SOUND WAVES See Demonstration 3A, Chap. 24, for two speakers as sources placed side by side.

12. PHASE CHANGE UPON REFLECTION An 11 cm microwave transmitter is placed beside metal sheet serving as reflector. Detector is connected to audio amplifier and speaker for audible detection. Explore interference pattern. Destructive interference at point B shows that there is 180° phase change of electric field of microwave beam upon reflection. Analog of Lloyd's mirror experiment with visible light.

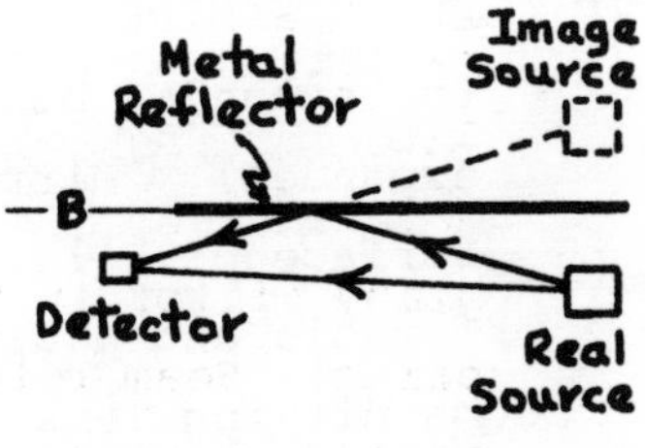


13. INTERFERENCE WITH NEWTON'S RINGS Light from H-4 100 W mercury lamp produces brilliant colored rings when used to illuminate at close range air gap between thin prism and flat glass plate clamped loosely together. Observe interference rings by reflected light using long focal length lens to project on screen. Laser source may be substituted.

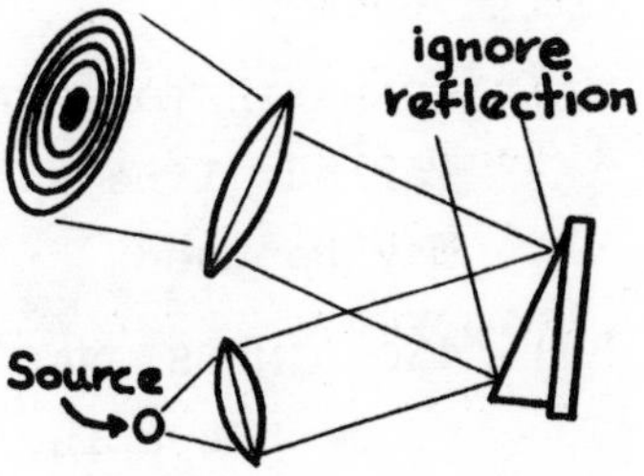

14. SOAP FILM INTERFERENCE Use 35 mm projector to reflect white light from thin soap film placed on end of horizontal Plexiglas tube (∿ 7 cm dia.). Roll on film with small photographic roller. Focus reflected light on screen with lens (f ∿ 35 cm). Since film is vertical, it assumes wedge shape and multicolored interference fringes are formed. Show effect of several colored gelatin filters. For films lasting ∿ 45 min, mix several days before using: 71 gm Joy detergent, 184 gm glycerine, and 227 gm distilled water.

15. INTERFERENCE WITH MICA SHEET Reflect light from H-4 100 W mercury source using thin mica sheet ∿ 15 cm square to large screen several meters away. Limit source aperture to ∿ 1x3 cm.

16. INTERFEROGRAM Place high intensity sodium light source in far corner of room and remove any shield. Allow ample warm-up time for lamp to reach high intensity. Pass among class large acetate-framed transmission holograms ∿ 11 cm square available from Edmund Scientific Co. Sharper image produced at greater distance from sodium lamp. Sharpest image produced by expanded laser beam.

17. LASER DEMONSTRATIONS A 1-2 mW laser may be used but 3.5 mW preferred. A large or poorly darkened room requires the higher power. Extreme caution should be exercised to prevent the reflected beam from striking the audience.

A) DIFFRACTION - Use single slit of fixed or variable width.

B) INTERFERENCE - Use double slit.

C) LLOYD'S MIRROR - Place small piece of plane front-surface mirror in the expanded beam (6-8 cm F.L. negative lens preferred as good beam expander). Mirror should be just below center of beam with its surface parallel to beam direction. An aluminized screen is preferable and a distance of 5-8 m works well. A long focal length magnifying lens may be used to enlarge the image.

D) FRESNEL BIPRISM - Use expanded beam and start with biprism several meters from laser to show two beams. Move in continuously to show overlapping. Fringes appear with biprism a few cm from beam expander.

E) TRANSMISSION GRATING - Place in unexpanded laser beam gratings of various line spacings; 100-1000 lines/cm work well. Ronchi rulings may be used.

F) TWO-DIMENSIONAL GRATING - Place in unexpanded laser beam wire cloth of mesh spacing 100-400 wires per inch (for source see Demonstration 5, Chap. 27). Larger diffracting angles obtained using photographic mesh grating 500-1000 lines/inch available from same source.

G) LAUE PATTERN ANALOG - Place two of above mesh gratings in series in unexpanded laser beam and rotate one with respect to other. Discuss x-ray diffraction and application to structure of solids, DNA, etc.

H) REFLECTION DIFFRACTION GRATING - Use engraved steel ruler placed in laser beam at grazing incidence. Reflect beam from rulings at edge where closest spacing occurs. Now move ruler so beam reflects from wider spaced rulings at greater distances from edge.

I) MULTIPLE REFLECTIONS IN GLASS - Place piece of thin wall glass tubing with its axis perpendicular to beam so that beam grazes circumference. Diameters from 1 to 4 cm work well, larger ones are preferable.

J) CIRCULAR FRESNEL DIFFRACTION - Placement of components is somewhat critical. Place pinhole in the diverging beam just beyond focal point of expander where beam is slightly larger than pinhole. Shift pinhole forward and backward to show constructive and destructive interference at center of circular pattern.

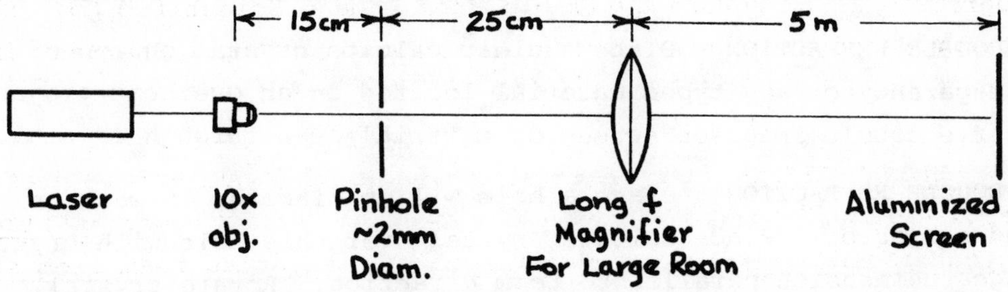


K) POISSON SPOT - Expand laser beam using ∿ 10 cm F.L. positive or negative lens. Use large cork as holder for straight pin with round head (or ball bearing ∿ 1 mm dia. held on end of cylindrical magnet). Place pinhead in beam ∿ 2 m from laser where beam dia. is 2-3 times pinhead dia. Observe diffraction pattern on screen as far away as possible, at least 5-8 m. For large class, form image on distant ground glass screen and use CCTV. Or, place long focal length projection lens between pinhead and screen for magnification.

L) MICHELSON INTERFEROMETER - See Demonstration 1, Chap. 28.

18. RESOLUTION

A) RESOLVING POWER - Show film loop of same title, number 80-2082, available from Holt, Rinehart and Winston, Inc.

B) ANGULAR RESOLUTION OF EYE - Place two black dots ∿ 2 mm apart on light background and observe from an increasing distance until unable to resolve. Determine angular resolution by ratio of dot separation to viewing distance. Apply to resolution of auto headlights.

19. POLARIZATION

A) BY DICHROIC MATERIAL - Place sheet of Polaroid on overhead projector and rotate second sheet above first.

B) BY SCATTERING - Observe blue sky through Polaroid in general northerly direction at right angles to sun's rays. Rotate Polaroid.

C) BY SCATTERING - Use a 50 W spot projection bulb to illuminate from above a battery jar or large beaker of water to which has been added few drops of condensed milk or powdered cream. Place sheet of Polaroid so that observer views light scattered at right angles (horizontally) to incident light. Rotate Polaroid.

D) BY REFLECTION - Use beam from 35 mm projector to illuminate pile of 5 to 10 glass plates at Brewster's angle. Observe effect of rotating piece of Polaroid in both reflected and refracted beams (almost totally and partially polarized, respectively).

E) BY REFLECTION - Rotate sheet of Polaroid to examine light reflected from polished floor or glossy painted table surface or from floor along long hall illuminated by strips of overhead fluorescent lights.

F) BY DOUBLE REFRACTION - Place a clear calcite crystal on top of a transparency of any typed material located on an overhead projector. Observe double image on screen of material seen through crystal.

G) BY DOUBLE REFRACTION - Place a hole $\sim$ 1 mm diameter in mask on overhead projector. Place calcite crystal over this hole with crystal's longest dimension parallel to beam direction. Rotate crystal, observing that it is extraordinary ray which moves. Rotate Polaroid above crystal to show two beams are plane-polarized at right angles.

H) INTERFERENCE - Place sheet of cellophane between two sheets of Polaroid. Rotate cellophane slightly between "crossed" and "parallel" Polaroid sheets. Increase thickness of cellophane. Clear cellophane tape also works well. Use on overhead projector. Make American flag by using different numbers of layers of tape.

I) HALF WAVE PLATE - Most commonly available thickness of cellophane tape is equivalent to $\sim \lambda/2$ plate for central region of visible spectrum. Cigarette wrapper cellophane is about same thickness.

J) DOUBLE REFRACTION DUE TO STRESS - Place sheet of Polaroid on overhead projector and tape second sheet, "crossed" to first, over focusing mirror/lens to give sizable working region between Polaroids. Stretch polyethylene sheet held close to stage to observe production of double refraction by stress. (Note: not all clear plastic films are polyethylene so try several types.)

K) STRESS ANALYSIS - Use overhead projector arrangement in J to examine models of beams, rings, triangles, etc., made from doubly refracting plastic when stressed. One source of such plastic is Photolastic, 67 Lincoln Hwy., Malvern, PA 19355.

L) 3-D COLOR SLIDES - Use 3-D "glasses" to view two slides of same scene superimposed on <u>aluminized</u> screen. Slides should be taken using identical cameras placed side by side and projected using projectors with polarizing filters over lenses. Transmission plane of one filter is at +45 degrees to horizontal and other at -45 degrees.

M) MECHANICAL ANALOG - See Demonstration 2, Chap. 21.

# 27
# GEOMETRIC OPTICS

## CLASSROOM DEMONSTRATIONS

1. PLANE MIRRORS

A) GLASS SHEET - Place battery jar of water on stand behind glass pane ∿ 40x50 cm. Place candle on same type stand in front. Candle appears to class to "burn" under water. Alternative is to place identical light bulbs in identical sockets, one bulb and socket on each side of glass. Turn on front bulb and rear one appears to light.

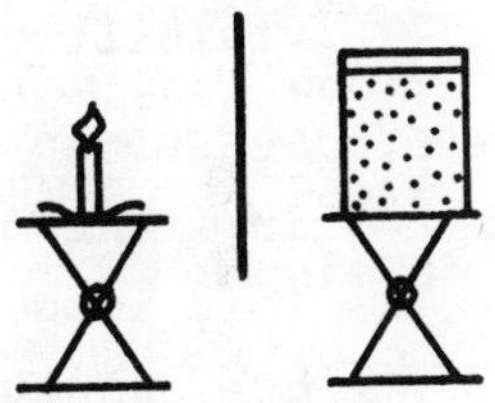

B) PARALLEL FACING MIRRORS - Place two mirrors, each 50-80 cm in each dimension, parallel and facing one another. Place object between them and have students view just past edge of one mirror to see multiple images of "barber shop" effect. CCTV may be used for large class with appropriate change of focus to see clearly images successively further away. Note that only alternate images are perverted. Draw ray diagrams and explain.

C) MIRRORS AT AN ANGLE - Arrange two mirrors, each 50-80 cm in each dimension so that one edge of each forms vertex of angle, θ. Place object in area between mirrors and observe multiple images when angle is 360° divided by whole number. Alternative is to mount small mirrors on board to pass among class. Have students examine central image when θ = 90° to "see themselves as others do", i.e., not perverted.

D) CORNER CUBE - Mirror "tiles" used for home decorating (∿ 30 cm square) can be mounted to form corner cube with retro-reflecting property. Have students close first one eye and then the other to observe which eye's image is at corner. Smaller mirrors may be so mounted to pass among class. Or, use chalk dust to make incoming and reflected laser beam visible (BE CAREFUL with reflected beam). Discuss retro-reflecting panel placed on moon by astronauts.

2. SPHERICAL MIRRORS

A) RAY DIAGRAM - See Demonstration 2, Chap. 26.

B) OSCILLATRON TOY - Discuss optics of item found in novelty stores consisting of hemispherical reflector made of plastic with small colored ball hanging at center of curvature.

C) IS THERE A BULB IN SOCKET? - At center of curvature of large spherical mirror (40-60 cm dia.), place box with two light sockets, one outside and one inside box. Wire inner one to illuminate 60-100 W bulb. Outside socket is empty but has dummy wires attached for realism. (Note: Positioning of mirror to get center of curvature at point between socket bases is important.) Place on rotating platform or use CCTV for good visibility for large classes.

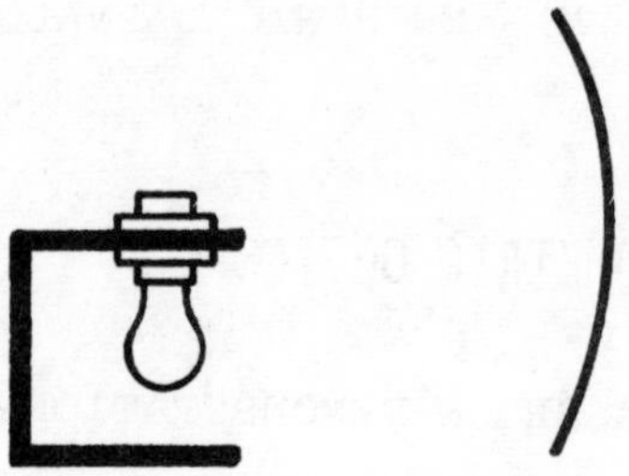

D) SPHERICAL ABERRATION - Place light bulb in front of mirror described in C) and form large image on screen 5-7 m away. Use annulus of Masonite in various sizes to hang over front of mirror and block out rays from periphery of mirror. Mark "stops" in "f" numbers (ratio of focal length to stop diameter). Start with small opening, say f:2, and proceed to f:1.4 and f:1. Discuss f numbers relating to cameras. May also use these apertures to show increase of depth of field (reasonably good focus) with decreased aperture size.

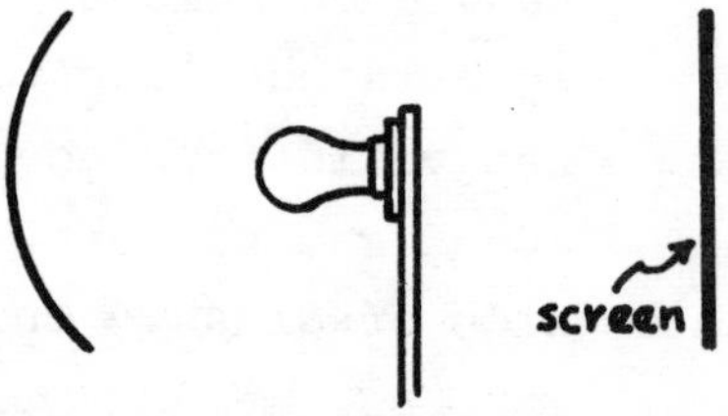


E) REFLECTION GRATING - Use concave mirror reflection grating to show combined focusing and diffracting properties. Use 100 W mercury lamp such as H-4 to get bright spectrum. To get appreciable ultra-violet radiation, carefully break off outer glass protective envelope which will expose inner quartz element. Place fluorescent card to show presence of UV beyond visible violet in spectrum. SAFETY NOTE: Use care with exposed quartz element, both against breakage and excessive UV exposure. SHIELD CLASS FROM DIRECT LIGHT.

F) CONVEX MIRROR - Mount large diameter (40-60 cm) convex mirror for class to see virtual images. Discuss why image always smaller and always behind mirror.

3. REFRACTION

A) BLACKBOARD OPTICS KIT - Use blackboard optics kit (Leybold) to show parallel displacement of rays by parallel-sided Lucite block and effect of positive and negative lenses on rays.

B) GIANT PRISM - Show dispersion with blackboard optics kit and large Lucite prism. Alternate is to use hollow Lucite prism filled with water, carbon disulfide or ethyl cinnamate (larger index but expensive).

C) MINIMUM DEVIATION - Show with apparatus in B or use Demonstration 4, Chap. 26.

D) WATER TANK - Add eosin (fluorescin) to tank (10 gal aquarium works nicely) filled with water. Use 35 mm projector equipped with 12 mm Al "slide" as source and shine parallel beam through tank horizontally. Show refraction of converging and diverging glass lenses under water. Illustrate effect of relative index with hollow, air-filled lenses and prism. Make converging and diverging air-filled lenses from watch glasses (double convex air lens is negative!). Show effect of one hollow lens filled with water and ask students to explain. Use small plane mirror to divert beam and show refraction at water surface. Change incident angle to near grazing incidence. See Question 4 in text.

4. LENSES

A) LENS ACTION - Place clear envelope bulb with coiled filament such as used in automobiles at end of tube 30-40 cm long. Cover other end with black paper and aim tube at screen several meters away. Punch tiny hole in paper to give pinhole image of coiled filament on screen. Punch several more scattered holes. Enlarge one hole to show effect. Add projection lens between paper and screen to show addition of all images into one. Tear out remaining paper to show increased intensity of image.

B) POSITIVE AND NEGATIVE LENSES - Use technique in Demonstration 2A, Chap. 25, along with glass or Lucite two dimensional lens models to show ray behavior.

C) FOCAL LENGTH DEPENDS ON INDEX - Place a slide of any type (photo, irregular object cut in aluminum, etc.) in projector and use mirror at 45° to focus image on ceiling. Place ring stand over mirror and watch glass on ring stand. Pour water in watch glass and show image out of focus. Refocus, then empty water and replace with carbon tetrachloride ($n = 1.46$), acetone ($n = 1.45$) or benzene ($n = 1.50$) to show change of focus. To reduce spherical aberration, use aperture of few cm diameter placed on stand under watch glass. SAFETY NOTE: Use care with these fluids. Do not spill. Reduce evaporation to room as much as possible by pouring back into container quickly.

5. ABERRATIONS This group of four demonstrations uses 35 mm projector as source with usual projector lens removed. Substituted for this is 10-15 cm dia. lens with focal length 20-40 cm. Make following stops out of thin aluminum or Manila folder so that outside diameter of stop fits outside of lens mount:

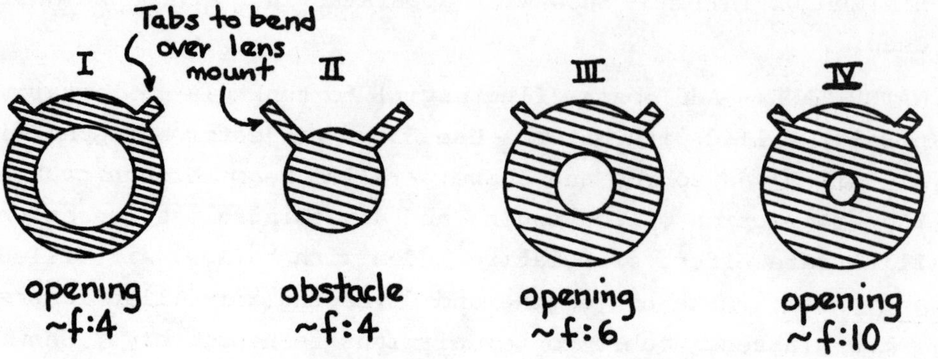


As projector "slide", use apertures referred to at beginning of Chap. 26 Demonstrations. Other useful "slides" are screen wire mesh mounted in usual 35 mm cardboard photo mounts or wire cloth available from Small Parts, Inc., 6901 N.E. Third Avenue, Miami, Fla. 33138. Suggested are meshes 10, 20, 40, 60, 100, 200, 400 wires per inch. These latter ones make good two dimensional gratings with unexpanded laser beam. For Demonstrations A, B, and C, mount red filter (Kodak Wratten 25) in slide holder and use in addition to other object slide referred to.

A) SPHERICAL - Use aluminum slide of small holes, ∿ 1 mm dia., drilled in array forming school's initials. Focus with stop IV, then replace with I and III. Also compare I and II.

B) COMA - Use "slide" of 3 mm aperture and rotate lens so its axis is 10-20° from direction of light. Again use stops I, III and IV to show improvement in image quality with decreasing stop diameter. Use I and II to discuss portions of lens producing respective parts of comatic image.

C) ASTIGMATISM - Use slide of 20 or 40 mesh wire cloth (spacing 0.5-1 mm) with lens rotated so its axis is 10-20° from direction of light. Obtain reasonable focus of horizontal wires of mesh then show change of lens position necessary for reasonable focus of vertical wires. Again use stop IV to improve overall image.

D) CHROMATIC - Use slide in A and good violet color filter (Kodak Wratten 47 B) adjacent to it. Focus on distant screen after eyes partially dark adapted. Replace violet filter by red (Wratten 25) to see image badly out of focus. Not as effective if order of filters reversed.

# 28
# SPECIAL RELATIVITY

CLASSROOM DEMONSTRATIONS

1. <u>MICHELSON INTERFEROMETER</u> Fringes may be projected for large class by using a 2-3 mw laser with beam expander as source. Use naked beam for initial adjustment of interferometer mirrors. Place instrument 3-4 m from screen. May also wish to place Polaroid over each mirror to show interference only occurs when beams have at least some portion in same plane of polarization.

2. <u>DOWEL ROD AXES</u> To aid in explaining fixed and moving axes, glue 3 dowel rods, 8 mm dia and 30 cm long into small wood block for x, y, z axes. Paint each axis different color. Make a second set shorter than first to represent S' axes.

3. <u>TIME DILATION</u> Show 16 mm sound movie <u>Time Dilation, An Experiment With Mu-Mesons</u> available from United World Films, Inc., 221 Park Avenue South, New York, N.Y. 10003.

4. <u>RELATIVITY</u> Show film loop <u>A Relativistic Ride</u> available from Educational Development Center, Newton, MA 02158.

5. <u>ULTIMATE SPEED</u> Show 16 mm sound movie <u>The Ultimate Speed</u> available from United World Films, Inc., 221 Park Avenue South, New York, N.Y. 10003.

6. <u>DOPPLER EFFECT</u> Refer to four suggestions in Demonstration 2, Chap. 24, for non-relativistic effect with sound waves.

# 29
# THE ELECTRIC FIELD

CLASSROOM DEMONSTRATIONS

The following materials are suggested for demonstrations with charged bodies: rods of Lucite, hard rubber, and glass; cloths of silk (ladies' scarf) and wool; cat's fur; and acetate sheet. Most effective way of charging by friction is to hold cloth vertically by thumb and forefinger and "whip" the cloth with rod held in other hand. Lucite rods (∿ 2-3 cm dia.) are preferred. Strips of acetate sheet used on overhead projectors acquire high charge when rubbed with silk cloth. Note that frosted and polished end of standard glass rods used for charging acquire negative and positive polarities, respectively, when rubbed with silk.

Electrostatic generators include familiar Wimshurst and Toepler-Holtz machines and van de Graaf generators. A more recent addition is Dirod generator (Macalaster Scientific Co.).

Numerous demonstrations in this and subsequent chapters may be performed with Pasco Electrostatics Demonstration System which includes electrometer with projection meter.

1. <u>CHARGING BY CONTACT</u> Rub Lucite with wool and use charged electroscope to show rod and cloth have charge of opposite sign.

2. <u>ATTRACTION - REPULSION</u>

   A) RODS AND STIRRUP - Freely suspend glass, rubber, or Lucite rods in stirrups of paper, string, or wire. Use different rods to show attraction and repulsion.

   B) SHEETS OF ACETATE - Two strips of charged acetate show dramatic attraction when held close.

   C) ALUMINIZED PING PONG BALLS - Use needle to pass sewing thread through ping pong ball for 40-50 cm suspension. Spray ball with aluminum paint to form conducting surface. Use as giant pith balls for attraction-repulsion demonstrations.

3. <u>FIELDS</u>

   A) BALL DANCE - Make box with Lucite ends and bottom and thin aluminum angle sides (ethylene dichloride is good solvent for gluing Lucite). Connect aluminum sides to electrostatic generator to form parallel plate capacitor. Place in box 10-20 sugar balls ∿ 3 mm dia. with silvery coating (used for decorating cakes). With field applied from generator, balls serve as carriers of charge from one plate to another. Place on overhead projector to increase visibility.

   B) GRASS SEED DETECTORS - Sprinkle grass seed of long, narrow, variety such as Fescue 31 on Lucite bottom of capacitor in A. Connect plates to electrostatic generator and tap base lightly to assist seed in rotating against friction. Place on overhead projector for increased visibility.

   C) ELECTRIC FIELD CONFIGURATIONS - Two dimensional configurations for many combinations of geometric shapes are contained in kit from

Electret Scientific Co., P.O. Box 4132, Star City, WV 26505. Included are grass seed and shaker, electrode connectors and 11 glass plates having metal foil conductors in combination of patterns.

4. INDUCED CHARGES

A) 2X4 - Balance wood 2x4 of length $\sim$ 2 m with narrow edge on inverted watch glass as low friction pivot. Place charged Lucite rod parallel to long axis of 2x4 and near one end. Attraction of induced charge causes 2x4 to rotate on pivot. Cause motion to cease and reverse by placing rod near opposite face of 2x4. Repeat with charged rubber rod to prove 2x4 was not initially charged.

B) BALLOON - Rub inflated toy balloon briskly on hair or trousers and then "stick" to vertical glass blackboard or smooth wall.

C) DEFLECTING WATER STREAM - Form fine stream of water using glass tube drawn to fine point. Or use fine stream issuing from lab faucet equipped with adapter for hose connection. Bring charged rod or acetate sheet near stream to deflect it.

# 30
# CALCULATION OF ELECTRIC FIELD

## CLASSROOM DEMONSTRATIONS

1. FIELDS Various electrode arrangements given in text may be illustrated with Demonstration 3C, Chap. 29.

# 31
# CONDUCTORS IN ELECTROSTATIC EQUILIBRIUM

## CLASSROOM DEMONSTRATIONS

1. ZERO FIELD

A) CHARGE ON CONDUCTOR - Attach metal beaker to electroscope and charge it either positively or negatively. Use metal ball mounted on insulating handle as proof plane to remove charge from beaker by touching it to either inside or outside and then grounding it before touching beaker again. When beaker is touched on inside, there is no change in electroscope deflection showing no removal of charge. Charge is removed, however, if beaker is touched on outside. Shows charge resides on outside surface of conductor.

B) SHIELDED ELECTROSCOPE - Place grounded screen cage over charged electroscope. Show that any number of charged bodies brought near electroscope produce no effect as long as they remain outside cage.

2. CHARGING BY INDUCTION

A) ELECTROSCOPE - Discuss how electroscope detects different kinds of charge. Then charge one with negative rod by induction and use same negative rod to show difference in response of this electroscope to one charged by contact using negative rod. When charging by contact, use rod having small charge and touch carefully to prevent damage to electroscope leaf.

B) ELECTROPHORUS - Glue unwanted phonograph record ($\sim$ 30 cm dia.) onto flat, insulating base. Attach insulating handle to center of $\sim$ 1 mm Al disk of same diameter. Charge phonograph record by rubbing with cloth and cover with piece of Plexiglas ($\sim$ 1 mm thick) of same size. Al disk may now be placed on top of Plexiglas and charged repeatedly by induction with no loss of charge from phonograph record. Many students believe conservation of energy is violated here. Explain source of energy to separate charge.

3. ELECTRIC ANALOG TO MAGNET An electret made of Carnauba wax is available from source given in Demonstration 3C, Chap. 29. This device has permanent electric dipole moment analogous to "electric magnet."

# 32
# ELECTRIC POTENTIAL

CLASSROOM DEMONSTRATIONS

1. VAN DE GRAAF Show and explain operation of this generator. See Demonstration 1A, Chap. 31.

2. DIELECTRIC BREAKDOWN Connect generator to pair of sphere electrodes with adjustable gap between them to show increased breakdown potential of larger gaps.

3. HIGH FIELDS

A) IONIC DRIVE - Show principle of ionic space engine with sharp pointed metal pinwheel which can rotate freely. Note only one connection to electrostatic generator is needed. More rapid rotation produced if connected with positive polarity.

B) SMOKE PRECIPITATOR - Commercially available for use with electrostatic generators, a set of sharp points is connected to the positive terminal of generator with single electrode at the opposite end of insulating chamber connected to negative terminal. Tobacco smoke in chamber is quickly precipitated by attraction of ionized smoke particles. Discuss application to pollution control.

C) ELECTRIC WIND - Place lighted candle between plates of parallel plate capacitor connected to electrostatic generator. Predominantly positively charged candle flame is "blown" toward negative plate. More pronounced effect when sharp point replaces positive electrode plate.

# 33
# CAPACITANCE, ELECTROSTATIC ENERGY AND DIELECTRICS

## CLASSROOM DEMONSTRATIONS

Good quantitative measurements may be obtained for many demonstrations on these topics with Pasco Electrostatics Demonstration System.

1. FIELDS IN CAPACITORS See Demonstration 3C, Chap. 29.

2. ENERGY STORAGE

A) SPHERE GAP WITH CAPACITOR - Use pair of spheres with adjustable gap to show thin but frequent sparking (low energy). Add capacitor, such as Leyden jar or aluminum plates separated by Lucite sheet, in parallel with gap to produce fatter, less frequent spark discharges (higher energy).

B) SHORTING CAPACITOR - Charge 10 μf 1000 VDC capacitor to ∿ 1000 V, disconnect source, and then short capacitor with large screwdriver. WARNING - Small screwdriver may be damaged upon dissipation of large energy stored. Use care with high voltage!

C) BATTERY REPLACEMENT - Use 10 μf 1000 VDC capacitor charged to ∿ 1000 V as energy source for relaxation oscillator. Blinking lamp of oscillator shows that energy stored in capacitor is used very slowly. Typical values shown.

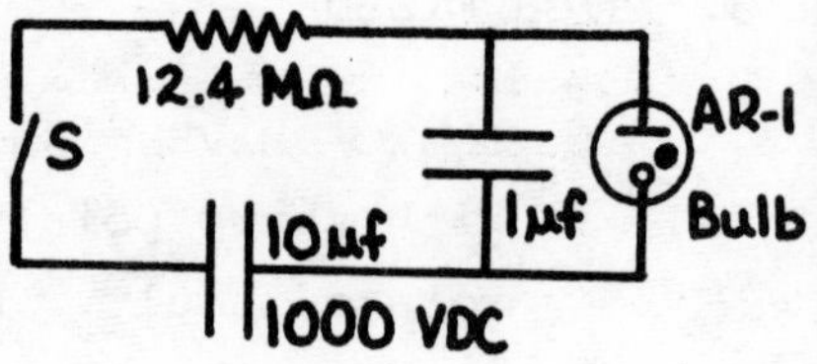


# 34
# ELECTRIC CURRENT

CLASSROOM DEMONSTRATIONS

1. CONDUCTIVITY Mount light socket on insulator with two wire electrodes protruding ∿ 10 cm below insulator. Wire so 120 VAC plug is in series with electrode, lamp, and second electrode. 25 W lamp serves as current detector. Place electrodes in solutions of sugar, distilled water, sulfuric acid and salt to detect which has larger number of ions to enhance current. USE CARE WITH EXPOSED 120 VAC. ISOLATION TRANSFORMER, NOT AUTOTRANSFORMER, RECOMMENDED TO REDUCE SHOCK HAZARD TO GROUND.

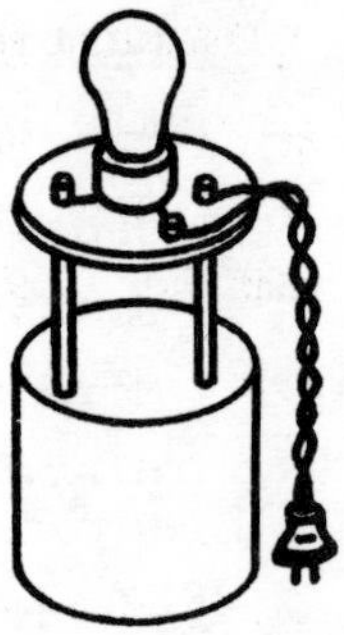

2. OHM'S LAW Mount several identical lengths of wires of same diameter but of different metals on board and connect wires in series so they carry same current. Use digital meters to measure voltage across each and current. Current must be kept low since digital meters typically read in mA range. Calculate resistances by $R = V/I$.

3. RESISTIVITY Use digital multimeter to measure directly resistance of wires in 2 above. Compare resistivities.

4. TEMPERATURE COEFFICIENT OF RESISTANCE See Demonstration 1A, Chap. 17.

5. MECHANICAL ANALOG OF RESISTANCE Drive nails at random into board ∿ 20 cm wide so that ∿ 2.5 cm ball bearing can roll between them. Attach rails to keep bearings from rolling off sides. Ball bearings moving through maze of nails simulate current flow in wire. Construct second board with different nail spacings to show change of mean free path. Use different number of balls to show change of number of charge carriers. Incline board at different angles to show effect of different applied emfs.

6. EMF - LEMON BATTERY Insert strips of galvanized iron and copper into a lemon 90-120° apart and read emf (∿ 0.95 volt) on digital meter.

7. POWER - LIGHT BULBS Measure cold resistance of 200 W and 25 W bulbs with digital meter. Use $P = V^2/R$ and show R inversely proportional to P. Compute R(hot) to show change of R with temperature.

# 35
# DIRECT-CURRENT CIRCUITS

## CLASSROOM DEMONSTRATIONS

1. INTERNAL RESISTANCE - LEMON BATTERY See Demonstration 6, Chap. 34. Connect "battery" to 0-10 kΩ load. Vary load and read current and terminal voltage of "battery". Plot load R vs. 1/i. Slope of graph is emf (∿ 0.95 volt) and intercept is internal resistance (∿ 1800 Ω).

2. KIRCHHOFF'S LAWS Solve simple circuit, then show by measuring currents and voltages with digital meters that theoretical values are confirmed. Discuss errors in measurement and meter errors as desired. Typical values shown.

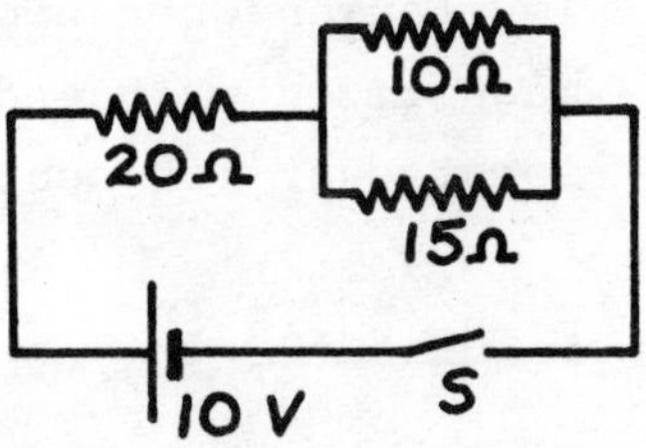


3. RC CIRCUIT

A) CHARGING/DISCHARGING - Place digital meter across capacitor and measure change of voltage with time for circuit with long time constant. Typical values shown.

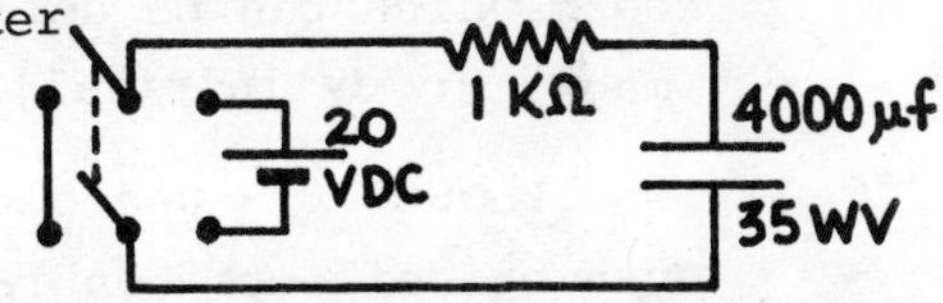


B) CHARGING/DISCHARGING - Connect oscilloscope to square wave generator to show sharp rise and fall of voltage. Load generator with capacitor and resistor and observe change of voltage across each component with time. Typical values shown.

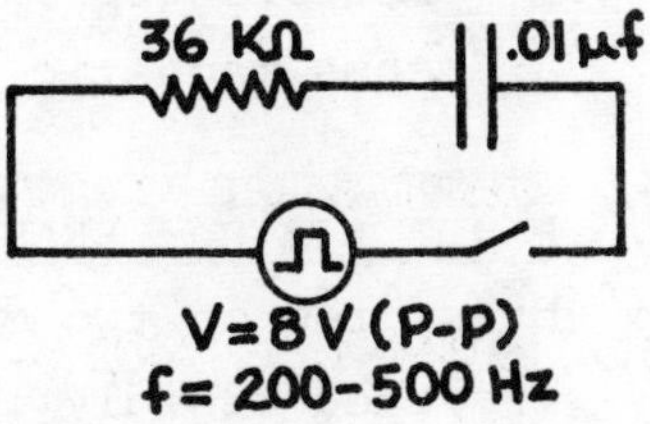


C) RELAXATION OSCILLATOR - Construct relaxation oscillator as shown in circuit diagram, close S and observe regularity of flash of AR-1 bulb. Open S and connect oscilloscope to capacitor terminals. With oscilloscope sweep set at ∿ .5 sec/cm and sensitivity at ∿ 20 volts/cm on DC input, close S and observe voltage across capacitor as function of time.

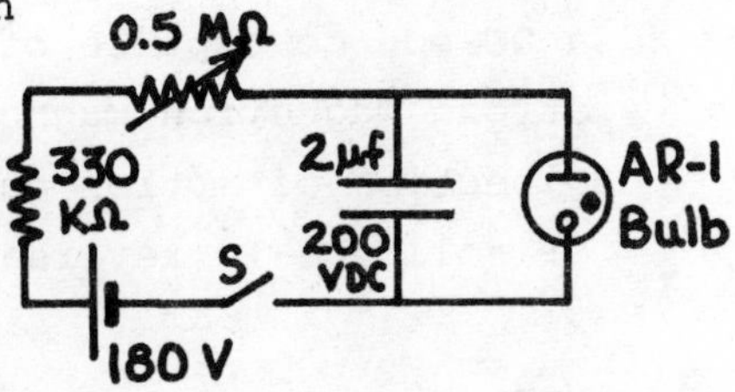

CLASSROOM DEMONSTRATIONS

1. VECTOR NATURE OF FIELD Seal loop made from paper clip between two sheets of paper or Manila folder cut in shape of arrow. Attach string to loop and use to explore direction of field of magnets. Better results with strong "magnetron" magnets.

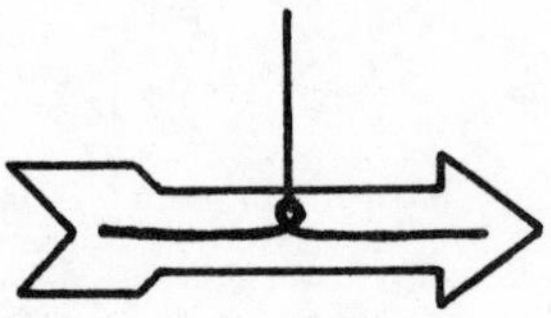

2. MAGNETS IN MAGNETIC FIELD - LEVITATION TOY Two strong cylindrical magnets are located in light frame as shown. Lower magnet is fixed in place while upper magnet can be removed. Levitation occurs when upper magnet oriented with like poles together; loss of levitation occurs when orientation of upper magnet reversed. Another pair with frame produces levitation when upper magnet oriented either way. These magnets are magnetized with ends having like poles, with opposite pole in each located at its center. Available commercially.

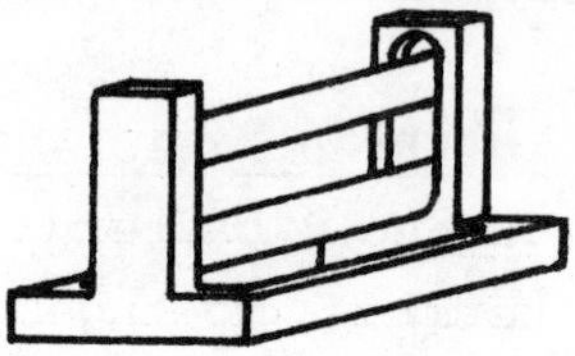

3. $\vec{F} = q\,\vec{v} \times \vec{B}$

   A) DISCHARGE TUBE - Commercially available tubes excited by induction coil produce electron beam which can be deflected by relatively weak magnets: cylindrical, bar or horseshoe.

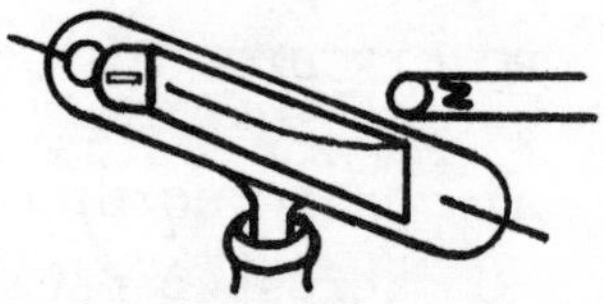

   B) OSCILLOSCOPE - Use old, cheap oscilloscope to show electron beam spot can be deflected on face of tube as magnetic pole is brought close to oscilloscope. Can also use compact solenoid carrying current. Discuss magnetic deflection in TV sets.

4. $\vec{F} = I\,\vec{\ell} \times \vec{B}$ - BRASS ROD Rest length of brass rod on two other level brass rods inserted rigidly into piece of 2x4 clamped to table. Connect to these two level rods a DC source capable of delivering ∿ 15 A. Strong magnetron magnet provides field such that moveable rod will roll. Direction of motion can be correlated with vector equation. Show change of roll due to reversal of current or magnetic field.

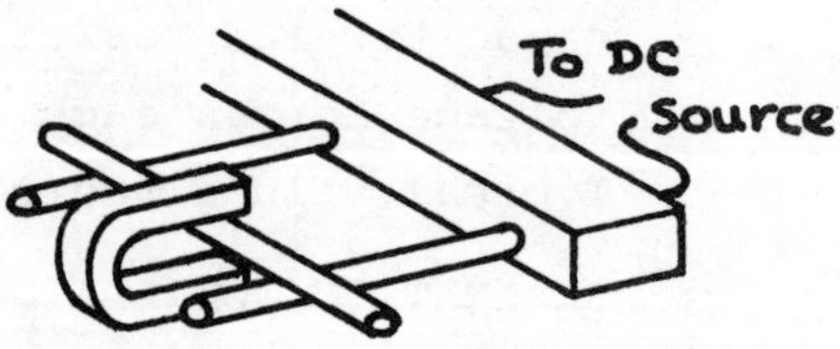


5. TORQUE This group of demonstrations utilizes Helmholtz coils 70-100 cm in diameter such as are commercially available with Sargeant-Welch e/m

apparatus. Requires DC source capable of ∿ 10 A.

A) MAGNETIC AS COMPASS - Suspend small magnet to detect presence of earth's field and/or field inside coils. Discuss period of oscillation as means of finding relative field strengths.

B) FLAT AND SOLENOID COILS - Suspend in field of Helmholtz coils both flat and solenoid shaped coils made from ∿ 100 turns of copper wire. Wire #20 to 26 works well. Crude string suspensions are satisfactory. Battery eliminators providing up to 5 A work well as current sources.

C) GALVANOMETER - If reasonably good mechanical suspension, somewhat more elaborate than B above, is outfitted with spring for restoring torque, coils in B can be used as demonstration galvonometer.

6. <u>MOTOR</u> Model motors are available with both split ring commutators and slip rings for use with DC and AC. Discuss use of generators as motors. Scrapped car generators and alternators are good models. Also see Demonstrations 4C and 4D, Chap. 38.

# 37
# SOURCES OF THE MAGNETIC FIELD

CLASSROOM DEMONSTRATIONS

1. <u>PARALLEL WIRES - ROGET'S SPIRAL</u> Helical wound coil of copper wire is hung vertically with its two wire ends bent to lie on vertical axis. Lower wire rests with about 1 mm immersed in small mercury filled cup. Connecting 6-10 VDC between upper end and cup causes spiral to contract, breaking contact with mercury. Oscillations occur. Shadow project for large class. SAFETY NOTE: Cover mercury with thin film of water to prevent release of mercury vapor to atmosphere.

2. <u>FIELD MAPPING</u>

A) BAR AND HORSESHOE - Place a thin sheet of Lucite or shallow tray of Lucite over bar or horseshoe magnet and sprinkle iron filings into tray. Place on overhead projector for greater class visibility.

B) STRAIGHT WIRE - Use tray above with straight wire fastened underneath. Battery eliminator capable of delivering 5-10 A works well.

C) ONE LOOP - Drill two holes in sheet of Lucite and use length of #14 or #16 copper wire to form loop with axis of loop in plane of sheet. Sprinkle iron filings on sheet to show concentric circles of magnetic field path.

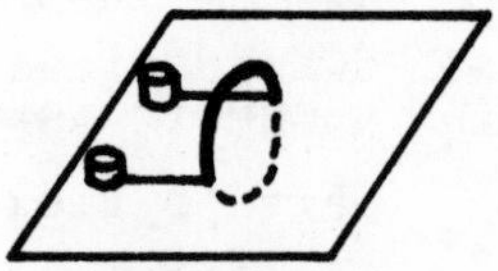

D) SOLENOID - Wind several loops through Lucite sheet as in C to form solenoid with axis in plane of sheet.

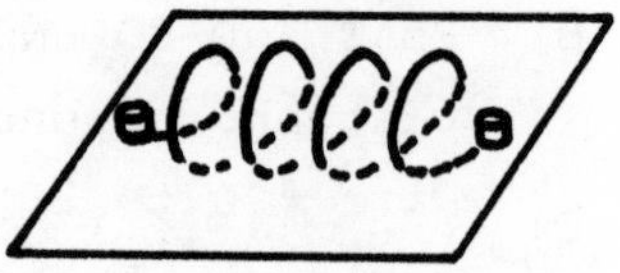

## 38
## FARADAY'S LAW

CLASSROOM DEMONSTRATIONS

1. MOTIONAL EMF

A) JUMP ROPE - See Demonstration 1A, Chap. 40.

B) MAGNET IN LOOSE COIL - Form 10-15 cm dia. coil of several turns from jump rope in A and connect to galvanometer. Note deflection of galvanometer as bar magnet is inserted and withdrawn at different speeds and polarities. Add additional turns to coil. Show that it doesn't matter which of two, coil or magnet, is moved - only relative motion required.

C) MAGNET IN SOLENOID - Connect outer coil described in 3A below to galvanometer. Note deflection of galvanometer as bar magnet is inserted and withdrawn at different speeds and polarities.

D) WIRE IN MAGNETIC FIELD - Use equipment described in Demonstration 2E, Chap. 14. Pluck wire with fingers so it vibrates first perpendicular and then parallel to magnetic field. Latter case difficult to achieve with horseshoe or magnetron magnets.

E) FLIP COIL - An "earth inductor", available commercially, has coil of $\sim$ 1025 turns which can be rotated 180° in either horizontal or vertical plane. Possible to measure horizontal and vertical components of earth's magnetic field when used with ballistic galvanometer.

2. LENZ'S LAW AND EDDY CURRENTS

A) PUMP RING - Suspend Aℓ ring (typically 6.35 cm O.D. x 5.72 cm I.D. x 1.4 cm long) from bifilar suspension. By inserting and withdrawing one pole of bar magnet, it is possible to "pump" ring much as child "pumps" swing.

B) MAGNETIC BRAKING - Pendulum bob made of sheet copper or aluminum swings freely between poles of strong electromagnet when current off. But pendulum comes to quick halt when current on due to eddy current damping. Replace solid sheet with one of same shape and material in which slots have been cut to restrict circulation of eddy currents. Pendulum now swings freely with current on or off. Discuss application of magnetic brake on laboratory beam balance.

C) MAGNETIC BRAKING - Suspend bar magnet so it can swing as pendulum. Pendulum comes to quick halt when copper sheet is placed horizontally just beneath lowest point of swing. Replace with slotted sheet as in B.

D) MOTOR DISK WITH STRONG MAGNETIC - Use equipment in Demonstration 3F, Chap. 9. Have student bring up strong magnetron magnet so that disk passes between magnet poles. Produces dramatic effect. SAFETY NOTE: Hold base of motor securely!

E) MAGNETIC LEVITATION - Use equipment in Demonstration 3F, Chap. 9. Attach very strong, light-weight magnet (Edmund Scientific sells 1 1/2 oz. "Super Magnet" of 7000 gauss) with double-sided masking tape to piece of Manila folder ∿ 2.5 cm x 20 cm. Magnet will levitate about 1 cm above rotating Aℓ disk when held near periphery. Show that levitation height depends on linear speed by moving magnet toward axis of rotation. Convince students that air currents not responsible by using duplicate piece of Manila folder without magnet. For large class, illuminate apparatus from side and use long focal length lens (f = 35 cm) to form large image of magnet and disk on screen.

F) INDUCTION STIRRER - Magnetic stirrer is excellent example of eddy current induction motor.

G) BACK EMF IN MOTOR - See Demonstration 1B, Chap. 40.

3. <u>FARADAY'S LAW</u>

A) SOLENOIDS - Primary and secondary coils are available commercially. One has many turns and is designed to be placed over other. Current can be passed through primary while secondary is connected to galvanometer. Show induced emf due to different rates of change of current and due to reversal of primary current.

B) HELMHOLTZ COILS - Use coils similar to ones described in Demonstration 5, Chap. 36 as flux-producing coils. Place near axis of coils second set of coils having various combinations of turns and areas. Combinations which work well are one coil 10 x 20 cm (I) and two coils

20 x 20 cm (II and III) all having 100 turns. These should be wound so as to be as nearly coplanar as possible, thereby sensing the same flux changes. Adding II to III doubles number of turns keeping area constant. Comparing II and I doubles area keeping same number turns. Flux from Helmholtz coils can be brought to zero by opening switch or reversing switch can be used.

C) INDUCTION COIL - Use commercially available coil for use with gas discharge tubes or use automobile ignition coil to show large emf produced when primary circuit is opened. Discuss operation of former type to produce pulsating high voltage.

4. <u>ELIHU THOMPSON APPARATUS</u> Commercially available, this apparatus has numerous accessories to be used with large iron core solenoid. See also Demonstration 3A, Chap. 40. CAUTION: Do not operate coil without core at least part way into coil. Coil without any core has insufficient impedance to prevent serious overheating.

A) JUMPING RING - Place solid ring of aluminum (Demonstration 2A, Chap. 38) over iron core protruding above end of coil. Energize coil to throw ring into air. Connect digital voltmeter to ends of similar ring having saw gap to show induced emf of several hundred mV between ends.

B) HEATED RING - Place solid ring over end of core protruding from core. Allow to levitate minute or longer or push ring down toward coil into strong field region and hold. Note heating effect.

C) SHADED POLE MOTOR - Place iron core flush with coil end and cover 30-40% of core end with thin flat plate of copper or aluminum (non-magnetic materials). Over exposed core adjust position of small non-magnetic disk on friction free bearings to simulate watt-hour meter operation. Adjust position of "shading" sheet and spinning disk as necessary for greatest speed of rotation.

D) SPINNING FLOATING BALL - Copper or other non-magnetic ball floating in beaker of water can be used to replace disk in C and ball will spin while floating.

5. <u>INDUCTANCE-RESISTANCE CIRCUIT</u>

A) INDUCED EMF - Closing switch in circuit shown first lights 15 W bulb due to large back emf across inductor. As steady state is reached 200 W bulb serves as detector of increased

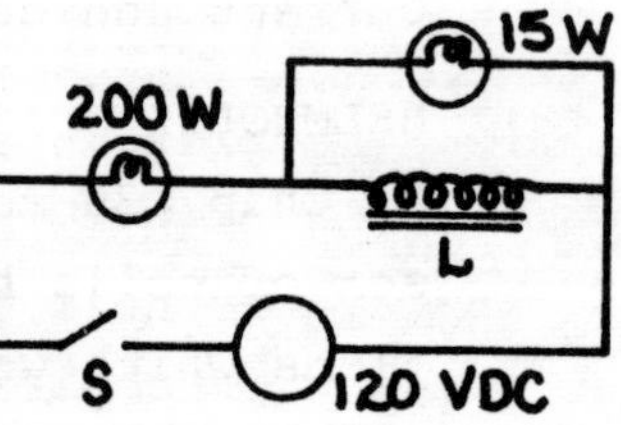

current. Opening switch produces momentary flash of 15 W bulb from back emf produced by sudden decay. Inductor must be several hundred henries such as found in demonstration kits having separate coils and core. If two coils used, be sure to connect in series, phased additively. SAFETY NOTE: Be careful with exposed 120 V DC!

B) GROWTH OF CURRENT - Inductor designed for slow AC demonstrations is commercially available and has L = 45,000 H with R = 10,000 Ω.

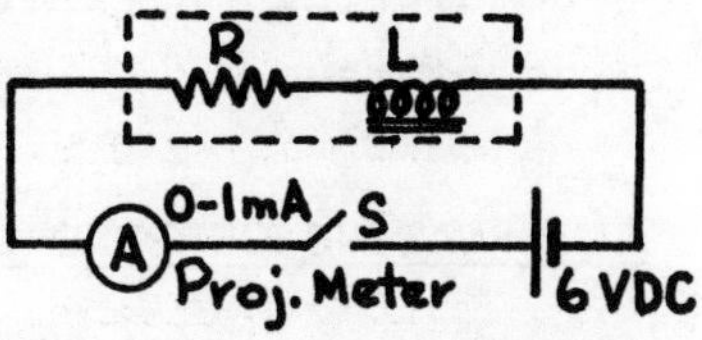


C) GROWTH AND DECAY WITH SQUARE WAVE - Typical Values R = 1800 Ω

L = 10-15 H

f = 10-30 Hz

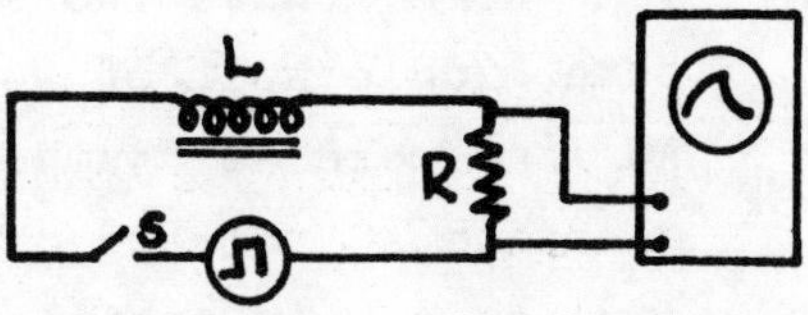


6. RLC RINGING CIRCUIT

Typical Values

V = 3-6 V DC  C = 0.03-1 μF

L = 10-30 H  R = 150-300 Ω

Sweep: 5-20 msec/cm

Sensitivity: 10-50 mV/cm

Ringing occurs when $CR^2 < 4L$

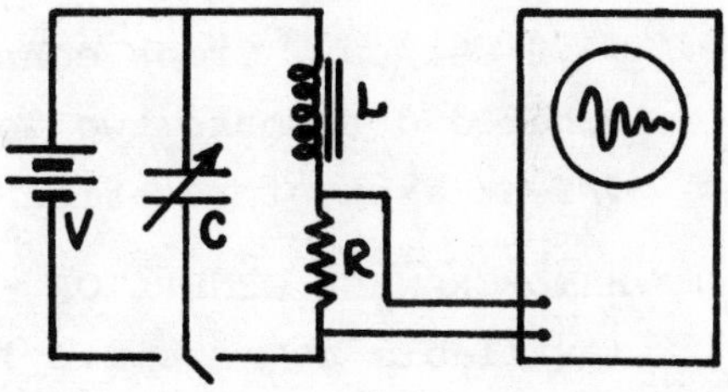


# 39
# MAGNETISM IN MATTER

## CLASSROOM DEMONSTRATIONS

1. MAGNETIC PERMEABILITY Use apparatus in Demonstration 3A, Chap. 38. Insert several pieces of iron wire (coathanger), one by one, as core and show increased emf produced in secondary due to core material.

2. MAGNETIC RELUCTANCE Inductor of 45,000 H referred to in Demonstration 5B, Chap. 38, has laminated core in two pieces. Compare growth rate of current with core solidly in place and then with several sheets of paper in gap. Finally remove part of core altogether. Similar effect can be noted with apparatus of Demonstration 5A, Chap. 38.

# 40
# ALTERNATING-CURRENT CIRCUITS

## CLASSROOM DEMONSTRATIONS

Use digital multimeters and CCTV to make circuit measurements visible to large classes.

1. ALTERNATING-CURRENT GENERATOR

A) JUMP ROPE - Have two students turn middle half of ∿ 40' of AC line cord as "jump rope" to generate AC voltage of ∿ 3 mv amplitude. An oscilloscope of at least 5 mV/cm sensitivity displays output; sweep rate ∿ .2 sec/cm. Cross connect a wire from one end to second wire at other end to make two loops out of "jump rope" and double signal. Orient axis of rotation East-West.

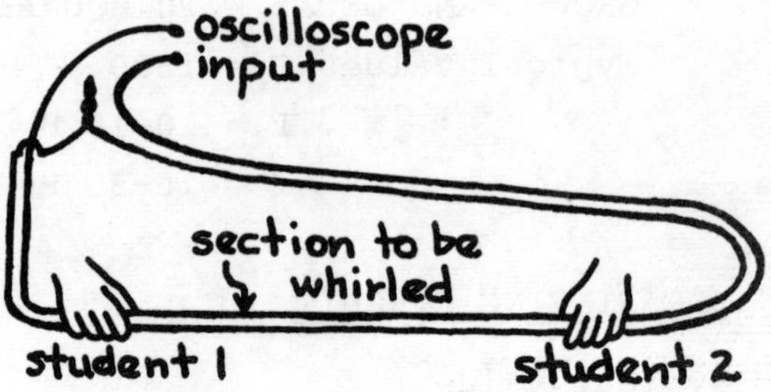


B) HAND-CRANKED GENERATOR - Light small bulb with hand-cranked generator (available commercially). Turn slowly to illustrate alternating nature of emf. Have student turn crank and show that turning is easier when bulb loosened to remove load. When bulb lit (and circuit closed) back emf is developed in generator windings which is felt when cranking generator. If effect of back emf not too noticeable, replace bulb with another which draws larger current.

2. RLC SERIES CIRCUIT Typical values: $R = 1600\ \Omega$, $C = 2.00\ \mu F$, $L = 12.0$ H, $R_L = 340\ \Omega$, and $V = 20.0$ V

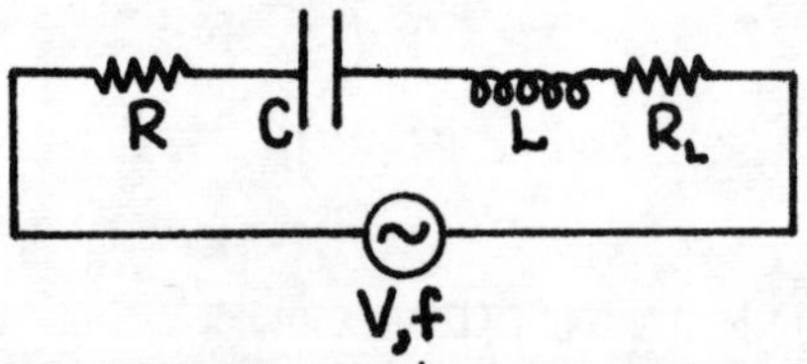


A) PHASE - Connect dual input oscilloscope across various components to show phase relationships between instantaneous current and voltage. Use $V_R$ to show phase of current. Place components being studied adjacent to R to eliminate ground connection problems; i.e., to measure phase for C, place C adjacent to R and connect oscilloscope ground between them. Polarity must be inverted for some components.

B) VOLTAGE DIAGRAM - Measure voltages across components and show how they must be combined on voltage vector diagram. Typical values for components specified and f = 60 Hz: $V_R = 8.4$, $V_C = 6.8$, and $V_L = 24$ (larger than applied V!). Voltages are in rms volts.

C) ADDING VOLTAGES - Calculate voltage across two adjacent components (e.g., R and C), and then measure and compare.

D) RESONANCE - Adjust f to achieve resonance by maximizing $V_R$ on digital meter or by making phase angle between V and $V_R$ zero (overlap traces on oscilloscope and set sweep rate high). Compare with theoretical value (∿ 32 Hz for circuit values shown).

3. TRANSFORMER

A) LIGHT UNDER WATER - A small flashlight bulb is attached to small coil. Bulb and coil are brought near larger coil of many turns having iron core (Elihu Thompson Electromagnetism Apparatus - see Demonstration 4, Chap. 38). Bulb glows when larger coil is connected to AC power source. Vary flux linkage by moving small coil and changing its orientation. Bulb and small coil may be immersed in water if well waxed.

B) EMF IN SPLIT RING - Allow iron core to protrude a few cm from the larger coil end of apparatus in A. Place Al ring which has been cut (open circuit) over exposed core. Digital voltmeter connected on either side of cut in ring will read several hundred mV when AC power source is connected.

C) PRIMARY CURRENT VS. SECONDARY LOAD - A 200 W bulb is connected to secondary of variable auto transformer. A second 200 W bulb is placed in series with primary. Current in primary, detected by change of lamp brightness, increases as current in secondary increases.

D) WELD NAILS - Weld pair of nails together with step-down transformer (6.3 V at 10.6 A works nicely) or transformer used with low voltage concentrated filament illuminator. Casually place fingers between nail ends before they make contact. Then bring points together allowing sparks to fly while nails quickly become red and then white hot. Use short, large diameter connecting wires soldered to terminals and make effort to minimize contact resistance.

4. MEASURE INDUCTANCE WITH A VOLTMETER Connect known resistor (R) in series with inductor ($L, R_L$). Apply DC source and measure $V_R$ and $V_L$ (call this value $V_{LDC}$). Calculate $I_{DC}$ from $V_R$ and R and then find $R_L$ ($=V_{LDC}/I_{DC}$). Substitute audio oscillator of frequency f and adjust until $V_R$ is same as before - this makes $I_{AC} = I_{DC}$. Measure $V_L$ (call it $V_{LAC}$). Then $\cos \phi = V_{LDC}/V_{LAC}$, and L can be found from $R_L$, $\phi$, and f.

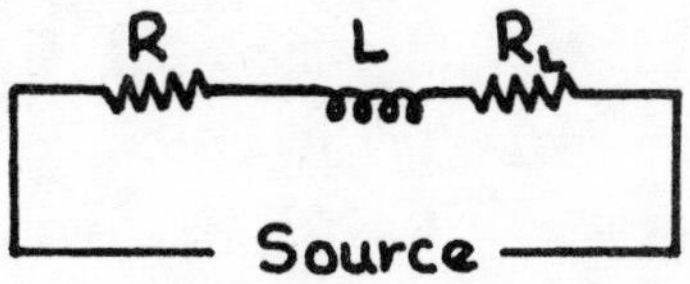


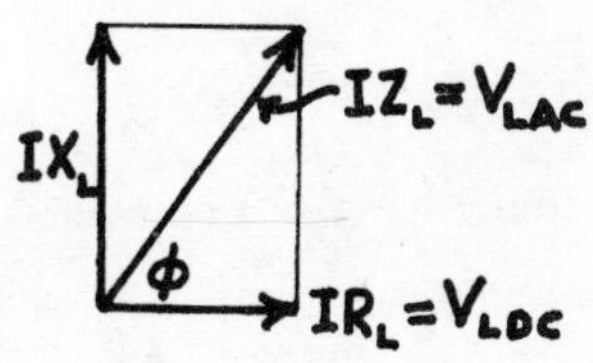

# 41
# MAXWELL'S EQUATIONS AND ELECTROMAGNETIC RADIATION

CLASSROOM DEMONSTRATIONS

1. MICROWAVES Various properties of electromagnetic waves may be illustrated with Demonstrations 1 and 12, Chap. 26.

# 42
# QUANTIZATION

CLASSROOM DEMONSTRATIONS

1. STANDING ELECTRON WAVES IN HYDROGEN ATOM Illustrate condition on allowed electron orbits in hydrogen atom with Demonstration 1E, Chap. 22.

2. PHOTOELECTRIC EFFECT Attach piece of freshly polished zinc or galvanized metal to electroscope and illuminate with open carbon arc. Focus beam on metal with quartz lens (no lens necessary if arc close to metal). A positivity charged electroscope will not discharge when light shines on metal but negatively charged electroscope quickly loses its charge. Shows that negative charges (electrons) are ejected from metal surface by light. To show that ultraviolet light is responsible for ejection of electrons, hold piece of window pane glass (which is opaque to uv) in beam to stop discharge process.

## FILM GUIDE

William R. Riley

This section presents a listing of film loops and 16-mm films for use at appropriate stages in the teaching of introductory physics. Most of the 16-mm films have sound tracks. All the loops suggested are available in Super 8 format and are silent; some are also available in silent 16-mm format. The 16-mm version is recommended where the lecture section is large, for example, more than 30 students, and where the lectures are presented in an auditorium such that the higher intensity projector light sources are required to get useful screen illumination. (Many Super 8 projector lamps are of 80 watts maximum; those in common 16-mm projectors range from 500 to 1000 watts.) The Super 8 version will be quite adequate in many situations, but the potential user should check its adequacy before investing in the Super 8 version for large lecture usage.

The information accompanying each 16-mm film listing includes title, producer, year of production, notation of whether film is in color, approximate running time in minutes, purchase or rental cost when available, distributor, review references in either the American Journal of Physics (AJP) or The Physics Teacher (TPT) when available, and a brief annotation.

It is suggested that you use "preview before purchase" rights when they are offered by a distributor. Many 16-mm films may be previewed before purchase; most of the commercially available loops cannot be previewed before purchase. The availability of the AAPT Repository Films, generally in Super 8 only, for showing at regional and sectional meetings of the American Association of Physics Teachers represents a preview option for that one source of loops.

Distributors of films often have a rental system. Rental charges vary widely. The three-day rate for most of the PSSC films is less than $10.00 for films of about 25 minutes duration, mostly in black and white. Rental charges for color films are usually greater, for example, Laser Light (37½ min) by Scientific American has a purchase price of $375 and rents at $37.50. Albert Einstein: The Education of a Genius (44 min) may be purchased for $550 and rented for $52.50. A rough rule of thumb would be that the rental cost is approximately 10 percent of the purchase cost. Known rental costs have been indicated.

Single copies of films for purchase and/or rental from distributors may also be available from one of the university libraries in your region of the United States. Film libraries or audio-visual educational centers, such as those at the University of Southern California, University of California at Berkeley, University of Michigan, Wayne State, the State University of New York system, Michigan State University, and many others, offer rental privileges on films. Their film rental fees are about the same as those set by distributors.

Various methods are used in showing physics films to students. Most frequently, where lecture sections are involved, appropriate films are shown as an integrated part of a lecture. Some of the lengthier films can probably best be used as optional extracurricular "cultural" material (yes, even for future physicists and engineers) having a strong basic physics flavor. Fifty-seven-minute films are difficult to fit into a 48-minute "class hour," yet they have much value, can be helpful and interesting, and can be viewed by and contribute to a fuller understanding of physics for both physics and nonphysics students and faculty. I have in mind a sequence of (a) the seven Feynman-Messenger Lecture films, more than 50 minutes per film, rental EDC $20/lecture; (b) the Morrison series of ten half-hour films, Fabric of the Atom, describing the quantum nature of matter, rental EDC $15/film; (c) the History of Science Series distributed by IFB, 8 films, rental $10 to $22.50/film; (d) the HPP films The World of Enrico Fermi, People and Particles, and Synchrotron, (e) the UWF series on atomic physics, (f) the BBC-CERN film on high energy, Shadows of Bliss, and (g) the St. Andrews University film, Superfluid Helium. All of these could be profitably shown to students on an optional basis without consuming class lecture time if the latter is a major barrier to film usage.

Films loops are used occasionally in lecture halls, but more often in smaller recitation and laboratory sections. Myriad approaches are employed for showing film loops to students, among them, corridor displays using a single loop per day and library showings of the loop of the day or week.

Among the larger useful sources of physics film loops are BFA, EBEC, EDC, UEVA, and Ward's Natural Science Establishment. BFA now handles most of the loops formerly distributed by the Ealing Corporation and by Holt Media, including the following series:

Demonstrations in Physics, 10 loops (Schwartz)
Electromagnetism, 12 loops (Adler)
Kinetic Theory (Air Table), 6 loops (Daw)
Mechanics on an Air Track, 9 loops (Stull)
Quantum Physics, 9 loops (EDC)
Vector Kinematics, 6 loops (ESI)
Project Physics, 48 loops (HPP)

BFA also distributes the FMOSU Demonstrations. The 19 film loops in this series, all but one in color, were produced at Ohio State University under a grant from the National Science Foundation to Dr. Franklin Miller of Kenyon College. These provide a number of filmed demonstration experiments that can be classified as difficult or dangerous or one of a kind or too time-consuming to be set up live each time one lectures on a given topic. These are available from BFA in Super 8 format and from Ohio State University in the 16-mm format. If seriously interested in purchasing these in the 16-mm version, a single 16-mm reel containing all 19 films is available for preview purposes. This series includes basic films in areas of wave motion, magnetism, critical temperature, diffraction phenomena, the Tacoma Narrows Bridge collapse, and others.

EBEC has many film loops in the physical sciences. For a college physics course the following are among the more useful series:

Standing Waves Series, 20 loops (Baez)
Electrostatic Series, 19 loops (Baez)
Cathode Ray Oscilloscope Series, 16 loops (Baez)
Microwave Optics Series, 14 loops (Baez)

## Film Sources

AAPT - AAPT Executive Office, Graduate Physics Building, SUNY at Stony Brook, Stony Brook, NY 11794
AEF - American Educational Films, 132 Lasky Drive, Beverly Hills, CA 90212
BARNARD - History of Physics Laboratory, Barnard College, Columbia University, New York, NY 10027
BFA - BFA Educational Media, 2211 Michigan Ave., Santa Monica, CA 90404
BTL - Contact local Bell Telephone Company business office or Bell Laboratories, Audio/Visual Center, Room 1C-248, Murray Hill, NJ 07974
CERN - Public Information Office, CERN, 1211 Geneva 23, Switzerland
CONTEMPORARY - Contemporary/McGraw-Hill Films, 1221 Avenue of the Americas, New York, NY 10020
EAMES - The Charles Eames Studio, 901 Washington Blvd., Venice, CA 90291
EBEC - Encyclopaedia Britannica Educational Corporation, 425 North Michigan Ave., Chicago, IL 60611

EDC - EDC Distribution Center, 39 Chapel St., Newton, MA 02160
EPP - Elementry Penguin Productions, 1043-3 South Westmoreland, Los Angeles, CA 90006
FMOSU - 16 mm: Department of Photography and Cinema, 156 West 19th Ave, Columbus, OH 43210; super 8: BFA
FNL - Public Information Office, Fermi National Laboratory, P.O. Box 500, Batavia, IL 60510
HMCO - Houghton Mifflin Company, 110 Tremont St., Boston, MA 02107
HPP - 16 mm: Holt, Rinehart & Winston, 383 Madison Ave., New York, NY 10017; film loops: BFA
IBMFL - Purchase: IBM Motion Picture Library, c/o Modern Talking Picture Service, 1212 Avenue of the Americas, New York, NY 10036. Loan: IBM Regional Film Libraries, 412 West Peachtree St. NW, Atlanta, GA 30308; 160 East Grand Ave., Chicago, IL 60611; 1411 Slocum St., Dallas, TX 75207; 1145 North McCadden Pl., Los Angeles, CA 90038
IFB - International Film Bureau, Inc., 332 South Michigan Ave., Chicago, IL 60604
JFA - Professor J. F. Allen, F.R.S., University of St. Andrews, School of Physical Sciences, North Haugh, St. Andrews, Fife, KY 9SS, Scotland
KALMIA - Kalmia Company, Dept. P1, Concord, MA 01742
MFR - Modern Film Rentals, 2323 New Hyde Park Road, New Hyde Park, NY 11040
MGH - McGraw-Hill Book Company, College and University Division, 1221 Avenue of the Americas, New York, NY 10020
MLA - Modern Learning Aids Division, Ward's Natural Science Establishment, Inc., P.O. Box 312, Rochester, NY 14601
MSU - Michigan State University, Instructional Media Center, East Lansing, MI 48824
PFR - AAPT Film Repository, c/o Executive Office, Graduate Physics Building, SUNY at Stony Brook, Stony Brook, NY 11794
RPI - Office of Instructional Media, Rensselaer Polytechnic Institute, Troy, NY 12181
UEVA - Universal Education and Visual Arts, 100 Universal City Plaza, Universal City, CA 91608
WARDS - Ward's Natural Science Establishment, Inc., P.O. Box 1712, Rochester, NY 14603

## Chapter-by-Chapter Film Suggestions

The following list represents the potential usage that I would make of films when teaching introductory physics. Each film proposed will probably be found appropriate in the suggested context by many physicists teaching the course. However, the author's experience suggests that individual differences of taste and teaching techniques are such that a given film will not be viewed as wholly appropriate by all physicists teaching a given topic. So the listing offers recommendations; all readers are advised to preview before using any film on the list.

## Chapter 1. Introduction

Powers of Ten (Charles Eames Studio, 1968), color, 8 min, purchase $125, rental $10, EAMES. Reviewed AJP 40:1357 (1972), TPT 10:52-53 (1972). Indicates visually the entire range of distances we experience from the familiar to the observable extent of the universe at one extreme and to the dimensions of the atomic nucleus at the other.

Symmetry (Sturgis-Grant, 1967), color, 10 min, purchase $160, rental $15, CONTEMPORARY. An outstanding introduction to notions of geometric symmetries of reflection, rotation, translation, and their combinations.

The House of Science (IBM-Eames, 1968), color, 14 min, purchase $165, rental, IBMFL; purchase $185, rental $9, EBEC. A superbly animated description of the development of science and philosophy. Scientific procedure is shown to be a natural process arising from man's innate curiosity concerning the world in which he lives and from the expanding confidence that increased scientific understanding brings.

## Chapter 2. Motion in One Dimension

Straight Line Kinematics (PSSC, 1959), 34 min, purchase, MLA, rental $9, MFR. Graphs are generated for distance traveled, speed, and acceleration, using special equipment in a test car. The relationship between phenomena and graphs is shown.

Film Loops - A set of Super 8 loops appropriate for laboratory, library, or corridor study in this and other chapters is Calculus in Motion (8 loops): Functions, Derivatives, The Definite Integral, The Fundamental Theorem, Limits, Concavity and Points of Inflection, Rolle's Theorem and the Mean Value Theorem, and Taylor Polynomials (Bruce and Katherine Cornwell/Duane W. Bailey, 1973), purchase $300, HMCO.

## Chapter 3. Motion in Two and Three Dimensions

Uniform Circular Motion (AAPT, 1952), 8 min, purchase $65, MGH. When a particle moves around a circular path of fixed radius at constant speed, the motion is shown to be accelerated since the velocity vector is constantly changing direction. A centripetal acceleration equation is derived and centripetal force is illustrated by several animations. May be useful in Chapter 5 also.

Film Loops

Galilean Relativity (3 loops): Ball Dropped from Mast of Ship, Object Dropped from Aircraft, Projectile Fired Vertically (Project Physics), purchase $24.95 each, BFA.

Vector Kinematics (6 loops): The Velocity Vector, Velocity in Circular and Simple Harmonic Motion, The Acceleration Vector, The Velocity and Acceleration in Circular Motion, Velocity and Acceleration in Simple Harmonic Motion, Velocity and Acceleration in Free Fall (PSSC, 1962), purchase $13 each, EDC and MLA.

## Chapter 4. Newton's Laws

Newton's Equal Areas (Cornwell-Bork, 1968), color, 8 min, purchase $100, rental $5, IFB. Utilizes the advantages of animation and elementary geometry to show that, if all the forces on a moving body act toward a point, the line connecting the moving body and the point sweeps out equal areas in equal time intervals.

Frames of Reference (PSSC, 1960), 28 min, purchase $150, MLA, rental $9, MFR. This is an outstanding film. Physics is fun, as Hume and Ivey readily show. Interesting and clever demonstrations are presented showing bodies in inertial and noninertial frames of reference.

Film Loops

Inertial Forces - Translational Acceleration (FMOSU, 1962). Weight and apparent weight can be understood from this film involving a student standing on a spring balance in an elevator.

Inertial Forces - Centripetal Acceleration (FMOSU, 1962). This is an imaginative use of an amusement park ride to provide a good demonstration of centripetal force. May also be useful in Chapter 5.

Reference Frames (Skylab, AAPT, 1974). Moving astronauts as seen from fixed and moving camera.

## Chapter 5. Applications of Newton's Laws

Uniform Circular Motion (AAPT, 1952). See Chapter 3 listing.

Film Loop

Inertial Forces - Centripetal Acceleration (FMOSU, 1962). See Chapter 4 listing.

## Chapter 6. Forces in Nature

Planetary Motion and Kepler's Laws (M. L. Meeks, 1973), color, 9 min, purchase $95, HMCO. Excellent computer-animated film with sound track. Variation in the planetary distances from the sun and the resulting change in orbital speed are shown to agree with Kepler's second law. May also be useful in Chapter 16.

Forces, Excerpt (PSSC, 1962), 8 min, purchase $40, EDC. Reviewed AJP 31:400 (1963). Excerpt of a longer film. Shows recording tape, a yard stick, medicine bottles, and boxes of sand being used to set up gravitational forces to simulate the Cavendish experiment. Also useful in Chapter 16.

Force, Mass, and Motion (BTL, 1965), 10 min, loan, BTL. This computer-generated film illustrates the motion of massive bodies under the influence of gravity and other forces.

Film Loops

Inertial Forces - Translation; Inertial Forces - Centripetal Acceleration (FMOSU, 1962). See Chapter 4 listing.

Planetary Motion and Kepler's Laws (Meeks, 1973). Two loops, I and II, from the film described above.

## Chapter 7. Work and Energy

No films recommended.

Film Loops

Mechanics on an Air Track series (BFA-Ealing, 1964). These 9 loops on mechanics are appropriate for use selectively in Chapters 7 to 11 and 14.

A Method of Measuring Energy; Gravitational Potential Energy (HPP). These loops are appropriate both for this chapter and Chapter 9.

## Chapter 8. Potential Energy and Conservative Forces

No films recommended.

Film Loop

Conservation of Energy, from Mechanics on an Air Track series (BFA-Ealing, 1964). Appropriate both in this chapter and in Chapter 9.

## Chapter 9. Conservation of Energy

No films recommended.

Film Loop

Conservation of Energy (BFA-Ealing, 1964). See Chapter 8 listing.

## Chapter 10. Many-Particle Systems

No films recommended.

Film Loop

Center of Mass Pendulum, from Mechanics on an Air Track series (BFA-Ealing, 1964). May also be useful in Chapter 14.

## Chapter 11. Collisions and Reactions

No films recommended.

Film Loops

Pressure, Volume, and Boyle's Law (KALMIA). Available in 16-mm silent loop as well as in Super 8 format.

Collisions (Skylab, AAPT).

## Chapter 12. Rotation of a Rigid Body about a Fixed Axis

No films or film loops recommended.

## Chapter 13. Rotation in Space and Angular Momentum

Angular Momentum, A Vector Quantity (CPF-EDC, 1963), 27 min, purchase or rental, WARDS or UEVA. Uses various demonstrations to show that angular momenta add vectorially. Obtains zero sum from three wheels spinning and adding momenta such that no precession occurs. Also demonstrates that a resultant torque causes change in angular momentum.

Film Loops - The following loops from the Skylab-AAPT series are appropriate here: Human Momenta, Moving Astronauts, Acrobatic Astronauts, Games Astronauts Play, and Gyroscopes.

## Chapter 14. Oscillations

Simple Harmonic Motion (AAPT, 1953), 10 min, purchase \$65, MGH. An animated spring, mass, oscillator is set on a smooth horizontal surface. The mass is displaced from its equilibrium position and is then released. Its subsequent motion is studied and related to a circle of reference.

Film Loops

Oscillator series (10 loops): CO-1, Energy Transfer; CO-2, Other Oscillators; CO-3, Normal Modes; SF-1, Soap Film Oscillations; OS-5, Point Suspension; OS-6, Saddle Suspension; OS-7, Short Saddle Suspension; OS-9, Forced Damped Harmonic Oscillations; OS-10, Ring of Coupled Pendulums I, Normal Modes; OS-11, Ring of Coupled Pendulums II, Mixtures of Normal Modes (EDC, 1964-1968); CO-1, CO-2, CO-3, OS-10, and OS-11 are in color; 16-mm, EDC; Super 8, BFA and UEVA. Shows the physical behavior of several different oscillating devices and could be wholly shown in connection with this and the next chapter.

Coupled Oscillators - Equal Masses; Coupled Oscillators - Unequal Masses; The Wilberforce Pendulum (FMOSU).

Oscillations (Skylab-AAPT).

## Chapter 15. Damped and Forced Oscillations

No films recommended.

Film Loop

Damped Oscillations (Schwartz, BFA). Demonstrates damped oscillations and shows factors on which damping depends.

## Chapter 16. Gravity

Planetary Motion and Kepler's Laws (Meeks, 1973). See Chapter 6 listing.

Forces, Excerpt (PSSC, 1962). See Chapter 6 listing.

Film Loop

Measurement of "G", the Cavendish Experiment (FMOSU). Time-lapse film of the oscillatory motion of a Cavendish torsion balance.

## Chapter 17. Temperature

No films recommended.

Film Loops - Two outstanding series of loops are recommended for use in these next three chapters as the teacher deems appropriate.

Kinetic Theory (Pucks on an Air Table) series (6 color loops): Maxwellian Speed Distribution, Random Walk and Brownian Motion, Equipartition of Energy, Gravitational Distribution, Diffusion, Properties of Gases (Harold Daw), purchase $150, BFA. Reviewed AJP 37:117 (1969).

Kinetic Theory series (11 computer-animated loops): Pressure, Volume, and Boyle's Law; Temperature, Energy, and Thermal Equilibrium; Heating, Cooling, and Charles' Law; Avogadro's Principle; Ideal Gas Law; Dalton's Law; Gravitational Distribution; Maxwell-Boltzmann Distribution; Brownian Motion and Random Walk; Graham's Law; Deviations from Ideal Gas (J. T. Fitch, MIT); Super 8: purchase $24.95 each or $258 for set; 16 mm: $30.95 each or $320 for set; KALMIA.

## Chapter 18. Heat, Work, and the First Law of Thermodynamics

No films recommended.

Film Loops - Select from listings in Chapter 17.

## Chapter 19. The Availability of Energy

The Carnot Cycle: Kelvin Temperature Scale (AAPT, 1952), 8 min, purchase $65, MGH. Excellent animated sketches used to explain PVT relations for a piston sliding in a cylinder. The efficiency of a heat engine is then related to the Kelvin temperatures of the hot source and cold sink.

You Can't Go Back (Bent and Bent, 1973), color, 6 min, purchase $60, EPP. Reviewed AJP 42:804 (1974). An amusing, educational, nontechnical film on the second law of thermodynamics. By showing reversed film sequences of familiar events, irreversibility in nature is convincingly demonstrated.

Superfluid Helium (J. F. Allen, 1972), color, 16 min, purchase $130, JFA. Reviewed AJP 42:437 (1974). A beautiful presentation of the spectacular characteristics of superfluid $^4$He, produced and narrated by the discoverer of the fountain effect. Superb photography shows the transition between normal and superfluid, the fountain effect, the passage of superfluid He through densely packed fine powder, and the difficult mobile-film phenomenon.

Liquid Helium II, The Superfluid (A. Leitner, 1963), 38 min, rental $8.25, purchase, MSU. Reviewed AJP 33:414 (1965). A longer film showing many of the same phenomena listed in the Allen film; second sound is also discussed.

Film Loop

Critical Temperature (FMOSU). In this dangerous experiment, a glass tube containing ethyl ether is heated above its critical temperature (194°C) and is then cooled. The violence of the condensation and the reappearance of the meniscus are impressive.

## Chapter 20. Wave Pulses

Simple Waves (PSSC, 1959), 27 min, purchase, MLA; rental $8.00, MFR; loan, BTL. A particularly valuable film in which John Shive of BTL uses ropes, slinkies, and a torsion bar machine to demonstrate various wave characteristics. Motion usually repeated several times in normal and slow-motion photography.

Film Loops - Use here and in Chapters 21 to 25 selected loops from the Baez-EBEC set of 20 loops on standing waves: Pulses and Waves, Single Pulses in a Spring, Transverse Wave Apparatus, Reflection of Waves in a Spring, Computer-Animated Standing Waves, Superposition of Pulses, Reflection of Pulses I, Reflection of Pulses II.

## Chapter 21. Harmonic Waves in One Dimension

No films recommended.

Film Loops

Superposition of Pulses in a Spring; Superposition of Pulses - Computer Animated (Baez-EBEC).

## Chapter 22. Standing Waves

Standing Waves and the Principle of Superposition (Sorri-Baez, 1971), color, 11 min, purchase $150, rental $9.00, EBEC. Reviewed in AJP 41:53 (1971). Clearly illustrates the formation of standing waves by the superposition of identical wave trains moving in opposite directions. The concept of nodes in standing linear waves is demonstrated and extended to nodal lines in surface waves. Also useful in Chapter 23.

Film Loops

Transverse Standing Waves in Spring-Wave Groups; Transverse Standing Waves in a Spring - Continuous Wave Train; Longitudinal Standing Waves in a Spring; Computer-Animated Standing Waves in a Spring (Baez-EBEC).

## Chapter 23. Superposition of Waves of Different Frequency

Standing Waves and the Principle of Superposition (Sorri-Baez, 1971). See Chapter 22 listing.

A Pair of Paradoxes (Zajac and Shepard, 1965), 2 min, loan, BTL. A film in which the paradox is based on the Penrose triangle. A ball appears to bounce ever upward, accompanied by musical tones which appear to ascend indefinitely.

## Chapter 24. Spherical and Circular Waves

Doppler Effect (AAPT, 1952), 8 min, purchase $65, MGH. Effects shown by detailed, clear animation; equations "derived" for either or both source and observer in motion. Train horn and bell at crossings used to demonstrate effects detected when approaching or receding.

Doppler Effect and Shock Waves: RTWPS-V (CPF-EDC, 1962), 8 min, purchase or rental, WARDS or UEVA. Reviewed in AJP 32:62 (1964). Contains demonstrations of effects produced by a source of waves moving at various speeds with respect to the wave medium. The Doppler effect is clearly seen at several source speeds less than the wave velocity. For source speeds greater than the wave velocity, the formation of the shock wave and shock cone is clearly demonstrated.

Film Loops - The following Strickland-EDC Ripple Tank series loops are recommended: RT 9, Doppler Effect; RT 10, Formation of Shock Waves. Available 16 mm, EDC; Super 8, BFA and UEVA.

## Chapter 25. Wave Propagation

Bragg Reflection: RTWPS-IV (CPF-EDC), 10 min, purchase or rental, WARDS or UEVA. Reviewed in AJP 32:62 (1964). Waves scattered from a two-dimensional array produce a strong reflection when n = 2d sin $\theta$. Strength of the reflected signal is studied as the angle of incidence and the wavelength are varied.

## Chapter 26. Light

Measurement of the Speed of Light (AAPT, 1951), 8 min, purchase $65, MGH. Excellent, but brief animated presentation of the various measurements of the speed of light. A superb match for Section 26-3.

Joseph Fraunhofer: Dispersion (Leitner, 1975), color, 14 min, purchase $140, rental $11, RPI. A heliostat is used to direct sunlight through the slit of a simple prism spectrometer. Many Fraunhofer lines are observed in the spectrum. An historical excursion to the Deutsches Museum is filmed; Fraunhofer's efforts to design and construct superb lenses and teloscopes are narrated to us.

Joseph Fraunhofer: Diffraction (Leitner, 1975), color, 16 min, purchase $160, rental $12, RPI. Demonstrates an historic series of diffraction experiments, performed by Fraunhofer about 1820, which served as the founding of grating spectroscopy. The spectrum of sunlight produced by a reflection grating having 30,000 lines per inch is shown to have many weak dark lines in the 6 A region between the sodium D lines.

Interference and Diffraction: RTWP-II (CPF-EDC), 19 min, purchase or rental, WARDS or UEVA. Reviewed in AJP 32:62 (1964). Using a ripple tank, various interference patterns are demonstrated for waves emanating from two point sources. The effects of varying wavelengths, the separation of the sources, and the phase of the sources are shown. Multiple-slit diffraction is also shown.

Refraction, Dispersion, and Resonance (Leitner, 1973), color, 35 min, purchase $290, rental $22, RPI. Reviewed in AJP 42:1047 (1974). Qualitatively presents the "classical model" for refraction and dispersion of light by optical materials. The "model" is built by animation and experiment. The question of resonance is explored using a mechanical oscillator driven at various frequencies, with care given to the phase between response and driving force. Demonstrates well several crucial experiments in the history of optics and spectroscopy.

Film Loops

Diffraction - Single Slit; Diffraction - Double Slit; Resolving Power (FMOSU)

Microwave Optics series (14 loops): Refraction, Diffraction, Michelson Interferometer, Polarization, and three loops on interference are especially recommended (Baez-EBEC).

## Chapter 27. Geometric Optics

Refraction, Dispersion, and Resonance; Joseph Fraunhofer - Dispersion; Joseph Fraunhofer - Diffraction (Leitner). See Chapter 26 listing.

Film Loops

Microwave Optics series (14 loops): Transmission and Reflection, Total Internal Reflection, and Index of Refraction are appropriate here for discussing related concepts between light and microwaves (Baez-EBEC).

## Chapter 28. Special Relativity

A Relativistic Ride (E. Taylor-EDC, 1970), color, silent, 4 min, purchase \$25, rental \$10, EDC (also available in Super 8-T). Visual effects of the finite velocity of light are shown in this computer-animated sequence that depicts the view one would observe moving along a pole-lined road at ever-increasing speed. Time dilation and Penrose-Terrall rotation are illustrated.

The Ultimate Speed, An Exploration with High-Energy Electrons (CPF-EDC, 1962), 38 min, purchase or rental, WARDS or UEVA. Reviewed in AJP 32: 551 (1964). Time-of-flight techniques are used to measure the speed of electrons having VDG and linear accelerator supplied kinetic energies from 0.5 to 15 Mev. The kinetic energy of the electron is measured by calorimetry. The results suggest that the speed of light is the limiting particle speed, in agreement with special relativity.

Time Dilation, An Experiment with Mu-Mesons (CPF-EDC, 1963), 36 min, purchase or rental, WARDS or UEVA. Reviewed in AJP 31:342 (1963). Data taken on Mt. Washington, New Hampshire, and at Cambridge, Massachusetts, are shown to support the thesis that mu-mesons moving at 0.99 c "have clocks" that run at about one-ninth the rate of "clocks" associated with mesons at rest.

Two films that could be used to good advantage here or in Chapter 42 as "leavening agents" are:

Anti-Matter (UCLA, 1973), color, 12 min, purchase \$260, rental \$25, AEF. Reviewed in AJP 42:803 (1974). This is a cleverly presented animated film on a fascinating topic. It presents truths and suppositions regarding antimatter. It treats the topics of anti-atoms, antitime, antiworlds, antimeteors, and a pollution-free scheme for deriving energy from garbage. Its levity is a real plus in making some students aware of concepts they may not have encountered.

Shadows of Bliss (CERN-Tattooist, 1972), color, 44 min, 750 Swiss francs, CERN; loan, FNL. Provides a look at elementary-particle physics with a solid tie to classical physics and present-day large-scale research apparatus in the CERN accelerator. It attempts to clarify for the intelligent layman the meaning, method of experimentation, and some basic theoretical ideas in the subnuclear world of high-energy physics.

## Chapter 29. The Electric Field

Introduction to Electric and Magnetic Fields (Blum, 1973), color, 25 min, purchase \$350, MGH. Ronald Blum has assembled a five-part computer-animated sound film in which Coulomb's law and the Biot-Savart law are used to derive fields and forces for several situations normally dealt with in a good introductory course. The majority of this 16-mm film is available in the Super 8 format, in five silent loops, the titles of which outline much of the content of the 16-mm film: Coulomb's Law, Grounded Conducting Sphere and a Point Charge, Ampère's Law, and Force on a Line Current in a Uniform Magnetic Field. This film can be used in its entirety as an introduction to the next 11 chapters, be shown sectioned as in the loop format, or be used both as preview and review (e.g., at the end of Chapter 37).

Film Loops

Coulomb's Law (Baez-EBEC).

Coulomb's Law; Grounded Conducting Sphere and a Point Charge; Conducting Sphere Insulated from Ground and a Point Charge (Blum, 1973).

## Chapter 30. Calculation of the Electric Field

Introduction to Electric and Magnetic Fields (Blum, 1973). See Chapter 29 listing.

Film Loop

Coulomb's Law (Blum, 1973).

## Chapter 31. Conductors in Electrostatic Equilibrium

Volta and Electricity (Devons, 1974), color, 33 min, purchase $225, BARNARD. Reviewed AJP 43:659 (1975). An ingenious and genuine presentation treating the research of Alessandro Volta. Devons has produced a fine historical résumé of the 25-year span of Volta's activities. Experiments with the electrophorus and condensing electroscope are shown; these, along with the pile, are instruments invented by Volta. The film gives one a new look at the state of "electrical science" 150 to 175 years ago. Best shown here or in Chapter 32.

Film Loop

Conducting Sphere Insulated from Ground and a Point Charge (Blum, 1973), MGH.

## Chapter 32. Electric Potential

Volta and Electricity (Devons, 1974). See Chapter 31 listing.

Introduction to Electric and Magnetic Fields (Blum, 1973). See Chapter 29 listing.

## Chapter 33. Capacitance, Electrostatic Energy, and Dielectrics

No films recommended.

Film Loops

Conductors, Insulators, and Capacitors; Increasing the Potential of a Capacitor; Capacitance of Capacitor Combinations - Parallel; Capacitance of Capacitor Combinations - Series (Baez-EBEC).

## Chapter 34. Electric Current

## Chapter 35. Direct-Current Circuits

## Chapter 36. The Magnetic Field

No films recommended.

## Chapter 37. Sources of the Magnetic Field

Introduction to Electric and Magnetic Fields (Blum, 1973). See Chapter 29 listing.

Film Loops

Ampère's Law; Force on a Line Current in a Magnetic Field (Blum, 1973), MGH.

## Chapter 38. Faraday's Law

No films recommended.

Film Loops

Lenz Law I; Lenz Law II; Large Inductance: Current Buildup; Large Inductance: Free Oscillations (PFR).

Adler's Electromagnetism series of 12 loops (BFA) could prove useful here for students of this course who did not have "hands on" experience with the subject in high school physics.

## Chapter 39. Magnetism in Matter

No films recommended.

Film Loops

Paramagnetism of Liquid Oxygen (FMOSU, 1962). Available in 16-mm as well as Super 8 format. Demonstrated by pouring liquid oxygen over the poles of magnets. Paramagnetic oxygen clings to the magnet bridging the gap between poles of a horseshoe-shaped magnet. In another sequence, liquid nitrogen is poured into the region to show the contrasting effect when a diamagnetic substance is used.

Ferromagnetic Domain Wall Motion (FMOSU, 1962). Available in 16-mm as well as Super 8 format. A single crystal iron whisker covered with a colloidal suspension of magnetite is placed in a varying longitudinal magnetic field. The magnetite particles collected along the boundaries are observed to move as the domain boundaries change.

## Chapter 40. Alternating-Current Circuits

## Chapter 41. Maxwell's Equation and Electromagnetic Waves

No films recommended.

## Chapter 42. Quantization

Photons (PSSC, 1959), 19 min, purchase MLA, rental MFR. Reviewed AJP 30:772 (1962). The particle behavior of light is demonstrated using a photomultiplier and an oscilloscope. The dynode action of a photomultiplier is explained and a cryogenic trap for limiting "noise" is shown. Gives a good introduction to how a photon detector operated in 1959.

Interference of Photons (PSSC, 1959), 13 min, purchase MLA, rental MFR. Reviewed AJP 30:772 (1962). Companion film to Photons. The interference pattern of a weakly illuminated double slit reveals the wave and particle nature of light. Photomultiplier tube is used to detect the photons.

Matter Waves (PSSC, 1962), 28 min, purchase MLA, rental MFR. Reviewed AJP 33:63 (1965). This is a modern version of the original experiment which showed the wave behavior of the electron. Electron diffraction patterns are observed on a fluorescent screen. Similarity to an optical system showing the same pattern is presented.

Introduction to Lasers (EBEC, 1972), color, 17 min, purchase $220, rental $11, EBEC. Reviewed AJP 42:525 (1974). The development, structure, and uses of a laser are discussed by three prominent scientists closely related to the discovery of the "lasing" phenomenon. Animated sequences and laboratory demonstrations are used to illustrate their explanations. Some interesting uses of the laser also are presented.

Introduction to Holography (EBEC, 1972), color, 17 min, purchase $220, rental $11, EBEC. Reviewed AJP 43:203 (1975). Useful in conjunction with Introduction to Lasers to give a final summary of wave-particle duality. Animation is well used to explain how holograms are made from direct and reflected beams. The production of various types of holograms is illustrated, and several uses of holography are then mentioned.

Film Loops

Atoms to Molecules series (8 loops): Electrons and Electron Densities; Orbitals and the Building-Up Principle of Atomic Structure; The Covalent Bond: Forming the Hydrogen Molecule; The Ionic Bond: Forming the Lithium-Fluoride Molecule; Repulsion between Noble Gases: The Helium-Helium Interaction; Chemical Bonding in Polyatomic Systems: The Water Molecule especially recommended (Wahl and Blukis), MGH.

## ANSWERS TO EVEN-NUMBERED EXERCISES AND PROBLEMS

Stanley Williams

### Chapter 1

EXERCISES:

2. (a) length, velocity, acceleration; (b) length, $time^{-1}$; (c) length, $time^{-1}$.
4. (a) feet, ft/sec, $ft/sec^2$; (b) ft, $sec^{-1}$; (c) ft, $sec^{-1}$.
6. (a) $4.0 \times 10^7$ m; (b) $6.37 \times 10^6$ m.
8. 1.000 mi/h = 1.609 km/h.
10. $[G] = (length)^3/(time^2\text{-}mass)$; $m^3/(sec^2\text{-}kg)$.
12. $\pi/2$ radians
14. (a) 45°; (b) 270°; (c) 90°; (d) 30°; (e) 150°.
16. 1.0 rev/min = $\pi/30$ rad/sec = $1.05 \times 10^{-1}$ rad/sec = 6°/sec.
18. (a) $12\pi$ in = $3.77 \times 10^1$ in; (b) 20.9 in/sec.
20. (a) c = 8.25 in;

(b),(c)

| ∡ opposite | sine | cosine | tangent | ∡ |
|---|---|---|---|---|
| a | 0.243 | 0.970 | 0.250 | 14° 2' |
| b | 0.970 | 0.243 | 4.000 | 75° 58' |
| c | 1.000 | 0.000 | ∞ | 90° |

22. $2.158 \times 10^3$ mi
24. $a_1 = -2$, $a_2 = 3$, $a_3 = -4$, ... , $a_n = (-1)^n(n+1)$.
26. (a) 96.0; (b) 0.995; (c) 0.996.

PROBLEMS:

2. (a) C = 0.537 yr, n = 1.5; (b) $r = 5.11 \times 10^5$ km.
4. $[v] = L/T$, $[g] = L/T^2$, $\therefore [v^2/g] = L$ so $R \propto v^2/g$.
6. $\sin(\theta+\theta) = \sin\theta\cos\theta + \cos\theta\sin\theta = 2\sin\theta\cos\theta$.
8. (a) 8.66 mi from the N-S road and 5.00 mi from the E-W road; (b) 17.32 mi.
10.

| Term | $\frac{\frac{1}{2}n(n-1)x^2}{\text{E-26 Ans}}$ | $\frac{\text{Exact - E-26 Ans}}{\text{Exact}}$ |
|---|---|---|
| $(9.8)^2$ | $4.17 \times 10^{-2}$ % | $4.16 \times 10^{-2}$ % |
| $(.999)^5$ | $1.01 \times 10^{-3}$ % | $1.00 \times 10^{-3}$ % |
| $(1.002)^{-2}$ | $1.21 \times 10^{-3}$ % | $1.20 \times 10^{-3}$ % |

### Chapter 2

EXERCISES:

2. (a) 54.54 mi/h; (b) 54.54 mi/h; (c) 0; (d) 0.
4. (a) 0; (b) 1/3; (c) - 2; (d) 1.
6. 2.0 m/sec
8. (a) 1.0 m/sec; (b) 0.67 m/sec; (c) at t = 8.0 sec.
10. (b)

| time interval | 0-1 | 1-2 | 2-3 | 3-4 | 4-5 | 5-6 | 6-7 | 7-8 | 8-9 | 9-10 |
|---|---|---|---|---|---|---|---|---|---|---|
| $\bar{v}$ (m/sec) | 45 | 35 | 25 | 15 | 5 | -5 | -15 | -25 | -35 | -45 |

(c) v = 50 - 10t m/sec.

12. (a) 55 mi/h, 65 mi/h; (b) v = 45 + 10t mi/h.
14. (a) 8 $m/sec^2$ for both; (b) 8 $m/sec^2$.
16. (a) $2 < t < 3$; (b) $6 < t < 7$; (c) near t = 5, $8 < t < 9$, $10 < t < 11$; (d) $2 < t < 4$, $8 < t < 9$, $10 < t < 11$; (e) $0 < t < 4$, $t > 8$; (f) $4 < t < 7$.
18. $v = \omega A\cos\omega t$, $a = -\omega^2 A\sin\omega t = -\omega^2 x$. Use $a = -\omega^2 A\sin\omega t$ to find $\sin\omega t = -a/\omega^2 A$. Then $v = \omega A(1 - \sin^2\omega t)^{1/2} = \omega A[1 - (-a/\omega^2 A)^2]^{1/2}$, so that $v = \omega A$ when a = 0.
20. $x = 6t + x_0$
22. (a) v = - 9.8t; (b) $x = 100 - 4.9t^2$.

24. (a) $x(t) = x_0 + v_0 t + 1/6\, Ct^3$; (b) $v = 75/2$ m/sec, $x = 125/2$ m.
26. (a) 90 m; (b) $x(t) = x_0 + 3t + 3t^2$, $x(5) - x(0) = 90$ m.
28. (a) 1.0 m; (b) $1 \le t \le 2$: displacement = 1.17 m, $2 \le t \le 3$ sec: displacement = 3.17 m; (c) $\bar{v} = 2.17$ m/sec.
30. $x = 1/6\, t^3$, $x(3) - x(1) = 26/6$ m, $\bar{v} = 2.17$ m/sec.
32. 50 m
34. $t = -1$ sec, $x = 8$ m, $v = -3$ m/sec; $t = +\frac{1}{2}$ sec, $x = 8$ m, $v = 3$ m/sec.
36. $v_0 = 80$ ft/sec, $a = -32$ ft/sec$^2$. The ball rises until $v = 80 - 32t = 0$ and then falls striking the ground with velocity - 80 m/sec.
(a) Time in flight = 5.0 sec;
(b) The greatest height is attained when $v = 0$ at $t = 2.5$ sec. Thus $x = 80(2.5) - 16(2.5)^2 = 100$ ft.
(c) In general $x = 80t - 16t^2 = 96$ has two roots, $t = 2$ sec and $t = 3$ sec. At $t = 2$ sec, the ball is upward bound with speed 16 m/sec, while at $t = 3$ sec, the ball is falling with speed 16 m/sec.
38. $a = 0.71\, g = 22.8$ ft/sec$^2$, $t = 3.86$ sec.
40. Area of a circular ring of radius r and width $\Delta r$: $\Delta A \approx 2\pi r\,\Delta r$.
42. (a) Volume of a spherical shell of radius r (surface area $4\pi r^2$) and thickness $\Delta r$: $\Delta V \approx 4\pi r^2 \Delta r$;

(b) $\frac{dV}{V} = \frac{4\pi r^2 dr}{\frac{4}{3}\pi r^3} = 3\frac{dr}{r}$ ; (c) $\Delta V/V \approx 6\%$.

PROBLEMS:

2. In both cases t is in seconds and x in meters.

| | | |
|---|---|---|
| For Hare: | $x = 4t$ | $0 \le t \le 300$ sec = 5 min |
| | $x = 1200$ m | 5 min $\le t \le$ 140 min |
| | $x = 1200 + 4(t - 140.60)$ | $t \ge 140$ min |
| For Tortoise: | $x = t$ | |

Tortoise passes Hare fast asleep at t = 20 min. At t = 140 min Tortoise has covered 8400 m while Hare has managed only 1200 m and is 7200 m behind. When Tortoise crosses the finish line at x = 10,000 m, Hare is only at 7600 m and loses the race by 2400 m. Since Tortoise requires 10,000 seconds to cover the course while Hare needs only 2500 seconds when running, Hare may nap slightly less than 7500 seconds = 2 hr 5 min.

4. (a) $t_0$ and $t_1$; (b) $t_3$, $t_4$, $t_6$ and $t_7$; (c) $t_2$ and $t_5$; (d) $t_4$; (e) $t_2$ and $t_6$; (f) $t_0$, $t_1$, $t_3$, $t_5$, $t_7$.

6.

| Time | 1 | 2 | 3 | 4 | 5 | 6 | 7 | 8 | 9 |
|---|---|---|---|---|---|---|---|---|---|
| Fig. (a) acceleration | 0 | 0 | + | 0 | 0 | - | - | 0 | 0 |
| Fig. (b) acceleration | - | - | - | 0 | + | + | + | - | |

For Fig. (b), a is constant and not 0 from about 1 to 3, and from about 7.5 to 8.5 and v is zero near 2, 6 and just before 8. For Fig. (a), v is 0 at 3 and between 6 and 7 while a is constant and not zero between about 2.5 and 3.5 sec.

8. Police car equations:

| | | |
|---|---|---|
| $v = 5t$ | $0 \le t \le 24$ sec | |
| $v = 120$ mi/h | $t \ge 24$ sec | |
| $x = (\frac{5}{2}t)\frac{t}{3600}$ mi | $0 \le t \le 24$ sec | |
| $x = 0.40 + \frac{(t-24)}{30}$ mi | $t \ge 24$ sec | |

Speeder equations:

$v = 80$ mi/h
$x = t/45$ mi

In the equations the numerical value of t in seconds is to be used and speeds are in mi/h.
(a) Condition is $x_{police} = x_{speeder}$ or $0.4 + (t-24)/30 = t/45$ so $t = 36$ sec;
(b) Thus for both $x = 0.80$ mi.

10. If there is a collision, then $x_1 = v_1 t - \frac{1}{2}at^2 = x_2 = d + v_2 t$ determines its time of occurrence. Thus the collision time is

$$t = \frac{(v_1 - v_2) + \sqrt{(v_1 - v_2)^2 - 2\,ad}}{a}.$$

If $(v_1 - v_2)^2 > 2ad$, there is a positive root solution, hence a collision. Therefore, no collision occurs if $(v_1 - v_2)^2 < 2ad$ or if $d > (v_1 - v_2)^2/2a$.

14. (a) 24 ft; (b) 1.72 sec; (c) 39.2 ft/sec downward.

16. Alternatively, $\frac{dE}{dt} = mva = \frac{dE}{dx}\frac{dx}{dt} = \frac{dE}{dx} v$ so that $\frac{dE}{dx} = ma$.

18. The solution is $v = v_T(1 - e^{-Bt})$ where $v_T$ is the terminal velocity given by $v_T = g/B$.

## Chapter 3

EXERCISES:

2. 7.07 m at 135° in both cases.
4. (a) 14.1 m, 45°; 20m, 90°; 14.1 m, 135°; 0 m;
   (b) 14.1 m, 45°; 14.1 m, 135°; 14.1 m, 225°; 14.1 m, 315°;
   (c) equal magnitude, perpendicular;
   (d) equal magnitude, oppositely directed.
6. (a) $A_x = 8.66$ m, $A_y = 5.00$ m; (b) 3.54 m, 3.54 m; (c) 3.50 ft, 6.06 ft; (d) 0 ft, 5.0 ft; (e) - 13.0 ft/sec, 7.5 ft/sec; (f) - 5.0 m/sec, - 8.66 m/sec; (g) 0 m/sec$^2$ , - 8.0 m/sec$^2$.
8. $2(\underset{\sim}{i} + \underset{\sim}{j} + \underset{\sim}{k})$
10. (a) $\underset{\sim}{A}$: 8.06, 209.75°
   $\underset{\sim}{B}$: 3.61, 303.69°
   $\underset{\sim}{A} + \underset{\sim}{B}$: 9.06, 263.66°
   (b) 4.12, 284.04°
   6.32, 71.57°
   3.61, 33.69°
12.

| | $\underset{\sim}{A}$ | $\underset{\sim}{B}$ | $(\underset{\sim}{A} + \underset{\sim}{B})$ | $(\underset{\sim}{A} - \underset{\sim}{B})$ |
|---|---|---|---|---|
| x component | 1.41 m | 1.73 m | 3.14 m | -0.32 m |
| y component | 1.41 m | -1.00 m | 0.41 m | 2.41 m |

$(\underset{\sim}{A} + \underset{\sim}{B})$: 3.17, 7.44°, $(\underset{\sim}{A} - \underset{\sim}{B})$: 2.44, 97.56° .

14. Any vector of magnitude 5 and angle other than 53.13° will do.
16. $\underset{\sim}{A}$ parallel with $\underset{\sim}{B}$ or $\theta_B = 360° - \theta_A$.
20. 28.0 mi/h, 300.36°.
22. (a) $\pi/10$ m/sec; (b) 5 m, 180°; 5 m, 90°; 5 m, 36°; 5 m, 0°;
   (c) 0.20 m/sec, 180°; 0.28 m/sec, 135°; 0.31 m/sec, 107.9°;
   (d) $\underset{\sim}{v}(0) = 0.31$ m/sec, 90°.
24. (a) At both times v = 9.8 m/sec; (b) $\Delta\underset{\sim}{v} = 2(9.8) = 19.6$ m/sec, downward;
   (c) $\bar{a} = g$, downward.
26. (a) 10 ft/sec, decrease; (b) - 90°; (c) 50 m/sec, 143.1°; (d) 10 m/sec$^2$, 143.1°.
28. $\underset{\sim}{v} = 30\underset{\sim}{i} + (40 - 10t)\underset{\sim}{j}$, $\underset{\sim}{a} = - 10\underset{\sim}{j}$.
30. (a) 57.5 sec; (b) 23.9 mi; (c) 10 miles.
32. (a) g; (b) No; (c) If $\theta_o$ is the initial angle with the horizontal, then the angle between $\underset{\sim}{v}$ and $\underset{\sim}{a}$ starts at $90° + \theta_o$, decreases to 90° at the top and then to $90° - \theta_o$ upon impact with the horizontal.
34. $|\underset{\sim}{v}| = 50$ ft/sec, horizontal; $|\underset{\sim}{a}| = 32$ ft/sec$^2$, downward.
36. $a_{rotation} = 3.44 \times 10^{-3}$ g, $a_{orbital} = 6.07 \times 10^{-4}$ g.
38. 29.9 rev/min
40. (a) Increases by a factor 4; (b) is halved; (c) Sharp corners imply $r \to 0$ which implies $a \to \infty$ unless v is zero.
42. (a) 2 sec; (b) $\pi$ m/sec; (c) $- \underset{\sim}{j}$; (d) $\pi^2$ m/sec$^2$, $\pi/2$ m/sec$^2$; (e) 9.99 m/sec$^2$, 189°.
44. As the particle moves about the circle $\hat{\theta}$ assumes all possible directions. At any point there is a point 90° around the circle at which $\hat{r}$ points parallel to the direction of $\hat{\theta}$ at the first point. Obviously, these correspond to different times.

PROBLEMS:

2. $R = v_o^2 \sin 2\theta_o/g$, so $R(45° + \varphi) = v_o^2 \sin (90° + 2\varphi)/g = v_o^2 \cos 2\varphi/g$.
   $R(45° - \varphi) = v_o^2 \sin (90° - 2\varphi)/g = v_o^2 \cos 2\varphi/g$.
4. 2.25 ft
6. (a) The stationary observer sees $v_o = \sqrt{20^2 + 30^2} = 36.1$ mi/h at 56.3° above the horizontal;
   (b) Both see the ball in the air for 2.75 sec;
   (c) Observer on train sees no horizontal travel while the stationary observer records 80.7 ft;

(d) Train observer sees no velocity at top while the stationary observer sees it move horizontally at 20 mi/h;

(e) Both perceive an acceleration of 32 $ft/sec^2$ downward.

8. Let $\theta$ be the angle between $\underset{\sim}{v}$ and $\underset{\sim}{a}$. The direction of $\underset{\sim}{v}$ determines the tangent to the arc and the center of curvature is along the line perpendicular to $\underset{\sim}{v}$. The center is in the direction such that the radial component of $\underset{\sim}{a}$ which is $a \sin\theta = v^2/r$ is positive. Then $r = v^2/(a \sin\theta)$. For the projectile let the initial angle be $\theta_0$. At the top $v = v_0 \cos\theta_0$ where $v_0$ is the launch speed. Then $\underset{\sim}{v}$ is horizontal and makes an angle $90^o$ with $\underset{\sim}{a} = \underset{\sim}{g}$ which is downward toward the center of curvature. The radius of curvature is $r = (v_0 \cos\theta_0)^2/g$.

10. (a) $\underset{\sim}{v} = (6\underset{\sim}{i} + 4\underset{\sim}{j})t$, $r = 10\underset{\sim}{i} + (3\underset{\sim}{i} + 2\underset{\sim}{j})t^2$; (b) Path equation is $y = 2/3\ x - 20/3$.

12. (a) Yes, some 3.8 m short of the village edge; (b) 95.4 m/sec, 25 m/sec; (c) 6.84 sec.

14. The ball takes 0.4 sec to reach the wall at a height of 5.22 m with a vertical speed of 6.08 m/sec. These together with $v_x = 10$ m/sec form the initial conditions for the second part of the problem. Then $y = 5.22 + 6.08t - 4.9t^2 = 0$ yields $t = 1.825$ sec and $x = v_x t$ then yields $x = 18.25$ m so the ball hits the ground 14.25 m behind the boy.

16. 74.4 rev/min

## Chapter 4

EXERCISES:

2. (a) $1.5\ \underset{\sim}{F}_0$; (b) $1.5 \times 10^7\ m/sec^2$; (c) $3 \times 10^6\ m/sec^2$.
4. Find $a_x$ from the slope of the graph of $v_x$ versus t. Then $F = 10a_x$ is graphed versus time.
6. (a) Air resistance back along the path and tangent and weight downward;
   (b) mg downward, normal perpendicular to the plane, friction to plane and upward;
   (c) On the fluid in the tube: normal along the tube, weight downward;
   (d) Tension upward along string and weight downward.
8. 12 $ft/sec^2$
10. 48 N
12. $\underset{\sim}{a} = 3\underset{\sim}{i} - 1.5\underset{\sim}{j}\ m/sec^2$, $|\underset{\sim}{a}| = 3.35\ m/sec^2$.
14. 20 N down the incline
16. (a) 300 N; (b) 500 N.
18. (a) 12 kg-m/sec; (b) 18 kg-m/sec; (c) 6 kg-m/sec, - 3 kg-m/sec.
20. 490 N = 110 lb
22. 2723 kg
24. (a) 140 lb; (b) 122.5 lb; (c) 122.5 lb.
26. (a) (b)

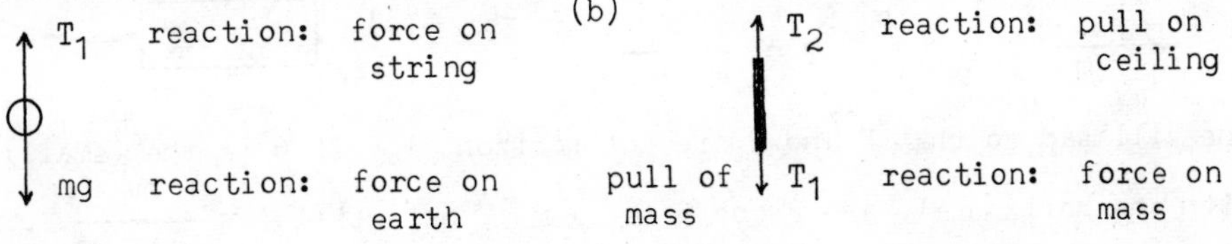


28.

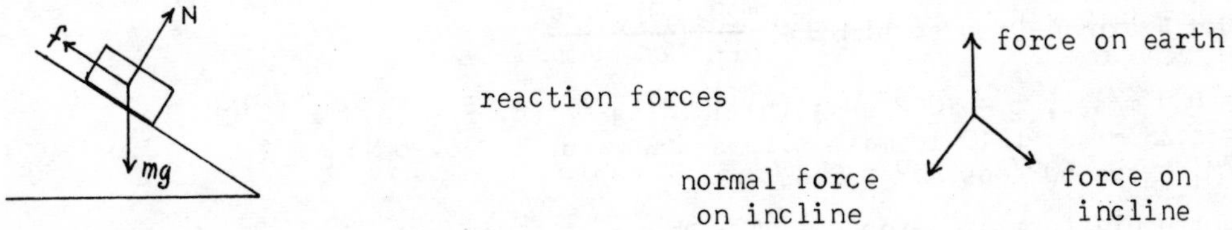


30. (a) $3.125 \times 10^3$ lb-sec; (b) 2.0 ft/sec.
32. (a) $v'_x + 3$; (b) $v'_x = 5/2$ m/sec, 5 m/sec, 15/2 m/sec; (c) $v_x = 11/2$ m/sec, 8 m/sec, 21/2 m/sec; (d) 5/2 $m/sec^2$ in either frame.
34. Since both ends are measured at some time t

$$x'_2 - x'_1 = x_2 + ut - x_1 - ut = x_2 - x_1 .$$

PROBLEMS:

2. Use a calibrated spring scale to accelerate the object. Measure a and use F = ma.
4. (a) 2.5 tons; (b) 2.0 tons; (c) 1.5 tons.
6. (a) $T = (mg/2) \sin\theta = (w/2) \sin\theta$;
   (b) $T \sin\theta + mg$ vertically, $T \cos\theta$ horizontally;

(c) $T = 57.4$ lb, on man vertical force = 165 lb and horizontal force = 57.2 lb;
(d) No, this would require $T = \infty$.
Yes, T in excess of $(w/2) \sin \theta_{initial}$ will produce an upward acceleration which if sufficient will carry the weight beyond the horizontal position.

8. (a) 20 cm/sec$^2$; (b) 1000 dynes; (c) 4000 dynes; (d) 500 dynes; (e) 4000 dynes.
10. (a) 100 kg-m/sec; (b) 260 N horizontally, 50 N vertically;
(c) $|\underset{\sim}{p}| = 2746$ kg-m/sec, 10.5° above horizontal and $|\underset{\sim}{v}| = 275$ m/sec.
12. (a) $a_c = v^2/R = 0.03$ m/sec$^2$; (b) 9.81 m/sec$^2$; (c) 981 N; (d) 978 N.
14. The car is turning to the observer's left with an acceleration 5.64 ft/sec$^2$ toward the center of curvature. Since $v = 50$ mi/h = 73.3 ft/sec, $r = (73.3)^2/5.64 = 953$ ft.

## Chapter 5

EXERCISES:

2. (a) 6 m/sec; (b) 9 m.
4. 2.25 lb
6. (a) 98 N; (b) 98 N; (c) 49 N each; (d) 49 N.
8. (a) 424 N; (b) $T = mg \sin \theta$.
10. $a = g/2 = 4.9$ m/sec$^2$, $T = 49$ N.
12. $a = g/3 = 327$ cm/sec$^2$, $T = 2/3\, m_1 g = 4/3\, m_2 g = 1.31 \times 10^5$ dynes.
14. (a) $a_2 = 0$, $a_4 = 0.75$ m/sec$^2$; (b) $a_2 = a_4 = 0.50$ m/sec$^2$;
16. 5.20 m/sec$^2$, upward
18. $m_1$ $m_2$
$f_1 \longleftarrow \bullet \longrightarrow p$ $\quad p \longleftarrow \bullet \longrightarrow f_2$
$f_1$ and $f_2$ are the respective forces on each boy due to the force he exerts on the ground. If $f_2 > f_1$, then boy 2 wins.
20. $T = m\omega^2 R = m(2\pi/T)^2 R = 0.5(2\pi/4)^2(6.0) = 7.40$ N.
22. 35.8 ft/sec = 24.4 mi/h.
24. 9.8 ft/sec
26. (a) 0.35 %; (b) 2.01 h.
28. (a) 900 kg/m$^3$; (b) 90 %.
30. (a) 10.3 m; (b) 0.74 m.
32. 5
34. If $a = g$ = constant, $v = gt = mg/b$ when $t = t_c = m/b$. Thus, the time $t_c$ is that point where the straight line $v = gt$ intersects the straight line asymptote $v = v_t = mg/b$.
36. Freely falling body in air; a stone dropped into a deep lake, etc.

PROBLEMS:

2. (a) $a = \dfrac{F}{m_1 + m_2}$; (b) $T = \dfrac{m_1}{m_1 + m_2} F$; (c)

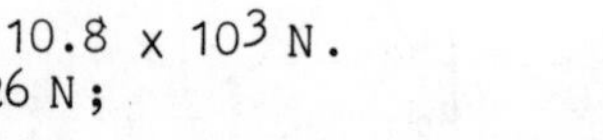


The rope will sag so that F and T are not horizontal. If θ is the (small) angle made with the horizontal, $a = F \cos\theta/(m_1 + m_2)$, but still $T = \dfrac{m_1}{m_1 + m_2} F$. Also, $T \sin\theta + F \sin\theta = m_2 g$ so $\sin\theta = \dfrac{m_2 g}{F}\left(\dfrac{m_1 + m_2}{2m_1 + m_2}\right)$.

4. (a) $\bar{v} = 600$ m/sec, $t = 10^{-3}$ sec; (b) 10.8 kg-m/sec, $\bar{F} = 10.8 \times 10^3$ N.
6. (a) $a = 4.48$ m/sec$^2$, 10 lb mass slides downward, $T = 6.26$ N;
(b) $m_2/m_1 = \cos 50°/\cos 40° = 0.84$.
8. (a) For the platform of weight $w_p$, $T - N - w_p = \dfrac{w_p}{g} a$ where N is the force exerted on the platform by the girl. For the girl one has $F + N - w_g = \dfrac{w_g}{g} a$. Since the rope "is" massless $F = T$ and thus $2T = w_p + w_g + \dfrac{w_p + w_g}{g} a = 170$ lb. So $T = 85$ lb.
(b) Set $a = 0$ and find $T = 80$ lb.
10. $\mu(m_1 + m_2)g$
12. (a) $a = \dfrac{m_1 - m_2}{m_1 + m_2} g$, $T = \dfrac{2m_1 m_2}{m_1 + m_2} g$; (b) $t = \sqrt{\dfrac{2L}{g}\left(\dfrac{m_1 + m_2}{m_1 - m_2}\right)}$ from $L = \frac{1}{2} at^2$;
(c) $dt/t \le 0.25$ so $t \ge 4$ sec, thus $(m_1 + m_2)/(m_1 - m_2) \ge 26.1$ or $m_1/m_2 \le 1.08$. Thus, for example, $m_1 = 900$ gm and $m_2 = 835$ gm would do.

14. The acceleration down the incline is $g \sin \theta$ and this has a vertical component $g \sin^2 \theta$. Thus, if $w_a$ is the apparent weight (the force exerted vertically by the scale on the girl), then $mg - w_a = mg \sin^2 \theta$ or $w_a = mg \cos^2 \theta = 90$ lb.

16. $T_2 = 4\pi^2 f^2(m_2L_1 + m_2L_2)$, $T_1 = 4\pi^2 f^2(m_1L_1 + m_2L_1 + m_2L_2)$.

22. $F = 2.0 \times 10^7$ lb

## Chapter 6

EXERCISES:

2. $1.97 \times 10^{30}$ kg
4. $g/4$ approximately, 2.45 m/sec using $r = 2R_{earth}$.
6. $r = \sqrt{2}R_e$, so $h = (\sqrt{2} - 1)R_e = 1660$ mi.
8. (a) $6.25 \times 10^{12}$; (b) 0.225 N.
10. $1.20 \times 10^{-1}$ $\mu$C
12. $8.20 \times 10^{-2}$ $\mu$N
14. $2.30 \times 10^3$ N, $2.8 \times 10^{10}$ is the ratio of nuclear to electric forces here.
16. (a) $F_{gravity} = F_{spring} = 49$ N; (b) $\Delta x = 24.5$ cm.
18. (a) $k = 3.3$ N/cm; (b) 4.9 m/sec$^2$.
20. (a) 16 ft/sec$^2 = g/2$; (b) 242 ft.
22. 42.3 mi/h
24. $1/16 = 6.25 \times 10^{-2}$
26. (a) $1.67\ g = 16.3$ m/sec$^2$; (b) 19.6 N; (c) No.
28. Parabolic path across the floor of the car. Looks like the path of a ball thrown horizontally.
30. (a) $\tan \theta = 5/g = 0.510$, $\theta = 27.0°$;
    (b) Inertial frame -- acceleration view          Box car view -- equilibrium view

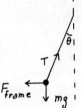

PROBLEMS:

2. $\frac{GMm}{r^2} = m\frac{v^2}{r} = m\left(\frac{2\pi r}{T}\right)^2 \frac{1}{r}$ or $T^2 = \frac{4\pi^2}{GM} r^3 \equiv Cr^3$ .
4. $6.45 \times 10^{23}$ kg
6.

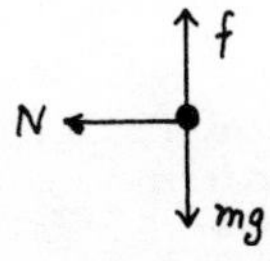


$f = mg$, $N = m\frac{v^2}{r}$, $f = \mu_s N$ at maximum so this yields $v \geq \sqrt{\frac{gr}{\mu_s}}$.

8. $F = \frac{\mu_s mg}{\cos \theta + \mu_s \sin \theta}$ is the functional form.

12. If half the unstretched spring length is d and the angle made with the horizontal is $\theta$, then each half becomes $\ell = d/\cos \theta$ long so that the stretch is $-d + d/\cos \theta$. Equilibrium demands $2F \sin \theta = mg$ and since $F = k\Delta x = kd[(1/\cos \theta) - 1]$ one has $\tan \theta - \sin \theta = mg/2kd$. The sag is $d \tan \theta$. Here $\theta = 22.75°$ and the sag is 6.29 cm.

14. (a) $kx = mv^2/(x_o + x)$; (b) 4.62 cm; (c) $x \approx 5.33$ cm; (d) The next approximation yields 4.53 cm.

16. $f = 1.8 \times 10^{-18}$

18. $\sqrt{rg \frac{\tan \theta - \mu}{1 + \mu \tan \theta}} \leq v \leq \sqrt{rg \frac{\tan \theta + \mu}{1 - \mu \tan \theta}}$, $\tan \theta = \frac{v_o^2}{rg} = 1.681$

so 37.0 mi/h $\leq v \leq$ 77.1 mi/h.

20. (a) The conditions that the 4-kg mass tries to slide upward are $f + 4g \sin 30° - mg = 0$ and $N = 4g \cos 30°$. Thus $f = mg - 4g \sin 30° \leq \mu_s N = (0.4)(4g \cos 30°)$ so $m \leq 3.39$ kg. The conditions that the 4-kg mass tries to slide down yield $m \geq 0.61$ kg; (b) 9.8 N.

22. (a) $F_N = m\omega^2 r$, $\omega = (\pi/30)B$ (rad/sec);

(b) Let the ceiling height be h. Choose unit vectors $\underset{\sim}{i}$ and $\underset{\sim}{j}$ for the inertial observer and $\underset{\sim}{i}'$, $\underset{\sim}{j}'$ for the compartment observer. At t = 0 these are coincident but at some later time t they are related as shown with $\theta = \omega t$. The position of the inerial origin from the compartment one is $\underset{\sim}{d}$.

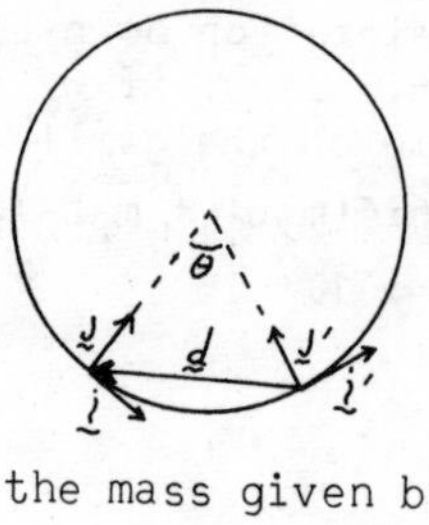


The inertial observer records a position vector $\underset{\sim}{r}$ for the mass given by

$$\underset{\sim}{r} = \omega(r-h)t\,\underset{\sim}{i} + h\underset{\sim}{j}$$

and therefore a velocity

$$\underset{\sim}{v} = \omega(r-h)\,\underset{\sim}{i}\,.$$

Then $\underset{\sim}{i} = \underset{\sim}{i}'\cos\theta - \underset{\sim}{j}'\sin\theta$, $\underset{\sim}{j} = \underset{\sim}{i}'\sin\theta + \underset{\sim}{j}'\cos\theta$ and $\underset{\sim}{d} = -r\sin\theta\,\underset{\sim}{i}' + r(1-\cos\theta)\,\underset{\sim}{j}'$ used to transform these shows that the moving observer claims a centrifugal acceleration

$$\underset{\sim}{a}_{centrifugal} = -\omega^2(r-h)[\underset{\sim}{i}'\sin\theta + \underset{\sim}{j}'\cos\theta]$$

and thus a coriolis acceleration

$$\underset{\sim}{a}_{coriolis} = \omega^2(r-h)(1-\cos\theta)\,\underset{\sim}{j}' + \omega^2(r-h)\sin\theta\,\underset{\sim}{i}'\,.$$

At t = 0, $\underset{\sim}{a}_{coriolis} = 0$ and $\underset{\sim}{a}_{centrifugal} = -\omega^2(r-h)\,\underset{\sim}{j}'$ which he attributes to his (pseudo) frame force. If this observer stands head toward the ceiling such that the rotation is counterclockwise (i.e., he moves toward his right from an outside view), then he sees the object fall but because it acquires a velocity it is subject to the (pseudo) coriolis force and hence moves to his left.

(c) The inertial observer sees the position of the floor at a point radially outward from the initial position of the mass as $\underset{\sim}{r} = r\sin\theta\,\underset{\sim}{i} + r(1-\cos\theta)\,\underset{\sim}{j}$ with velocity $\underset{\sim}{v} = r\omega\cos\theta\,\underset{\sim}{i} + r\omega\sin\theta\,\underset{\sim}{j}$ and acceleration $\underset{\sim}{a} = -\omega^2 r\sin\theta\,\underset{\sim}{i} + \omega^2 r\cos\theta\,\underset{\sim}{j}$. Just after t = 0 he sees this spot accelerate toward the mass at the rate $\omega^2 r$.

## Chapter 7

EXERCISES:

2. 12 J
4. (a) by $F_x$, 196 J; (b) by friction, - 196 J.
6. 1.00 N = 0.225 lb, 1.00 m = 3.28 ft, 1.00 J = 0.738 ft-lb.
8. 9 C
10. (a) 3.125 ft-lb; (b) 4.24 J.
12. (a) 60 J; (b) 4.90 m/sec.
14. (a) 30 J; (b) 23.5 J; (c) 6.48 J; (d) 2.55 m/sec.
16. (a) 7.5 J, 1.94 m/sec; (b) 3.0 J, 1.22 m/sec.
18. (a) $4.0 \times 10^5$ ft-lb; (b) $4.0 \times 10^5$ ft-lb; (c) 0.5.
20. (a) Normal force of plane, no work; friction, - 11.8 J work done by; gravity, 102 J work done by; (b) 90.2 J; (c) 5.48 m/sec.
22. (a) 133 lb, 100 lb, 80 lb; (b) 400 ft-lb in each case; (c) The longer plank requires less applied force.
24. (a) 9.8 J; (b) 3.13 m/sec; (c) horizontally opposite A; (d) It slides back and forth repeating the initial motion and its reverse back to A.
26. Applied force by some outside agent in moving an object over a horizontal surface, the work done by friction, etc.
28. (a) 392 J; (b) 4.9 m, 9.8 m/sec; (c) 296 J, 96 J; (d) 0.4 m, 7.84 J, 384 J.
30. (a) 78.4 watts; (b) - 78.4 watts; (c) 156.8 J.
32. (a) $v = \frac{1}{2}t$, $x = \frac{1}{4}t^2$; (b) 5 watts; (c) 5/2 t.
34. $1.32 \times 10^7$ ft-lb = 4.97 kw-h.
36. 18
38. (a) - 18; (b) - 4; (c) 0.
40. (a) 6 W; (b) - 49 W; (c) 0 W.

PROBLEMS:

2. (a) 2.6 J; (b) 2.6 J + 24 J = 26.6 J; (c) 4.2 m/sec; (d) 3.4 J; (e) 4.3 m/sec.

4. (a) Work = - change in potential energy = 0.9 J;
(b) Work of friction = - fd = - $\mu$mgd = - 2.94 x $10^{-1}$ J;
(c) $\frac{1}{2}$ $mv^2$ = Work done on block = 6.06 x $10^{-1}$ J, v = 49.2 cm/sec;
(d) It will move until all its kinetic energy is expended against friction. That is until fx = 6.06 x $10^{-1}$ J or x = 6.18 cm.
(e) At equilibrium $E_K$ = 6.06 x $10^{-1}$ J, Ep = 0. The mass comes to rest when $E_K$ = 0 and $E_P = \frac{1}{2} kx^2$. Friction will have done work - fx so 6.06 x $10^{-1}$ + 0 - fx = 0 + $\frac{1}{2}$ $kx^2$ which has a positive root x = 2.02 cm. At this point its energy is 4.08 x $10^{-1}$ J. It will move then to x = - 1.04 cm and then move back through equilibrium to x = 0.06 cm. At this point the spring force is less than the given force which is kinetic friction. Since static friction will be even larger, the mass ceases to move.

6. (a) Tension is perpendicular to the motion; it does no work. If L is the pendulum length, gravity does work mgL.
(b) $\frac{1}{2}$ $mv^2$ = mgL; (c) v = $\sqrt{2gL}$, but T - mg = m($v^2$/L), so T = mg + m(2gL/L) = 3 mg.

8. (a) Normal force -- does no work,
Friction -- does work - fx where x is distance along the incline,
Gravity -- does work - mgx sin $\theta$ where $\theta$ is the incline angle;
(b) $\frac{1}{2}$ $mv^2$ - ($\mu$mg cos $\theta$)x - (mg sin $\theta$)x = 0 so x = 45.2 cm;
(c) The same as in (a) except gravity which does positive work; use x as the distance down the incline.
(d) 2.52 m/sec.

## Chapter 8

EXERCISES:

2. (a) 503; (b) 32 J, 18 J, 50 J; (c) 18 J, 32 J, 50 J.
4. Particle sliding down a rough incline.
6. (a) Kinetic energy decreases 300 J, potential energy increases 300 J, no change in total mechanical energy; (b) 400 J, 500 J.
8. The kinetic energy must decrease.
10. (a) The potential energy first increases, is constant while the speed is zero and then decreases.
(b) A mass attached to a spring, a mass sliding up a frictionless incline.
12. (a) The equation graphed is U = 10 h where h is in feet; (b) The equation graphed is U = 10(h - 25) where h is in feet.
14. (a) U = 6x; (b) U = 6(x - 5); (c) U = 6x + 50.
16. (a) By man: 15 ft-lb, by spring: - 15 ft-lb; (b) 15 ft-lb, 15 ft-lb.
18. (a) 10 cm; (b) 5000 N/m.
20. (a) 400 ft-lb; (b) Gravity is conservative, force by man is not.
22. (a) U = - $GM_em/r$, $GM_em/R_e^2$ = mg or g = $GM_e/R_e^2$. Thus $GM_e = gR_e^2$ so U = - $mgR_e^2/r$;
(b) - 6.24 x $10^7$ J, - 3.12 x $10^7$ J, - 2.08 x $10^7$ J.
24. (a) 50$\pi$ J; (b) 0; (c) Along x axis from x = 5 m, y = 0, z = 0, to the origin, then along y axis to x = 0, y = 5 m, z = 0, then along circular arc of radius 5 m to x = - 5 m, y = 0, z = 0.
26. 5.76 x $10^{-17}$ J = 360 eV.
28. (a) and (c)

| Point | Force | Eq. Pt. (?) | Type |
|---|---|---|---|
| A | 0 | yes | stable |
| B | 0 | yes | unstable |
| C | + | no | -- |
| D | 0 | yes | stable |
| E | - | no | -- |
| F | - | no | -- |

(b) F has maximum magnitude at point F.

30. (a) $F_x$ = - $4Ax^3$; (b) x = 0.
32.

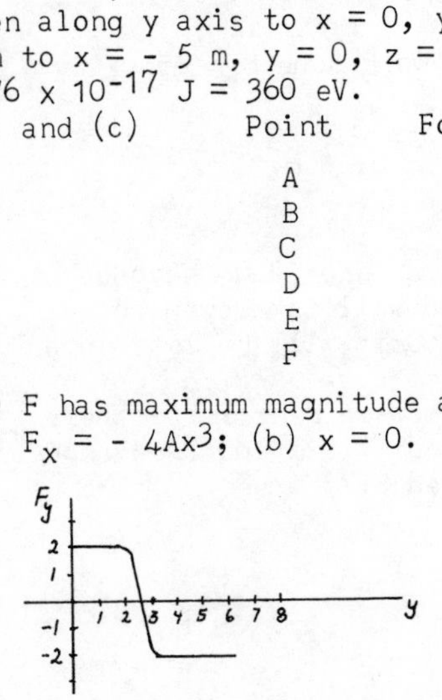

34. 1.44 MeV

36. (a) $1.67 \times 10^{-9}$ J; (b) U (relative to surface) = 294 J.

38. (a)

$$F_x = -\frac{Cx}{[x^2 + y^2 + z^2]^{3/2}} = -\frac{Cx}{r^3},\ F_y = -\frac{Cy}{r^3},\ F_z = -\frac{Cz}{r^3};$$

(b) $\frac{\partial F_x}{\partial y} = \frac{3Cxy}{r^5} = \frac{\partial F_y}{\partial x}$, etc.;

(c) $U = C/r$ and $\underset{\sim}{F} = -\frac{Cx}{r^3}\underset{\sim}{i} - \frac{Cy}{r^3}\underset{\sim}{j} - \frac{Cz}{r^3}\underset{\sim}{k} = -\frac{C}{r^2}\underset{\sim}{\hat{r}}$.

PROBLEMS:

2. (a)

| $x_f$ | - 4 | - 3 | - 2 | - 1 | 0 | 1 | 2 | 3 | 4 |
|---|---|---|---|---|---|---|---|---|---|
| Work (J) | - 6 | - 4 | - 2 | - 1/2 | 0 | 1/2 | 3/2 | 5/2 | 3 |

(b) The force is in one dimension and is a function of x only.

4. (a),(b) $U = -A/2x^2$; as x increases from zero, U becomes less negative so U increases.

6.

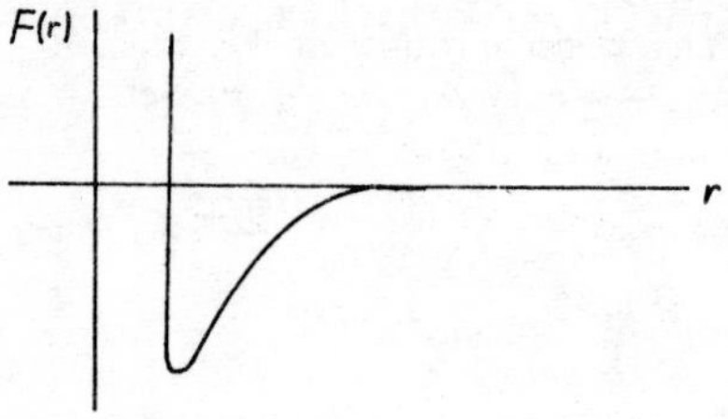


8. (a) $U = (m_2\ell_2 - m_1\ell_1)g \sin\theta$;
(b) If $m_2\ell_2 < m_1\ell_1$, U is a minimum at $\theta = -90°$.
If $m_2\ell_2 < m_1\ell_1$, U is a minimum at $\theta = 90°$.
(c) If $m_2\ell_2 = m_1\ell_1$, $U = 0$ for all θ.

10. (b) $F = -U_o \frac{a}{r} e^{-\frac{r}{a}}[\frac{1}{a} + \frac{1}{r}]$;

(c) $|F(r{=}a)| = \frac{2U_oe^{-1}}{a} = 6.77 \times 10^{15}$ MeV/m ,

$|F(r{=}2a)| = \frac{3U_oe^{-2}}{4a} = 9.34 \times 10^{14}$ MeV/m ,

$|F(r{=}5a)| = \frac{6U_oe^{-5}}{25a} = 1.49 \times 10^{13}$ MeV/m .

## Chapter 9

EXERCISES:

2. 25.51 m
4. (a) 49.5 cm; (b) The mass returns to the original height of 5 m.
6. (a) 3.16 m/sec; (b) 72.2 cm along the incline.
8. 1.4 m/sec
10. (a) The speeds are the same. (b) The ball thrown upward takes 2.04 seconds longer to reach the bottom. (c) The ball thrown upward will take even longer to reach the bottom and will do so with less speed since it will be acted upon for a longer time by the dissipative force of air resistance.
12. (a) The mass will reach a height of 7.5 m, slide back toward P arriving there with speed 7 m/sec, proceed further upward to a height of 7.5 m and then repeat this motion. (b) The mass will reach point Q with speed 6.78 m/sec. (c) 9.90 m/sec.
14. (a) $\frac{1}{2}kA^2$; (b) $\frac{1}{2}mv^2 + \frac{1}{2}kx^2 = \frac{1}{2}kA^2$, so $v = \sqrt{\frac{k}{m}(A^2 - x^2)}$.
16. $1.94 \times 10^4$ m/sec
18. $3.54 \times 10^4$ m/sec

20. (a) $6.25 \times 10^7$ J; (b) 17.4 kw-h; (c) \$ 41.67.
22. $F = - k\,e^2/r^2 = - m\,v^2/r$ so $E_k = \frac{1}{2}\,mv^2 = ke^2/2r$. Since $U = - ke^2/r$, $E = - ke^2/2r$.
24. (a) Both are open to the atmosphere; (b) $\frac{1}{2}\,\rho v_a{}^2 + \rho gh = \frac{1}{2}\,\rho v_b{}^2$;
(c) $v_a A_a = v_b A_b$ and $A_a \gg A_b$.
26. $5.24 \times 10^{-1}$ in

PROBLEMS:
2. (a) $dE/dt = - cE$; (b) $E = E_o e^{-ct}$; (c) $c = 1.05 \times 10^{-2}$ sec$^{-1}$; (d) 65.8 sec.
4. (a) $\frac{1}{2}\,mv^2 + U = E$, so $v = \sqrt{\frac{2}{m}(E - U)}$; (b) $v = dx/dt$, so $\frac{dx}{\sqrt{E - U(x)}} = \sqrt{\frac{2}{m}}\,dt$;
(c) $T/2 = \pi\sqrt{m/k}$.
6. (a) $8.82 \times 10^{-2}$ J; (b) $(0.9)^N H$; (c) 44; the maximum height will be just a bit less than 1 % of H.
8. (a) $\Delta v_e/v_{e\text{-surface}} \approx - \frac{1}{2}\,\Delta r/R_e$; (b) $v_{e\text{-}200\text{ mi}} = 2.44 \times 10^4$ mi/h.
10. (a) From exercise 22, $E = - ke^2/2r = - ke^2/2N^2 r_o = - |E_1|/N^2$ where
$|E_1| = \frac{1}{2}\,k(e^2/r_o) = 13.6$ eV;
(b) $E_2 - E_1 = - (13.6/4) - (- 13.6) = 10.2$ eV,
$E_3 - E_1 = - (13.6/9) - (- 13.6) = 12.1$ eV;
(c) $3 \to 1$, 12.1 eV; $2 \to 1$, 10.2 eV; $3 \to 2$, 1.89 eV.
12. At the nozzle v must be 48 ft/sec. Therefore at the pump v must be 12 ft/sec since $v_p A_p = v_n A_n$. Thus, the gauge pressure $p - p_a = \frac{1}{2}\,\rho(v_n{}^2 - v_p{}^2) + \rho gh$ or $p - p_a = 2730$ lb/ft$^2$. Since $p_a = 2102$ lb/ft$^2$, $p = 2.3$ atm.
14. (a) $p_a + \frac{1}{2}\,\rho v_1{}^2 + \rho gh = p_a + \frac{1}{2}\,\rho v_2{}^2 + 0$. Provided $v_1 \ll v_2$, $v_2 \approx \sqrt{2gh}$;
(b) $v_1 A_1 = v_2 A_2$, and $v_1 = - dh/dt = \frac{A_2}{A_1}\,v_2 \approx \frac{A_2}{A_1}\sqrt{2gh}$;
(c) $h = (\sqrt{H} - \frac{A_2}{2A_1}\sqrt{2g}\;t)^2$; (d) 1.77 h.
16. (a) The velocity of the emerging water is $v_x = \sqrt{2g(H - h)}$. Its height above the surface is h, so it takes $\sqrt{2h/g}$ to reach the surface during which time it travels $x = 2\sqrt{(H - h)h}$.
(b) For fixed x, one has $h^2 - Hh + x^2/4 = 0$ or $h = (H/2) \pm \frac{1}{2}\sqrt{H^2 - x^2}$;
(c) $\frac{dx}{dh} = \frac{H - 2h}{\sqrt{h(H - h)}} = 0$ yields $h = H/2$; $x_{max} = 2\sqrt{\frac{H}{2} \cdot \frac{H}{2}} = H$.

## Chapter 10

EXERCISES:
2. (a) 2/3 m/sec to the left; (b) 4 kg-m/sec to the left.
4. (a) 15 kg-m/sec; (b) $v_x = + 15/7$ m/sec.
6. (a) $\underset{\sim}{a} = 2\underset{\sim}{i}$, $\underset{\sim}{r}(0) = 4\underset{\sim}{j}$, $\underset{\sim}{r}(1) = 2\underset{\sim}{i} + 4\underset{\sim}{j}$, $\underset{\sim}{r}(2) = 4\underset{\sim}{i} + 4\underset{\sim}{j}$, $\underset{\sim}{r}(3) = 6\underset{\sim}{i} + 4\underset{\sim}{j}$;
(b) $\underset{\sim}{R}_{CM} = \frac{1}{2}\,\underset{\sim}{r}$ is the center of mass position;
(c) $\underset{\sim}{A} = \underset{\sim}{i}$, $\underset{\sim}{R}(t) = 2\underset{\sim}{j} + t\underset{\sim}{i}$, $\underset{\sim}{R}(0) = 2\underset{\sim}{j}$, $\underset{\sim}{R}(1) = \underset{\sim}{i} + 2\underset{\sim}{j}$, etc.
8. 3.27 m/sec down the incline.
10. 8.33 cm
12. To the right
14. (a) $8 \times 10^4$ kg-m/sec; (b) $8 \times 10^4$ kg-m/sec; (c) 0.8 m/sec; (d) $3.5 \times 10^4$ J, $3.2 \times 10^4$ J.
16. (a) $P_{east} = 11{,}000$ lb-sec, $P_{north} = 4583\ 1/3$ lb-sec. (One could also use $P_e = 2.4 \times 10^5/g$ lb-mi/h, $P_n = 10^5/g$ lb-mi/h.)
(b) $v = 32.5$ mi/h, 67.4°.
18. (a) Zero in both cases; (b) 3.
20. (a) 600 J; (b) $v_2 = 12$ m/sec, $v_1 = - 8$ m/sec; (c) 672 J after, 72 J before;
(d) $\Delta E = 600$ J.
22. (a) 25 J; (b) 2 m/sec, 10 J; (c) $v_2 = 3$ m/sec, $v_3 = - 2$ m/sec; (d) 15 J.
24. (a) Translate only; (b) Rotate about axis through center of mass.
26. 45/16 = 2.81 cm.

28.

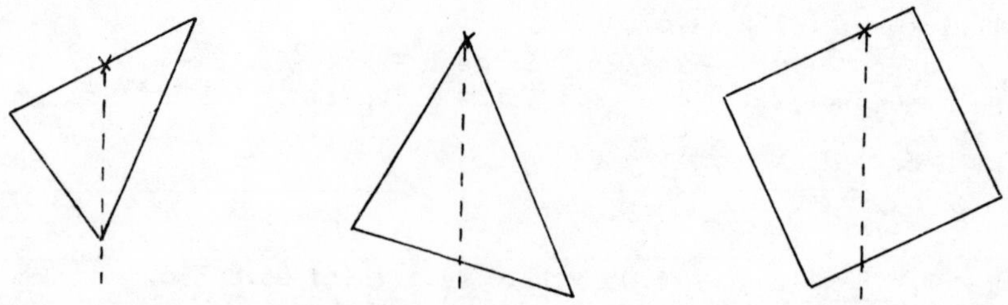

30. $x_{CM} = \dfrac{2m(2.5) + m(7.5)}{3m} = \dfrac{12.5}{3}$ in , $y_{CM} = \dfrac{2m(2.5) + m(7.5)}{3m} = \dfrac{12.5}{3}$ in .

PROBLEMS:

2. The center of mass lands where the projectile would have had it not split. Thus

$$x_{CM} = \frac{v_o^2 \sin 2\theta}{g} = 35.4 \text{ m} .$$

Since m lands at x = 20 m, the 2m mass must land at x such that

$$m(20) + 2m(x) = (3m)(35.4)$$

or x = 43.0 m.

4. Clearly $x_{CM} = 0$. $y_{CM} = \frac{1}{A}\int y\, dA = \frac{2}{\pi R^2}\int_0^R y\sqrt{R^2 - y^2}\, dy = \frac{4}{3}\frac{R}{\pi}$ .

6. Consider whole sphere of unit mass. Its radius is r and the origin is taken at its center. The actual sphere then has mass of 7/8 since if $\frac{4}{3}\pi r^2 \rho = 1$, then $\frac{4}{3}\pi(\frac{r}{2})^3 \rho = \frac{1}{8}$ which is the mass removed by the hole. Thus

$$R_{CM} = \frac{1(0) - \frac{1}{8}(\frac{r}{2})}{\frac{7}{8}} = -\frac{r}{14} .$$

8. First brick; 10 v = 110 u, u + v = 20: v = 5/3 ft/sec, v = 55/3 ft/sec.
Second brick in u = 5/3 ft/sec frame; 10 v = 100 u, u + v = 20: u = 20/11 ft/sec.
Thus relative to ground fixed frame

$$u_f = \frac{20}{11} + \frac{5}{3} = \frac{115}{33} = 3.48 \frac{\text{ft}}{\text{sec}} .$$

## Chapter 11

EXERCISES:

2. (a) 7.0 N-sec; (b) 13/3 m/sec = 4.33 m/sec.
4. 8250 lb-sec
6. 4/3 N
8. (a) $8(\underset{\sim}{j} - \underset{\sim}{i})$ N-sec; (b) $4(\underset{\sim}{j} - \underset{\sim}{i})$ N.
10. 10
12. 1.5 N
14. $\bar{F} = 1/3$ N, P = 0.104 N/m$^2$.
16. 1231 m/sec
18. (a) $1.99 \times 10^{-4}$ sec; (b) $3.32 \times 10^{-4}$ m; (c) $5.02 \times 10^4$ N, $\bar{F}/w = 1.7 \times 10^3$, impulse approximation is very good.
20. (a) 2.5 m/sec; (b) 502.5 m/sec, $1.26 \times 10^3$ J.
22. (a) 16 J, 4 J; 16 J, 16 J; (b) 12 J, 0 J; 12 J, 12 J;
(c) $\frac{1}{2}(m_1 + m_2)v_{CM}^2 = 4$ J in each case.
24. (a) Fig. (a): 42 J, 0 J; Fig. (b): 42 J, 42 J;
(b) Fig. (a): 73.5 J, 31.5 J; Fig. (b): 73.5 J, 73.5 J;
(c) In each case $\frac{1}{2}(m_1 + m_2)v_{CM}^2 = \frac{1}{2}\cdot 7 \cdot 9 = 31.5$ J.
26. $v_4 = 3$ ft/sec, $v_1 = 8$ ft/sec.
28. (a) $v_{10\ kg} = 4.90$ m/sec, $v_{100\ gm} = 9.90$ m/sec; (b) 3.96 %.
30. (a) 7 m/sec; (b) $m_1$: before, 3 m/sec; after, - 3 m/sec; $m_2$: before, - 2 m/sec; after, 2 m/sec; (c) $m_1$: 4 m/sec; $m_2$: 9 m/sec; (d) 275 J; (e) $E_k^{rel} = 30$ J, $\frac{1}{2}(m_1 + m_2)v_{CM}^2 = 245$ J.

32. (a) $\underset{\sim}{P}_i = 3\ mv_0 \underset{\sim}{i}$

$$\underset{\sim}{P}_f = (\sqrt{5}\ mv_0 \cos\theta_1 + 2\sqrt{2}\ mv_0 \cos\theta_2)\underset{\sim}{i} + (\sqrt{5}\ mv_0 \sin\theta_1 - 2\sqrt{2}\ mv_0 \sin\theta_2)\underset{\sim}{j}$$

$$= (mv_0 + 2\ mv_0)\underset{\sim}{i} + (2\ mv_0 - 2\ mv_0)\underset{\sim}{j} = 3\ mv_0\underset{\sim}{i} = \underset{\sim}{P}_i\ ;$$

(b) $E_k^i = \frac{1}{2} m\, 9 v_0^2$, $E_k^f = \frac{1}{2} m\, 5 v_0^2 + \frac{1}{2}\, 2m\, 2 v_0^2 = \frac{9}{2} mv_0^2$ ;

(c) $v_{CM} = v_0$

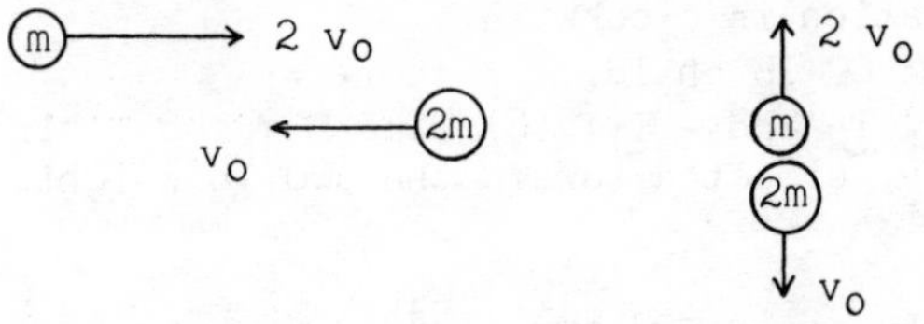


Before　　　　After

34. 0.998 ft/sec upward plus, 0.298 ft/sec in the original direction of the ball's motion, $|v| = 1.04$ ft/sec.
36. 45.9 cm
38. 7.11 ft
40. 3.30 MeV
42. (a) $H_2$ incident on proton requires more energy because $\frac{m_p + m_{H_2}}{m_{H_2}} \approx \frac{3}{2}$ while $\frac{m_{H_2} + m_p}{m_p} \approx 3$ ;

(b) $H_2$ incident: 13.44 eV, p incident: 6.72 eV.
44. (a) The 2 kg object moves left with speed 1.8 m/sec and the 3 kg object moves right with speed 1.2 m/sec.

(b) (2) ⟶ 5 m/sec　(3)　　　(2) ⟶ 0.2 m/sec　(3) ⟶ 3.2 m/sec

Before　　　　After

PROBLEMS:

2. (a) 40 kg-m/sec; (b) $\overline{F} = 8$ N; (c) 16 N.
4. For a 14 ft car the collision time estimate is 0.159 sec. The impulse is $\frac{3000}{32} \cdot 88 = 8.25 \times 10^3$ lb-sec, so $\overline{F} = 5.19 \times 10^4$ lb.
6. (a) 32 ft/sec; (b) 180 lb-sec; (c) $\Delta t \approx 3/16$ sec; (d) $\overline{F} = 960$ lb; (e) $\overline{F} = 5\ 1/3$ times the man's weight; approximation is only fair here.
8. The impulse imparted to each bead is $2(0.5 \times 10^{-3})\sqrt{2(9.8)(0.5)}$ so the average force is 100 times this and this average force is equal to mg. Thus m = 31.9 gm.
10. Use conservation of momentum.
12. The impulse is 3.0 N-sec. A tennis ball has diameter roughly 6.4 cm and assuming 1/2 deformation upon being hit, it travels 3.2 cm at an average speed of 25 m/sec, so the impulse time is about $1.28 \times 10^{-3}$ sec. The average force is then about $2.34 \times 10^3$ N.
14. $m_1 v = m_1 \frac{v}{4} + m_2 v_2$, $v_2 = \frac{3}{4}\frac{m_1}{m_2} v$. Thus, the height attained is $\frac{v_2^2}{2g} = \frac{9}{32g}(\frac{m_1}{m_2})^2 v^2$.

## Chapter 12

EXERCISES:

2. (a) $\frac{10}{9}\pi$ rad/sec; (b) $\frac{5}{9}\pi$ ft/sec, $\frac{50}{81}\pi^2$ ft/sec$^2$.
4. (a) 10 rad/sec; (b),(c) 25 rad or 7.6° less than 4 revolutions; (d) 15 ft/sec, 150 ft/sec$^2$.
6. (a) 50 rad/sec; (b) $a_t = 1.0$ m/sec$^2$, $a_r = 250$ m/sec$^2$.
8. (a) $\underset{\sim}{\omega} = -\omega\underset{\sim}{k}$, $\underset{\sim}{\alpha} = -\alpha\underset{\sim}{k}$, $\omega$ and $\alpha$ are positive;
   (b) $\underset{\sim}{\omega} = -\omega\underset{\sim}{k}$, $\underset{\sim}{\alpha} = \alpha\underset{\sim}{k}$, $\omega$ and $\alpha$ are positive.
10. (a) 56 kg-m$^2$; (b) 112 J.
12. $216/\pi^2 = 21.89$ kg-m$^2$.
14. (a) $I_x = 28$ kg-m$^2$; (b) $I_y = 28$ kg-m$^2$; (c) $I_z = 56$ kg-m$^2$.

16. (3/2) $MR^2$
18. (7/5) $MR^2$
20. 2 $MR^2$
22. (a) $- 7\pi/3$ rad/sec = - 7.33 rad/sec; (b) $- 3.59 \times 10^{-2}$ N-m.
24. $P = dE/dt = d(Fs)/dt = F\, ds/dt = FR\, d\theta/dt = \tau\omega$.
26. (a) 1000 lb; (b) 500 ft-lb; (c) $\omega = \frac{1}{2}$ rad/sec; (d) 250 ft-lb/sec = 0.45 hp.
28. $\tau_1 = 7.07$ ft-lb, $\tau_2 = - 9$ ft-lb, $\tau_3 = 3.46$ ft-lb, $\tau_4 = 0$,
$\tau_{net} = 1.54$ ft-lb, rotation is clockwise.
30. 40/7 = 5.71 ft from the 60 lb child.
32. (a) Force of the hinge, $\underset{\sim}{T}_2$ and $- \underset{\sim}{T}_1$; (b) Take $\Sigma\, \tau$ about hinge and use $T_1 = 500$ lb;
(c) 866 lb horizontally, directed toward the 500 lb weight.

PROBLEMS:

2. $E_{rot} = 2.60 \times 10^{29}$ J, $E_{orbital} = 2.68 \times 10^{33}$ J.
4. Start: $50 - \tau = I\alpha$, $\omega = \alpha t$ or $20\pi = 20\alpha$ so $\alpha = \pi$ rad/sec, $\therefore\ 50 - \tau = I\pi$,
Stop: $\tau = I\alpha'$, $\alpha' = 20\pi/120 = \pi/6$ rad/sec so $\tau = (\pi/6)I$.
(a) $I = 13.64$ kg-m$^2$; (b) $\tau = 7.14$ N-m.
6.

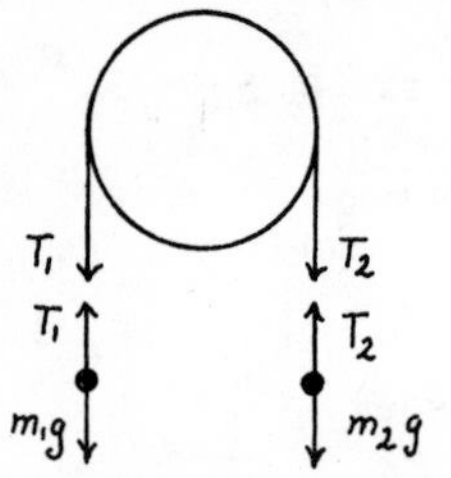


$I = m_p k^2 = 450$ gm-cm$^2$, $\quad m_2 g - T_2 = m_2 a$,

$a_1 = a_2 \equiv a$ (no string stretch), $\quad T_1 - m_1 g = m_1 a$,

$\alpha = \frac{a}{R}$ (no string slip), $\quad R(T_2 - T_1) = I\alpha = I\,\frac{a}{R}$,

$$(m_2 - m_1)g = a[(m_1 + m_2) + I/R^2].$$

(a) $a = 8.73$ cm/sec$^2$; (b) $T_1 = 4.944$ N, $T_2 = 4.953$ N;
(c) To neglect pulley, set $I = 0$. Then $a = 9.70$ cm/sec$^2$ and $T_1 = T_2 = 4.949$ N.
8. (a) $dI = r^2\, dm = \frac{m}{ab}\,(x^2 + y^2)\, dxdy$,

$$I = \int_0^b dx \int_0^a dy\, \frac{m}{ab}\,(x^2 + y^2) = \frac{m}{3}\,(a^2 + b^2);$$

(b) From parallel axis theorem: $\frac{m}{4}\,(a^2 + b^2) + \frac{m}{3}\,(a^2 + b^2) = \frac{7}{12}\, m(a^2 + b^2)$.
10. $(2/3)mR^2$
12. (a) $I = 4.0 \times 10^5$ gm-cm$^2$; (b) $I = 4.045 \times 10^5$ gm-cm$^2$,
% difference = 100 [(exact - approx)/exact] = 1.1 %.
14. (a) Because the floor is frictionless and because of symmetry, the floor exerts a force vertically upward of 100 lb on each leg of the ladder.
(b) Take torques about upper ladder hinge:

$$L_1(T \cos\theta) = (L_1 + L_2)N \sin\theta$$

$$T = \frac{L_1 + L_2}{L_1}\, N \tan\theta$$

$$T = 2 \cdot 100 \cdot \tan 15^\circ = 53.6 \text{ lb};$$

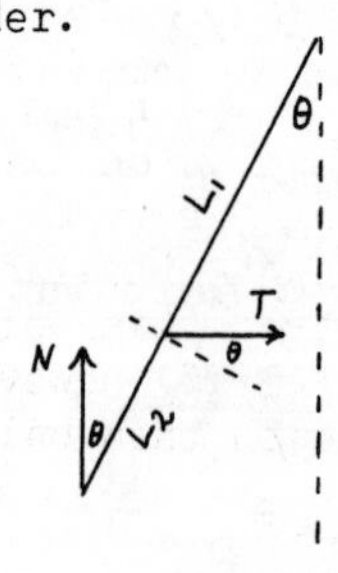


(c) $L_1 + L_2$ = constant, but $L_1$ increases, so T will decrease.

## Chapter 13

EXERCISES:

2. (a) $\underset{\sim}{\tau} = - 9.8\, \underset{\sim}{k}$ kg-m; (b) $- 9.8\, \underset{\sim}{k}$ kg-m.
4. Unless $\underset{\sim}{A}$ or $\underset{\sim}{B}$ is zero, $\underset{\sim}{A} = c\underset{\sim}{B}$ where c is a number (scalar).
6. $|\underset{\sim}{A} \times \underset{\sim}{B}| = AB \sin\theta = \underset{\sim}{A} \cdot \underset{\sim}{B} = AB \cos\theta$ implies $\theta = \pm 45^\circ$. (Note that $\theta = 135^\circ$ or $225^\circ$ is ruled out because magnitude $\underset{\sim}{A} \times \underset{\sim}{B}$ is positive so that $\underset{\sim}{A} \cdot \underset{\sim}{B}$ must be positive.)
8. (a) 30 kg-m$^2$/sec; (b) None, i.e., $\underset{\sim}{\tau} = 0$ because $\underset{\sim}{L}$ = constant.
10. (a) 60 kg-m$^2$/sec; (b) At closest approach the angular velocity is 0.8 rad/sec and decreases to zero as time increases.
12. $E_k = \frac{1}{2}\, mv^2 = \frac{1}{2}\, mr^2\omega^2 = \frac{1}{2}\, I\omega^2$, $L = I\omega$ so $E_k = \frac{1}{2}\,(L^2/I)$.
14. (a) Since $\underset{\sim}{F}$ is along r, $\underset{\sim}{\tau} = \underset{\sim}{r} \times \underset{\sim}{F} = 0$;

(b) $mv_1r_1 = mv_2r_2$ because L is constant. Thus $v_2/v_1 = r_1/r_2$.

16. (a) $90\pi$ kg-m$^2$/sec; (b) $3\pi$ N-m; (c) $10\pi$ N.

18. (a) $\underset{\sim}{L}$ due to C.M. motion is zero, so L has the same magnitude as before, $1.325 \times 10^2$ gm-cm$^2$/sec.

(b) $7.5 \times 10^2$ gm-cm$^2$/sec, $8.83 \times 10^2$ gm-cm$^2$/sec, $6.17 \times 10^2$ gm-cm$^2$/sec. If the coin spins counterclockwise as viewed from the top and if the point is to the left of the line viewed along the translation motion direction, then $\underset{\sim}{L}_{CM}$ and $\underset{\sim}{L}_{rot}$ have the same sense. If the point is on the right, then the two have opposite senses.

20. (a) $(m_1 - m_2 \sin\theta)gr$; (b) $(m_1 - m_2)vr + Iv/r$;
(c) $(m_1 - m_2 \sin\theta)g/[(m_1 - m_2) + I/r^2]$.

22. (a) 0.21 rev/sec; (b) $E_i = 6.17 \times 10^2$ J, $E_f = 5.14 \times 10^2$ J.

24. (a) $\omega = 0.352$ rad/sec; (b) The man has velocity 4.76 ft/sec relative to the rim point so he requires 6.60 second for one complete trip. Relative to the ground his angular velocity is 0.6 rad/sec so he travels 3.96 rad = 0.63 rev.

26. $A = \frac{b}{2}vt$, so $\frac{dA}{dt} = \frac{b}{2}v$. But $L = mvb$ so $\frac{dA}{dt} = \frac{L}{2m}$.

28. (a) $mgh = \frac{1}{2}mv^2 + \frac{1}{2}I\omega^2 = \frac{1}{2}mv^2 + \frac{1}{2}\frac{I}{r^2}v^2$. Write $I = kmr^2$ and find $v = [2gh/(1+k)]^{1/2}$.

(b) $mg\sin\theta - f = ma$, $fr = I\alpha = Ia/r$ so $a = \frac{g\sin\theta}{1+k}$ and $f = mg\sin\theta\,\frac{k}{1+k}$.

(c) $t = \sqrt{2d/a} = \sqrt{\frac{2h}{g\sin^2\theta}(1+k)}$.

Tabulated results:

| Object | k | v (m/sec) | f (N) | t (sec) |
|---|---|---|---|---|
| sphere | 2/5 | 5.29 | 4.2 | 1.51 |
| disk | 1/2 | 5.11 | 4.9 | 1.56 |
| hoop | 1 | 4.43 | 7.35 | 1.81 |

30. $F_1 - F_2 = ma_{CM}$ so $a_{CM} = 0.2$ m/sec$^2$, $(F_1 - F_2)r = I\alpha$ so $\alpha = 2/3$ rad/sec$^2$, $v_{CM} = 1.0$ m/sec and $\omega = 10/3$ rad/sec.

32. (a) 0.25 slug-ft$^2$, $20\pi$ rad/sec, $5\pi = 1.57$ slug-ft$^2$/sec;
(b) $8.1/5\pi = 0.51$ rad/sec, $10\pi^2/8 = 12.34$ sec;
(c) $2/5\pi = 1.27 \times 10^{-1}$ slug-ft$^2$/sec,

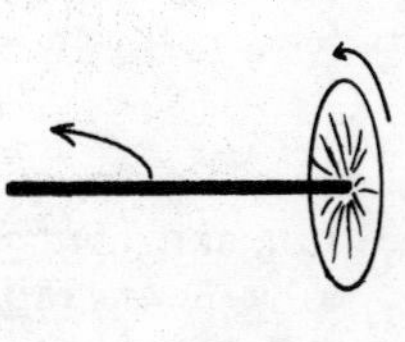

34. (a) $v_{CM} = \omega D = 10(5 \times 10^{-3}) = 5 \times 10^{-2}$ m/sec, $a_{CM} = v_{CM}^2/D = 0.5$ m/sec$^2$, $F_{CM} = 5(0.5) = 2.5$ N, directed toward axle. This force must be supplied by the bearings.

(b) The rotation axis must pass through the center of mass so the 100 gm weight should be at 25 cm from the axis opposite the C.M. of the disk. This still leads to imbalance dynamically since the C.M. would be .03 cm above the central plane of the disk. The situation is very like the unbalanced dumb-bell. If, however, 50 gm is placed on top the disk and 50 gm directly beneath then balance is restored.

PROBLEMS:

2. (a) $\underset{\sim}{L} = (yp_z - zp_y)\underset{\sim}{i} + (zp_x - xp_z)\underset{\sim}{j} + (xp_y - yp_x)\underset{\sim}{k}$,
$\underset{\sim}{\tau} = (yF_z - zF_y)\underset{\sim}{i} + (zF_x - xF_z)\underset{\sim}{j} + (xF_y - yF_x)\underset{\sim}{k}$;

(b) $\frac{dL_z}{dt} = v_xp_y + x\frac{dp_y}{dt} - v_yp_x - y\frac{dp_x}{dt} = v_xp_y - v_yp_x + xF_y - yF_x = \tau_z$

because $p_y = mv_y$ and $p_x = mv_x$ so that $v_xp_y - v_yp_x = 0$.

4. (a) Since the force is central, $\underset{\sim}{L}$ is constant, so $mvr = mv_0r_0 = L_0$. The tension is

$$T = m\frac{v^2}{r} = m\frac{L_0^2}{m^2r^2}\frac{1}{r} = \frac{L_0^2}{mr^3};$$

(b) $W = -\int_{r_0}^{r_f} T\,dr = \frac{L_0^2}{2m}\left(\frac{1}{r_f^2} - \frac{1}{r_0^2}\right)$;

(c) $v_f = \frac{v_o r_o}{r_f}$. Also $W = \frac{m^2 v_f^2 r_f^2}{2mr_f^2} - \frac{m^2 v_o^2 r_o^2}{2mr_o^2} = \frac{1}{2} mv_f^2 - \frac{1}{2} mv_o^2$ ;

(d) $L_o = (0.5)(3)(1) = 1.5$ kg-m$^2$/sec so $T = (1.5)^2/0.5r^3 \leq 200$ N. Thus $r^3 \geq (1.5)^2/(0.5)(200)$ or $r \geq 0.28$ m or else the string breaks.

6. Assume $\mathbf{f}$ opposite to $\mathbf{T}$.

(a) $T - f = ma_{CM}$, $Tr + fR = I\alpha = I \frac{a_{CM}}{R}$ so $f = \frac{2}{3}(\frac{1}{2} - \frac{r}{R})T$ ;

(b) $a_{CM} = \frac{2}{3}(1 + \frac{r}{R})\frac{T}{m}$ ; (c) Yes, $\frac{2}{3}(1 + \frac{r}{R})\frac{T}{m} > \frac{T}{m}$ implies $\frac{r}{R} > \frac{1}{2}$ ;

(d) If $r/R > \frac{1}{2}$, then f in part (a) is negative so $\mathbf{f}$ is parallel to $\mathbf{T}$ in this case.

8. (a) $v_r = v \cos \theta$, $v_t = v \sin \theta$;

(b) $\tan \theta = y/x$ or $\theta = \tan^{-1} y/x$ and $x^2 + y^2 = r^2$. So

$$\omega = d\theta/dt = -\frac{y}{r^2} v$$

$$= -\frac{v \sin \theta}{r} = -\frac{v_t}{r} .$$

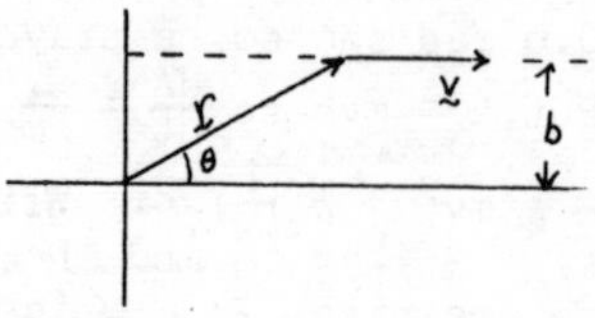


(The sign depends on the choice of direction of v.) But $y = b = r \sin \theta$, so $\omega = -(v \sin^2 \theta)/b$ or $+(v \sin^2 \theta)/b$ if $\mathbf{v}$ is chosen oppositely. Since $L = I\omega = mr^2(v \sin^2 \theta)/b$, $L = mvb$.

10. $(\mathbf{A} \times \mathbf{B})_x = A_y B_z - A_z B_y$,

$$\frac{d(\mathbf{A} \times \mathbf{B})_x}{dt} = \frac{dA_y}{dt} B_z - \frac{dA_z}{dt} B_y + A_y \frac{dB_z}{dt} - A_z \frac{dB_y}{dt} = (\frac{d\mathbf{A}}{dt} \times \mathbf{B})_x + (\mathbf{A} \times \frac{d\mathbf{B}}{dt})_x .$$

Similarly for the y and z components, so

$$\frac{d(\mathbf{A} \times \mathbf{B})}{dt} = \frac{d\mathbf{A}}{dt} \times \mathbf{B} + \mathbf{A} \times \frac{d\mathbf{B}}{dt} .$$

## Chapter 14

EXERCISES:

2. (a) $v = -15\pi \sin(5\pi t + \pi)$; (b) $v_{max} = \pm 15\pi$ m/sec; (c) at $x = 0$.
4. (a) $A = 5$ m, $\omega = 4\pi$ rad/sec, $f = 2$ cps, $T = \frac{1}{2}$ sec;
   (b) $v = -20\pi \sin 4\pi t$; (c) at $t = 0$, $v = 0$.
6. $x = (4/\pi) \sin \pi t$, $v = 4 \cos \pi t$, $a = -4\pi \sin \pi t$.
8. (a) $\omega = 50$ rad/sec, $f = 25/\pi = 7.96$ Hz, $A = 10$ cm $= 0.1$ m;
   (b) $x = 0.1 \cos 50t$, $v = -5 \sin 50t$, $a = -250 \cos 50t$;
   (c) $E_k = \frac{1}{2} \cdot 2 \cdot 25 \sin^2 50t = 25 \sin^2 50t$, $U = \frac{1}{2} kx^2 = 25 \cos^2 50t$, $E = E_k + U = 25$ J.
10. (a) $t = 1/12$ sec; (b) at $x = -5/6\pi$ cm $= -0.27$ cm;
    (c) $30\pi$ cm/sec$^2$ toward the origin; (d) $x = -(5/6\pi) \sin 6\pi t$ cm.
12. (a) $\sqrt{20}/6\pi = 0.237$ m $= 23.7$ cm; (b) $v_{max} = \sqrt{20}$ m/sec; (c) $6\pi\sqrt{20} = 84.3$ m/sec$^2$.
14. (a) $40\pi^2$ N/m; (b) $1/4\pi$ m.
16. $\sqrt{6}$ sec $= 2.45$ sec.
18. $(\pi/2)\sqrt{55}$ sec $= 11.65$ sec.
20. $(\pi/7)\sqrt{2}$ sec $= 0.635$ sec.
22. $5.03 \times 10^{-1}$ kg-m$^2$
24. (a) 5 J; (b) $A = (1/10)\sqrt{2}$ m $= 14.14$ cm, $T = (\pi/25)\sqrt{15}$ sec $= 0.49$ sec;
    (c) 20.02 cm.
26. (a) $t = \pi/15$ sec; (b) $4\sqrt{2}$ cm $= 5.66$ cm.

PROBLEMS:

2. (a) Yes; (b) $a = \omega^2 A \leq \mu_s g = 2.45$ m/sec$^2$ so $A \leq 5.59$ mm.
4. (a) $v = -57 \sin(9.5t + 1.0)$ cm/sec, $v_{max} = 57$ cm/sec which occurs when $x = 0$, $t = [(2n+1)\pi - 2]/19$ sec, $n = 0, 1, 2, \ldots$ ;
   (b) $a = -541.5 \cos(9.5t + 1.0)$ cm/sec$^2$, $a_{max} = 541.5$ cm/sec$^2$ which occurs when $x = \pm 6.0$ cm or $t = (n\pi - 1.0)/9.5$ sec, $n = 0, 1, 2, \ldots$ .
6. (a) Since spring 1 pulls left and spring 2 pushes left if the mass is moved to the right $F = -k_1 x - k_2 x$. So $-(k_1 + k_2)x = ma$ and $\omega = \sqrt{(k_1 + k_2)/m}$.
   (b) If the mass is pulled right an amount x and if $x_1$ is the stretch of spring

1 and $x_2$ that of spring 2 then $x = x_1 + x_2$. The force on the mass is $- k_2x_2 \equiv - kx$. Thus since the massless junction between the springs is not accelerated, $k_1x_1 = k_2x_2$. So $k_2x_2 = k(x_1 + x_2) = k(\frac{k_2}{k_1} + 1)x_2$. Thus $k = \frac{k_1k_2}{k_1 + k_2}$ or $\frac{1}{k} = \frac{1}{k_1} + \frac{1}{k_2}$. Alternatively, one can argue that the force which spring 1 exerts must equal that of spring 2 because of the massless junction. Then $x = x_1 + x_2$ so $- \frac{F}{k} = - \frac{F}{k_1} - \frac{F}{k_2}$ or $\frac{1}{k} = \frac{1}{k_1} + \frac{1}{k_2}$.

8. Describe the weight position by $y = - A \cos \omega t$ where $A = 7$ cm and $\omega = 8\pi$ rad/sec. Then the velocity is $v = \omega A \sin \omega t$ and the acceleration is $a = \omega^2 A \cos \omega t$.
   (a) The rock loses contact when a is negative and greater in magnitude than g. Thus contact is lost at

$$\cos \omega t = - \frac{g}{\omega^2 A} = - 0.222$$

   or $\omega t = 1.79$ rad so $t = 0.07$ sec $= 0.286\ T$ where T is the period, 0.25 sec.
   (b) $v = \omega A \sin \omega t = 1.72$ m/sec upward;
   (c) At the point of loss, $y = 1.55$ cm and the rock has upward speed of 1.72 m/sec. It therefore rises to a height of 15.09 cm above this point or to $y = 16.64$ cm.

10. (a) $T = 2\pi \sqrt{L/g}$, so $dT/T = - \frac{1}{2}\, dg/g$ or $\Delta T/T \approx - \frac{1}{2}\, \Delta g/g$;
   (b) Whatever the period, $\Delta T/T = - 90/(24 \cdot 3600) = - \frac{1}{2}\, \Delta g/g$ so $\Delta g = 2.08 \times 10^{-3}\ g = 2.04$ cm/sec$^2$.

12. (a) $A = 1.90$ m, $T = 3.44$ sec; (b) $A = 1.79$ m, $T = 2.81$ sec;
   (c) For case (a): $x = 1.90 \sin 1.83t$, the impulse is 4 kg-m/sec.
   For case (b): $x = 1.79 \sin 2.24t$, the impulse is 8 kg-m/sec.

14. $2.36 \times 10^{-1}$ rad

16. Eq. (14-19) will become

$$m \frac{d^2s}{dt^2} = - m_G \frac{g}{L} s$$

so that $\omega = 2\pi/T = \sqrt{m_G g/Lm}$ or $T = 2\pi \sqrt{mL/m_G g}$.

18.

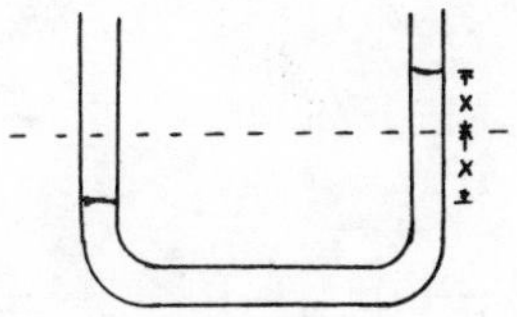

Mass of fluid not counterbalanced $= \rho A 2x$ which exerts a force on the system $- 2\rho Axg = m_s\ddot{x}$ where $m_s$, the system mass, is $\rho AL$. So

$$- 2\rho Axg = \rho AL\ddot{x} \quad \text{or} \quad \ddot{x} + \frac{2g}{L} x = 0 .$$

Hence $T = 2\pi \sqrt{L/2g}$.

20. $x_1(t) = 20 + 5 \cos \omega_1 t$, $x_2(t) = 30 - 5 \cos (\omega_2 t - \varphi)$, $\omega_1 = \omega_2 = \pi/2$, $\varphi = \omega_2 t_0$.
   $x_{rel}(t) = x_2 - x_1 = 10 - 5 \cos \frac{\pi}{2}(t - t_0) - 5 \cos \frac{\pi}{2} t = 10 - A \cos (\frac{\pi}{2} t - \delta)$,
   $\therefore A = \sqrt{50(1 + \cos \omega_2 t_0)}$, $\tan \delta = \sin \omega_2 t_0/(1 + \cos \omega_2 t_0)$.
   (a) $t_0 = 0$ so $A = \sqrt{100} = 10$ cm, $\delta = 0$, $x_{rel} = 10 - 10 \cos \frac{\pi}{2} t$, closest approach at $t = 4$ sec and $x_{rel} = 0$;
   (b) $t_0 = 1$, $\omega t_0 = \pi/2$, $A = \sqrt{50}$ cm, $\delta = \pi/4$, $x_{rel} = 10 - \sqrt{50} \cos (\frac{\pi}{2} t - \frac{\pi}{4})$, closest approach at $t = \frac{1}{2}$ sec and $x_{rel} = 2.93$ cm;
   (c) $t_0 = 2$, $\omega t_0 = \pi$, $A = 0$, $\delta = 0$, $x_{rel} = 10$, closest approach is $x_{rel} = 10$ for all t.

## Chapter 15

EXERCISES:

2. $x = A \cos \omega t$, $v = - \omega A \sin \omega t$, $v_{av}{}^2 = A^2\omega^2(\sin^2 \omega t)_{av} = \frac{1}{2} A^2\omega^2 = E/m$.

4. (a) $- \Delta A/A = \frac{b}{2m} T = .05 = 2b/100$, so $b = 2.5$ gm/sec;
   (b) $- \Delta E/E = \frac{b}{m} T = 2(- \Delta A/A) = 10\,\%$.

6. $A(t) = A_0 e^{-(b/2m)t}$, $A(t+T) = A_0 e^{-(b/2m)t} e^{-(b/2m)T}$, $A(t+T)/A(t) = e^{-(b/2m)T} = \text{const.}$

8. $f_0 = \frac{1}{2\pi}\omega_0 = \frac{1}{2\pi}\sqrt{\frac{100}{5/32}} = \frac{4}{\pi}\sqrt{10} = 4.03$ Hz, $\omega = 2\pi \cdot 5 = 10\pi = 31.42$, $F_0 = 108.4$ lb.

10. (a) $\frac{1}{\pi}\sqrt{10} = 1.01$ Hz; (b) $\frac{2}{\pi}\sqrt{10} = 2.01$ Hz; (c) $\frac{7}{20\pi}\sqrt{10} = 3.52 \times 10^{-1}$ Hz.

12. $P = Fv = (F_0 \sin \omega t)(\omega A \cos \omega t) = \frac{1}{2} F_0 A\omega \sin 2\omega t$,

$$P = \frac{1}{2} F_0\omega \sin 2\omega t \frac{F_0}{m(\omega_0^2 - \omega^2)} = \frac{F_0^2\omega \sin 2\omega t}{2m(\omega_0^2 - \omega^2)}, \quad \omega < \omega_0.$$

14. The damping force is $-bv$ and in general $v = \omega A \cos(\omega t - \delta)$

so $-bv = -Ab\omega\cos(\omega t - \delta) = -F_0 b\omega \cos(\omega t - \delta)/\sqrt{m^2(\omega^2 - \omega_0^2)^2 + b^2\omega^2}$.

At resonance $-bv = -\dfrac{F_0 b\omega_0 \cos(\omega_0 t - \pi/2)}{b\omega_0} = -F_0 \sin \omega_0 t = F_0 \sin(\omega_0 t + \pi)$.

16. The average power supplied to the system by the external force is

$$P_{av} = (Fv)_{av} = (F_0 \sin \omega t\, \omega A \cos(\omega t - \delta))_{av} = \frac{1}{2} F_0\omega A \sin\delta$$

$$= \frac{1}{2} F_0\omega \frac{F_0}{\sqrt{m^2(\omega^2 - \omega_0^2)^2 + b^2\omega^2}} \frac{b\omega}{\sqrt{m^2(\omega^2 - \omega_0^2)^2 + b^2\omega^2}} = \frac{1}{2}\omega^2 bA^2.$$

The average power dissipated in the damping material is

$$P'_{av} = (bv^2)_{av} = b\omega^2A^2(\cos^2(\omega t - \delta))_{av} = \frac{1}{2} b\omega^2A^2.$$

PROBLEMS:

2. $x = A_0 e^{-(b/2m)t} \cos(\omega' t + \delta)$ so

$v = -\frac{b}{2m} A_0 e^{-(b/2m)t} \cos(\omega' t + \delta) - \omega' A_0 e^{-(b/2m)t} \sin(\omega' t + \delta)$.

For weak damping $(b/2m) \ll \omega_0 \approx \omega'$ so the maximum of the damping force is approximately $b\omega' A_0 e^{-(b/2m)t} \approx b\omega_0 A_0 e^{-(b/2m)t}$. The restoring force is $-kx$ so its maximum value is $kA_0 e^{-(b/2m)t}$. The ratio is then $b\omega_0/k = b\omega_0/m\omega_0^2 = b/m\omega_0$.

4. For mass m the critical damping condition is $b = 2m\omega_0$. For a mass $M = 2m$, the natural frequency is $\bar{\omega}_0 = \sqrt{k/M} = \sqrt{k/2m} = (1/\sqrt{2})\omega_0$. Then

$$\omega' = \bar{\omega}_0[1 - (\frac{b}{2M\bar{\omega}_0})^2]^{\frac{1}{2}} = \bar{\omega}_0\sqrt{\frac{1}{2}} \neq 0,$$

so the motion with the 2 kg mass is damped motion but not critically damped.

6. $A = \dfrac{F_0}{[m^2(\omega^2 - \omega_0^2)^2 + b^2\omega^2]^{1/2}}$ so $\dfrac{dA}{d\omega} = \dfrac{2\omega F_0[2m^2(\omega^2 - \omega_0^2) + b^2]}{[m^2(\omega^2 - \omega_0^2)^2 + b^2\omega^2]^{3/2}} = 0$ yields

$$\omega^2 = \omega_0^2 - \frac{b^2}{2m^2} \quad \text{or} \quad \omega = \sqrt{\omega_0^2 - \frac{b^2}{2m^2}}.$$

10. $A^2 = \dfrac{F_0^2}{m^2(\omega^2 - \omega_0^2)^2 + b^2\omega^2} = \dfrac{1}{2}\dfrac{F_0^2}{b^2\omega_0^2}$.

Thus $(\omega^2)^2 - (\omega^2)[2\omega_0^2 - \frac{b^2}{m^2}] + [\omega_0^4 - \frac{2b^2\omega_0^2}{m^2}] = 0$

or $\omega^2 = \omega_0^2 - \frac{b^2}{2m^2} \pm \frac{1}{2}[4\omega_0^2\frac{b^2}{m^2} + \frac{b^4}{m^4}]^{\frac{1}{2}}$.

Since $\frac{b}{m} \ll \omega_0$ one has $\omega^2 \approx \omega_0^2 - \frac{b^2}{2m^2} \pm \frac{\omega_0 b}{m}$.

Therefore $\omega_+ \approx \omega_0[1 - \frac{b^2}{2m^2\omega_0^2} + \frac{b}{m\omega_0}]^{\frac{1}{2}} \approx \omega_0 + \frac{b}{2m} - \frac{b^2}{4m^2\omega_0}$

and $\omega_- \approx \omega_0 - \frac{b}{2m} - \frac{b^2}{4m^2\omega_0}$ so $\omega_+ - \omega_- \approx b/m$.

## Chapter 16

EXERCISES:

2. $(T_1/T_2)^2 = (r_1/r_2)^3$ so $r_1 = r_2(T_1/T_2)^{2/3}$;

$r_2 = 149 \times 10^6$ km, $T_2 = 1$y so $r_1 = 26.7 \times 10^8$ km.

4. 11.9 y
6. 84.6 min, $6.62\ R_e = 4.22 \times 10^7$ m.
8. $2.67 \times 10^{-9}$ N, $5.34 \times 10^{-10}$ N-m.
10. $GM_e/x^2 = GM_m/(r-x)^2$ or $x = r/(1 \pm \sqrt{M_m/M_e})$. Only the root $x < r$ will do. The other root corresponds to $\underline{g}_e = \underline{g}_m$ whereas the solution sought is $\underline{g}_e = -\underline{g}_m$. Thus $x = 0.900\ r = 3.46 \times 10^5$ km. The field also vanishes at $\infty$.
12. $g = 9.8$ m/sec$^2$ directed toward the earth's center.
14. $g_x = F_x/m_0 = -\dfrac{dU}{dx}\dfrac{1}{m_0} = -\dfrac{d(U/m_0)}{dx} = -\dfrac{dV}{dx}$.
16. $2Gmm_0/a$
18.

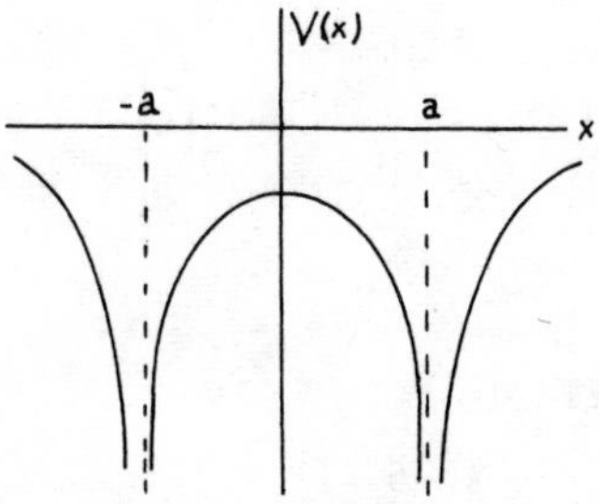


V(0) is a maximum point

20. (a) $|\underline{g}|$ is larger near the disk; (b) The field near the disk is essentially constant.
22. (a) Inside the shell $g(r) = 0 = -dV/dr$. Thus $V(r)$ is constant.
(b) $V(r) = -GM/r$, $r \geq$ shell radius.
24. $4.00 \times 10^{-10}$ J/kg

PROBLEMS:

2. (a) $g_x = -GMx/(r^2 + x^2)^{3/2}$; (b) at $x = \pm r/\sqrt{2}$.
4. (a) $-\kappa\theta = I\alpha = I\ddot{\theta}$ so $T = 2\pi\sqrt{I/\kappa}$;
(b) $I = 2 \times 10^4$ gm-cm$^2$ so $\kappa = 7.90 \times 10^{-1}$ dyne-cm/rad;
(c) $2F(L/2) = \kappa\theta$ or $F = 3.95 \times 10^{-5}$ dyne.
6. (a) $\sigma = M/\pi R^2$ (mass per unit area); (b) $dV = -G\sigma 2\pi r\, dr/\sqrt{r^2 + x^2}$;

(c) $V(x) = G\sigma 2\pi[x - \sqrt{R^2 + x^2}] = \dfrac{2GM}{R^2}[x - \sqrt{R^2 + x^2}]$; (d) $g(x) = \dfrac{2GM}{R^2}\left[\dfrac{x - \sqrt{R^2 + x^2}}{\sqrt{R^2 + x^2}}\right]$.

8. $g(r) = -\dfrac{GM}{r^2}$, $r \geq R_2$;

$$g(r) = -\frac{GM}{r^2}\frac{(r^3 - R_1^3)}{(R_2^3 - R_1^3)}, \quad R_1 \leq r \leq R_2;$$

$g(r) = 0$, $r \leq R_1$.

10. $dV = -\dfrac{G\lambda\, dx}{(x_0 - x)} = -\dfrac{GM\, dx}{L(x_0 - x)}$ so $V(x_0) = \dfrac{GM}{L}\ln\dfrac{x_0 - L/2}{x_0 + L/2}$.

For $x_0 > L/2$, $g(x_0) = -\dfrac{dV(x_0)}{dx_0} = -\dfrac{GM}{(x_0^2 - (L/2)^2)}$.

## Chapter 17

EXERCISES:

2. Yes, if the mass of gas is allowed to change.
6. $T_B = T_C$, $T_A \neq T_B$, therefore $T_A \neq T_C$.
8. (a) $-75°$C; (b) 2.18 atm.
10. (a) 22.0 mm Hg; (b) 2.18 K.
12. 1.0 atm = 14.70 lb/in$^2$.
14. (a) 12.7 lb/in$^2$; (b) 1.58 lb.
16. (a) 54.7 lb/in$^2$; (b) 112 in Hg.
18. (a) 90.29 K; (b) $-296.48°$F; (c) 162.52°R.
20. 56.7°C, $-62.2°$C.
22. 158°F
24. (a) 122 K; (b) 244 K, $-29.5°$C; (c) 1.44 atm.

26. (a) 44.1 lb; (b) 46.1 lb, 46.1 lb/3 $in^2$ = 15.4 lb/$in^2$; (c) 7.65 in.
28. $3.21 \times 10^8$
30. $m_{calc} = 1.66 \times 10^{-27}$ kg
34. $n = 4.06 \times 10^{-2}$ mole, $\langle KE \rangle = \frac{3}{2} nRT = 152$ J.
36. $1.0 + 8.8 \times 10^{-4}$ ft
38. 7.70 cm
40. $\sigma \equiv \lim_{\Delta T \to 0} \frac{\Delta A/A}{\Delta T}$. Square: $A + \Delta A = (L_1 + \Delta L_1)(L_2 + \Delta L_2) = A(1 + \alpha \Delta T)^2$;

Circle: $A + \Delta A = \pi(r + \Delta r)^2 = \pi r^2(1 + \alpha \Delta T)^2$.

PROBLEMS:

2. 400.5 K
4. $5.82 \times 10^{-1}$ ℓ
6. (a) $1.24 \times 10^{-19}$ J = 0.78 eV; (b) 12,234 -- 793 m/sec.
8. $L_B - L_A = L_{B_0} - L_{A_0} + (L_{B_0}\alpha_B - L_{A_0}\alpha_A)\Delta T = L_{B_0} - L_{A_0}$ which implies $L_{A_0}/L_{B_0} = \alpha_B/\alpha_A$. L = 182 cm. If both were brass, $\Delta L = 3.46 \times 10^{-1}$ cm.
10. $T_{pendulum} = 2\pi\sqrt{\ell/g}$. For small changes

$$\Delta T_p \approx dT_p = \frac{1}{2}\frac{d\ell}{\ell} T_p \quad \text{or} \quad \Delta T_p \approx \frac{1}{2}\alpha T_p \Delta T.$$

For $T_p = 1.00$ sec, $\alpha = 19 \times 10^{-6}$ and $\Delta T = 10°$, $\Delta T_p = 9.5 \times 10^{-5}$ sec. In one 24 hr day the clock will now record $24 \times 3600/T_p(26°)$ seconds and be 8.2 seconds slow at day's end.
12. (a) $\langle KE \rangle = \frac{3}{2} nRT = 11973$ J; (b) $\langle KE \rangle_{molecule} = \frac{3}{2} kT = 8.28 \times 10^{-21}$ J;
(c) $P = nRT/V = 19.7$ atm;
(d) $\rho = \frac{m}{V} = \frac{nM}{V}$ so $M = \frac{\rho V}{n} = \frac{1.68 \times 10^{-2} \frac{gm}{cm^3} \times 4 \times 10^3 \ cm^3}{2.4 \text{ mole}}$ or M = 28.0 gm/mole;
(e) Probably nitrogen.

Chapter 18

EXERCISES:

2. (a) $1.26 \times 10^7$ J; (b) $1.45 \times 10^2$ watts.
4. 20.84°C
6. 74.3 kcal
8. 10.95°C
10. (a) $5.0 \times 10^3$ cal = $2.09 \times 10^4$ J; (b) $1.57 \times 10^3$ J = 375 cal.
12. (a) 1.17 gm; (b) No.
14. 35.7°C
16. Heat is a flow of energy due to a temperature difference. Yes, the internal energy is higher.
18.

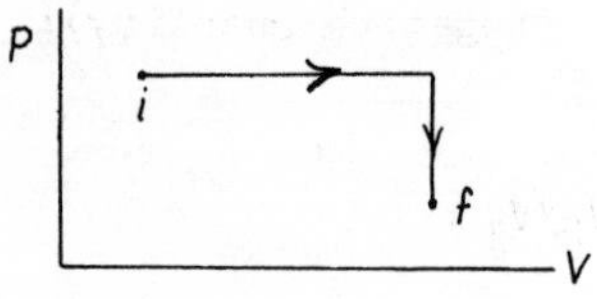


(a) W = 6 lit-atm = 608 J;

(b) $\Delta Q = 912 - 456 + 608 = 1064$ J.

20.

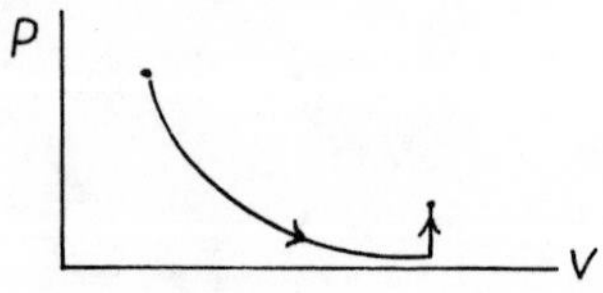


(a) W = 334 J;

(b) $\Delta Q = 790$ J.

22. (a) 608 J; (b) 1200 K; (c) 300 K; (d) 608 J.
24. (a) 3.99 moles; (b) 3570 cal; (c) 19.8 cal/K.
26. There are five degrees of freedom, three of which are translational. The rigid rotor dumbbell has the necessary two more. The others have too many.
28. (a) Vibrating dumbbell -- rotor; (b) dumbbell -- rotor (rigid); (c) rigid, non-rotating sphere -- i.e., point particles.
30. (a) $\Delta U = \Delta Q = 1493$ cal, W = 0; (b) $\Delta Q = 2090$, $\Delta U = 1493$, W = 597 cal;
(c) $P_iV_i = R(300)$, $P_iV_f = R(600)$, $P\Delta V = 300R = 597$ cal.
34. $PV^\gamma = \text{const} = P(nRT/P)^\gamma = (nR)^\gamma(T^\gamma/P^{\gamma-1})$, so $T^\gamma/P^{\gamma-1}$ = const.

36. (a) 192°C; (b) 114°C.

PROBLEMS:

2. While the ice is heated the temperature is $T = -10 + (23.89/50)t$. At $t = 20.9$ sec, the ice reaches 0°C where it remains for 334.7 sec while it absorbs 8000 cal; total time to water at 0°C is 355.7 sec. While the water is heating the temperature is given by $T = (23.89/100)t'$, for $355.7 \leq t \leq 774.3$ and $t' = t - 355.7$. At $t = 774.3$ sec, the water is at 100°C where it remains for the 2260 seconds required to absorb 54,000 cal to convert it to steam. Total time to steam is 3035 sec. After this time the temperature is given by $T = 100 + (23.89/50)t''$ where $t'' = t - 3035$ seconds. At $t = 3056$ seconds, the steam is at 110°C.
4. (a) $Q = 9702$ cal; (b) The initial volume is 18 $cm^3 = 18 \times 10^{-3}$ liter and from $PV = nRT$ the steam volume is 30.6 liter. Thus the volume change is essentially 30.6 liter. The work done is 30.6 liter-atm = 3100 J = 741 cal. Thus, (c) $\Delta U = 8961$ cal; (d) Since there is virtually no volume change as the ice melts the work done by the system is zero, so by the first law $\Delta U \approx Q \approx 18\ L_f$. Actually the density of ice is less than water (ice floats) so the volume actually decreases slightly. Thus, the system does a small amount of negative work. Hence $\Delta U$ is actually slightly greater than $18\ L_f$.
6. (a) 2.9°C; (b) To bring the 200 gm of ice to 0°C requires 2000 cal. At 2.9°C the calorimeter plus 600 gm of water can give up but 1860 cal to go to 0°C. Thus 1.75 gm of the 600 gm must freeze. So there will be 201.8 gm of ice. (c) The answer will be the same.
8. Consider a point where the adiabatic expansion curve and isothermal expansion curves intersect. There $PV^\gamma = P_iV_i^\gamma$ = constant and $PV = nRT = P_iV_i$ defines the two processes. For the former $dP/dV = -\gamma(C/V^{\gamma+1})$ and at the point this is $-\gamma(P_i/V_i)$. For the isothermal process $dP/dV = -nRT/V^2 = -P_iV_i/V_i^2 = -P_i/V_i$. Since $\gamma > 1$, the adiabatic expansion curve has steeper slope.
10. (a) To three figures accuracy $T_a = 244$ K, $T_b = 731$ K, $T_c = 366$ K, $T_d = 122$ K;
(b) Using R = 2.0 cal/mole-K,

| Path | a → b | b → c | c → d | d → a |
|---|---|---|---|---|
| Heat added to gas | 2435 cal | - 1095 cal | - 1220 cal | 366 cal |

(c) Path a → b: W = 40 liter-atm = 968 cal,
Path b → c: W = 0,
Path c → d: W = - 20 liter-atm = - 484 cal,
Path d → a: W = 0;
(d) $U_a = 732$ cal, $U_b = 2193$ cal, $U_c = 1098$ cal, $U_d = 366$ cal;
(e) $W_{net} = 484$ cal, $Q_{net} = 484$ cal (because of round-off, the sum in (b) is 486 cal).

12. (b) $\Delta U = 0$ (isothermal process) so $Q = W = \int_{V_1}^{V_2} P\,dV = nRT \int_{V_1}^{V_2} dV/V$ or $Q = nRT \ln (V_2/V_1)$;
(c) $\Delta U = 0$, $Q_{added} = W_{done\ by} = nRT \int_{V_3}^{V_4} dV/V = nRT \ln (V_4/V_3)$ (negative quantity);
$Q_{rejected} = -Q_{added} = nRT \ln (V_3/V_4)$, which is positive.
(d) $T_cV_4^{\gamma-1} = T_hV_1^{\gamma-1}$, $T_cV_3^{\gamma-1} = T_hV_2^{\gamma-1}$, therefore $V_3/V_4 = V_2/V_1$.
(e) $\dfrac{Q_c}{Q_h} = \dfrac{nRT_c \ln (V_3/V_4)}{nRT_h \ln (V_2/V_1)} = \dfrac{T_c}{T_h}$ so $e = 1 - \dfrac{Q_c}{Q_h} = 1 - \dfrac{T_c}{T_h}$.

## Chapter 19

EXERCISES:

2. (a) 28.7 %; (b) 71.33 cal.
4. (a) 5/3; (b) 37.5 %.
6. (a) A: T T F F (b) All but the second entry; (c) Yes.
B: T F T F

8. If the K-P statement is false, add a perfect engine to this refrigerator.

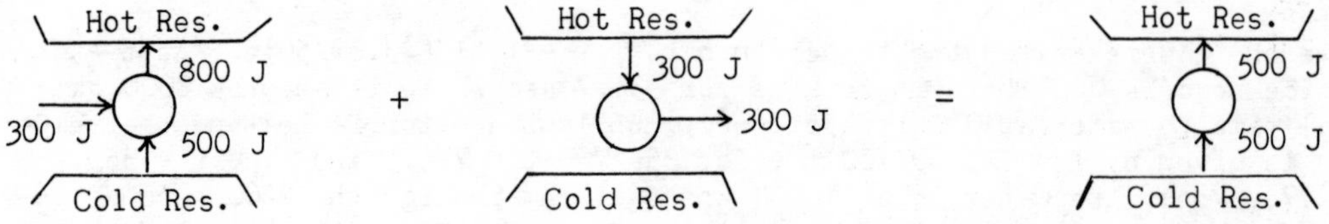


Actual refrigerator, 300 J work input | Perfect engine, 300 J work output | Perfect refrigerator

10. Run the first as a refrigerator and add a "more efficient" engine.

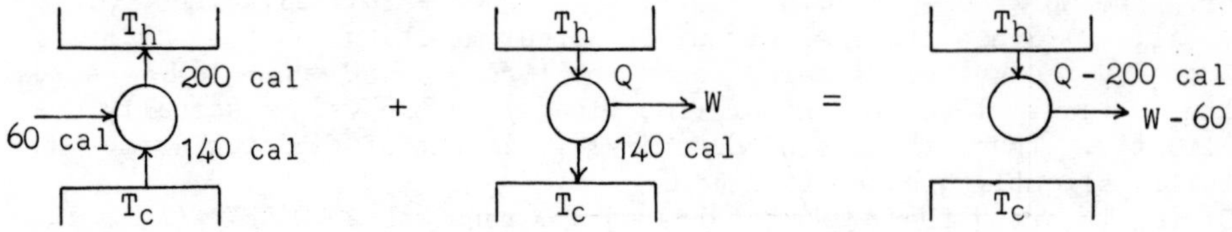


Since the hypothesized efficiency of the second engine is greater than 30 %, W will exceed 60 cal and Q will exceed 200 cal by the same amount. Thus we would have a perfect engine.

12. (a) 33.33 %; (b) Assume a refrigerator with $\eta > 2$. Combine with Carnot engine and show that this leads to a perfect refrigerator violating the Clausius statement of the second law.
14. 26.8 %
16. (a) 13.65; (b) 8.77.
18. $366\frac{1}{4}$ K
20. (a) The same because the initial and final states of the gas are the same. (b) Greater because of irreversibility.
22. (a) 0; (b) 266.7 K.
24. 0.234 cal/K
26. (a) $5.86 \times 10^4$ cal/K; (b) $-5.86 \times 10^4$ cal/K; (c) With the universe as defined $\Delta S = 0$. For the lake to remain at exactly the same temperature, however, the surrounding earth and air would have to give up heat energy to the lake.
28. (a) 20 %; (b) $\Delta S_{engine} = 0$, $\Delta S_h = -2.5$ cal/K, $\Delta S_c = 4.0$ cal/K, $\Delta S_{universe} = 1.5$ cal/K; (c) 50 %, 500 cal; (d) In general if an engine absorbs $Q_h$ at $T_h$ and rejects $Q_c$ to the reservoir at $T_c$, the entropy change of the universe is $\Delta S_u = Q_c/T_c - Q_h/T_h$. But if W is the engine work, $Q_c = Q_h - W$, so

$$T_c \Delta S_u = Q_c - Q_h T_c/T_h \quad \text{or} \quad T_c \Delta S_u = Q_h\left(1 - \frac{T_c}{T_h}\right) - W = W_{Carnot} - W.$$

30. 125 cal
32. (a) Energy wasted = 500 J, $\Delta S_u = \frac{5}{3}\frac{J}{K} = 1.67$ J/K;
    (b) Maximum work possible is 250 J so this is lost or wasted. Thus (a) is more wasteful in terms of potential work lost. $\Delta S_u = 0.833$ J/K.

PROBLEMS:

2. $T_i = 321.4$ K, $T_f = 243.6$ K, $T_a = 121.8$ K;
   $Q_{out} = \frac{7}{2} R(121.8)$, $Q_{in} = \frac{5}{2} R(199.6)$;
   E = 14.6 %.

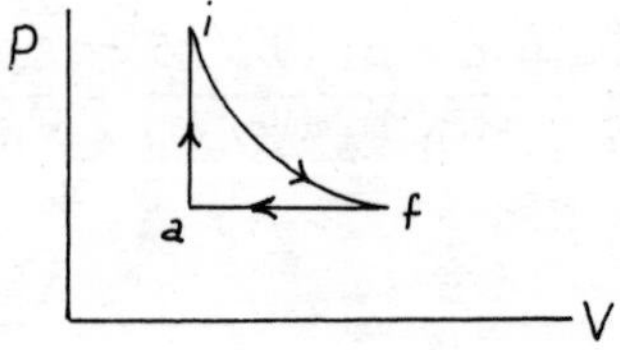


4. 13.2 %
6. (a) 8.21 ℓ; (b) PV = 32.84 ℓ-atm, $PV^{\gamma} = 76.23$ ℓ-atm$^{1.4}$;
   (c) 24.63 ℓ; (d) PV = 24.63 ℓ-atm, $PV^{\gamma} = 88.73$ ℓ-atm$^{1.4}$.
8. (a) $\eta = Q_c/W = Q_c/\epsilon Q_h = T_c/\epsilon T_h$; (b) $\eta = Q_c/W = Q_c/(Q_h - Q_c) = T_c/(T_h - T_c)$;
   (c) Increase $T_c$.
10. No.
12. $\Delta S = \int_{T_1}^{T_2} dQ/T = \int_{T_1}^{T_2} C_p\, dT/T = C_p \ln (T_2/T_1)$. Yes.

14. (a) $\Delta S_u = 19.3$ cal/K; (b) $\Delta S_u = 11.0$ cal/K;
(c) $\Delta S_u = 5.85$ cal/K.

Take N reservoirs at temperatures $200 + \frac{200}{N}k$, k = 1, 2, ..., N.

$$\Delta S = 69.3 - 100 \sum_{k=1}^{N} \frac{200/N}{200 + 200k/N} = 69.3 - 100 \sum_{k=1}^{N} \frac{1}{N+k} .$$

In the limit as $N \to \infty$ this becomes

$$69.3 - 100 \ln 2 = 0 .$$

## Chapter 20

EXERCISES:

2. At t = 3 sec, for example.

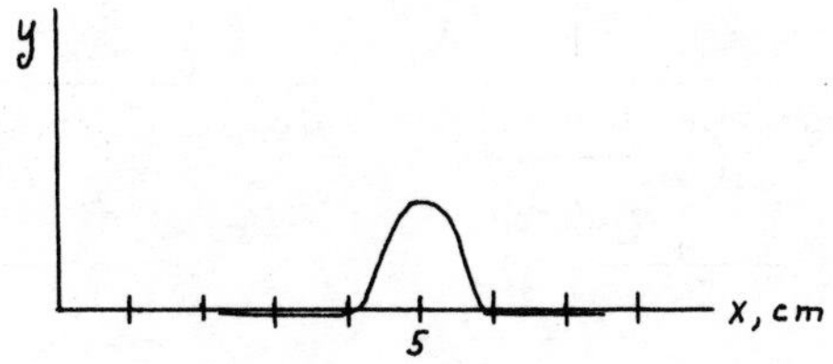


4.

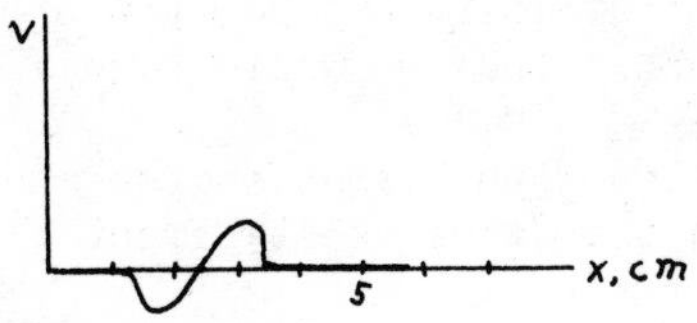


6. At t = 2 sec, for example.

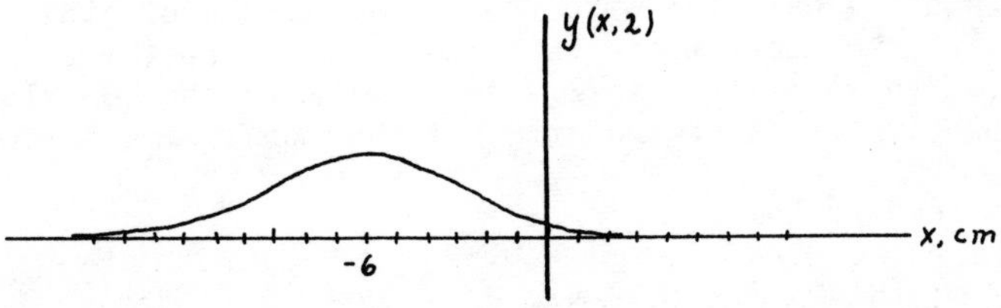


8.

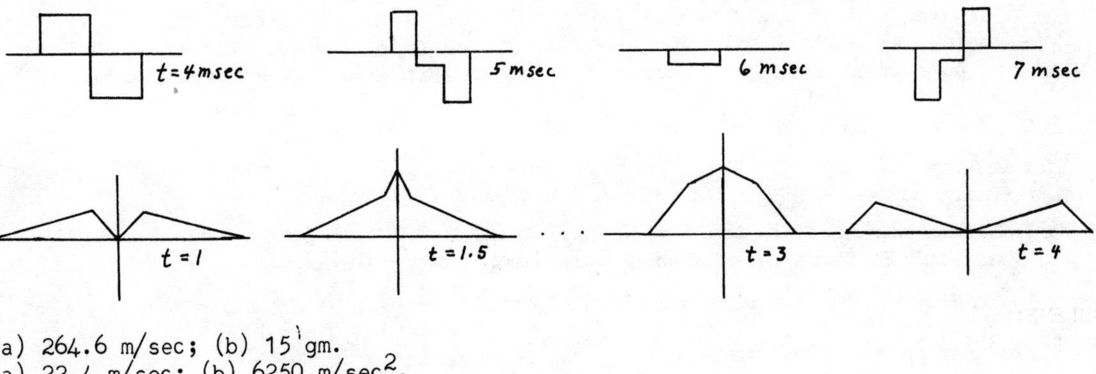


10.

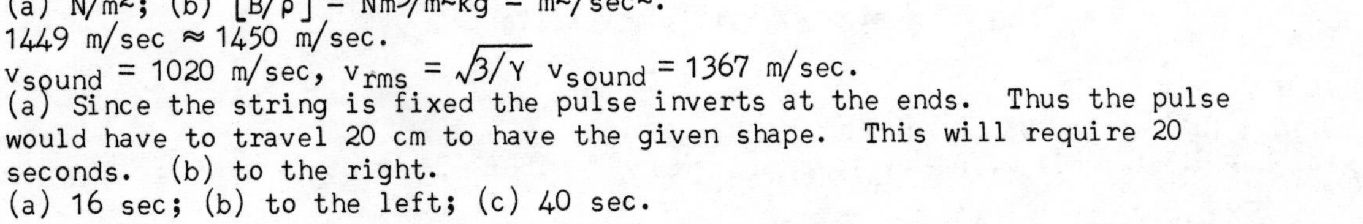


12. (a) 264.6 m/sec; (b) 15 gm.
14. (a) 22.4 m/sec; (b) 6250 m/sec$^2$.
16. (a) N/m$^2$; (b) $[B/\rho] = Nm^3/m^2kg = m^2/sec^2$.
18. 1449 m/sec $\approx$ 1450 m/sec.
20. $v_{sound} = 1020$ m/sec, $v_{rms} = \sqrt{3/\gamma}\ v_{sound} = 1367$ m/sec.
22. (a) Since the string is fixed the pulse inverts at the ends. Thus the pulse would have to travel 20 cm to have the given shape. This will require 20 seconds. (b) to the right.
24. (a) 16 sec; (b) to the left; (c) 40 sec.
26.

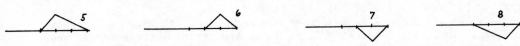

PROBLEMS:

2. Time clap to echo = $\frac{1}{2}$ time clap to clap = 1/2N. Wave front moves distance 2L, so 2L = v/2N or v = 4 LN.

4. (b) $\Delta T = 40$ N.
6. (a) Treat in analogy with sound waves. $\Delta P = -k\Delta x/A$ where A is cross-sectional area. Then $\Delta v = \Delta x A$ and $v = AL$, so "B" $= kL/A$. Then $\rho_0 = m/LA$ so $v = \sqrt{L^2k/m} = L\sqrt{k/m}$.
(b) $v = \sqrt{\frac{T}{\mu}} = \sqrt{\frac{kL}{m/L}} = L\sqrt{\frac{k}{m}}$. This assumes $L \gg L_0$ so that stretch is $L - L_0 \approx L$ and $\mu = m/L$.
8. (a)

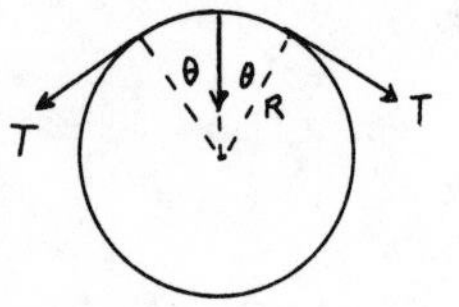


Centripetal force is $2T\sin\theta \approx 2T\theta = m\omega^2R$.
$m = \mu(2\theta R)$, so $2T\theta = 2\mu\theta\omega^2R^2$ or $T = \mu\omega^2R^2$ or $T = \mu v_0{}^2$.

(b) $v = \sqrt{T/\mu} = v_0$;
(c) Pulse will travel once around the loop for each loop revolution.

<u>Chapter 21</u>

EXERCISES:

2.

| f | $\lambda_{air}$ | $\lambda_{water}$ |
|---|---|---|
| 20 | 17 m | 75 m |
| 20,000 | 1.7 cm | 7.5 cm |

4. $7.5 \times 10^{14}$ Hz, $4.29 \times 10^{14}$ Hz.
6. (a) $-x$, 5 m/sec; (b) 0.1 m, 50 Hz, 20 msec; (c) 1.0 mm.
8. (a) The vibrations are parallel with the slot. If the original wave had no component parallel with the slot, there is no wave. In case (b) there will be no wave while in case (c) there will be a wave parallel with the 45° slot whose amplitude is 0.71 times the amplitude of the original wave that came through the vertical slot.
10. Sound waves are longitudinal.
12. $3.65 \times 10^{-5}$ m
14. (a) $1.04 \times 10^{-5}$ m; (b) $2.08 \times 10^{-5}$ m.
16. .071 m
18. 2A
20. (a) $5\sin(kx - \omega t + \psi)$, $\psi = 53.1°$; (b) $6.08\sin(kx - \omega t + \psi)$, $\psi = 34.7°$.
22. $\eta A$ = energy per unit length, and $\Delta E = \eta A v \Delta t$, so $\Delta E/\Delta t = \eta A v$.
24. (a) For same pressure and temperature, $\rho \propto m$. Since $s_0$ and $\omega$ are the same $I_{O_2}/I_{H_2} = \frac{32}{2}\frac{(317)}{(1286)} \approx 4$.
(b) $I_{O_2}/I_{H_2} = \frac{1}{4}$; (c) $s_{O_2}/s_{H_2} = \frac{1}{2}$, $p_{O_2} = 2p_{H_2}$.
26. (a) 20 dB; (b) 100 dB.
28. $\beta_2 = 10\log(2I/I_0) = 10\log 2 + 10\log(I/I_0) = 3.0\text{ dB} + \beta$.
32. (b) $2kx = A + B$, $2\omega t = A - B$, so $A = kx + \omega t$, $B = kx - \omega t$.
$\therefore y = A\sin kx\cos\omega t = \frac{A}{2}\, 2\sin kx\cos\omega t = \frac{A}{2}\left[\sin(kx + \omega t) + \sin(kx - \omega t\right]$,
or $y = y_1 + y_2$, $y_1 = \frac{A}{2}\sin(kx + \omega t)$, moves left;
$y_2 = \frac{A}{2}\sin(kx - \omega t)$, moves right.

PROBLEMS:
2. $3.14 \times 10^{-1}$ m/sec, 98.6 m/sec$^2$.
4. (a) $d = 0.34(2n+1)$ m, $n = 0, 1, 2, \ldots$; (b) $d = 0.68n$ m, $n = 0, 1, 2, \ldots$; $4I_0$; (c) $2I_0$.
6. (a) 790 milliwatts; (b) Tension up by $10^4$, frequency up by a factor of 10, amplitude up by a factor of 10; (c) frequency.
8. $I = I_0\,(\sin^2 2\delta/\sin^2(\delta/2))$. Maxima at $\delta = 2n\pi$, $n = 0, 1, 2 \ldots$ of intensity. $I = 16I_0$. There are zeros at $\pi/2$, $\pi$, $3\pi/2$, and $2n\pi$ plus these values where $n = 1, 2 \ldots$. Between the zeros of intensity at $\pi/2$ and $\pi$ there is a secondary maxima of intensity $(32/27)I_0$. This occurs at $\varphi$ such that $\cos\delta = -2/3$. All such secondary maxima are located at $\delta = \cos^{-1}(-2/3)$. The intensity is the same as the interference pattern for 4 slits.

10. $I_1 = I_0 \times 10^7$, $I_2 = I_0 \times 10^{7.3}$, $I_3 = I_0 \times 10^8$.
$I = I_1 + I_2 + I_3 = I_0 \times 10^7 [1 + 10^{.3} + 10] = 1.3 \times 10^8 I_0$.
Thus $\beta = 81.1$ dB. Eliminating the two least intense sources only reduces the sound level by 1.1 dB, but this is a 23% reduction in intensity from $1.3 \times 10^{-4}$ watt/m$^2$ to $1.0 \times 10^{-4}$ watt/m$^2$.

## Chapter 22

EXERCISES:

2. 1533.3 N
4. 180 m/sec
6. $y = y_0 \cos \omega t \sin kx$ is the general form. $\omega = 2\pi f_n = 2\pi(nv/2L) = n\pi(v/L)$. $k = 2\pi/\lambda_n = 2\pi n/2L = \pi(n/L)$.
8. (a) $10\pi$ cm, $150/\pi$ Hz; (b) 1500 cm/sec; (c) 62.8 cm.
10. (a) (b) $\pi/250$ sec;

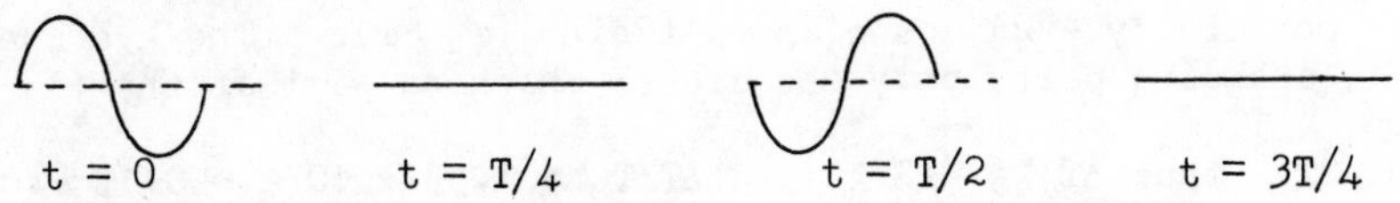


(c) It remains; the left half has velocity downward (upward) and the right half has velocity upward (downward).
12. (a) 2.66 m; (b) 0.67 m; (c) 159.8 m/sec.
14. (a) 5/3, 7/5; (b) Harmonics must be only odd multiples of $f_1$ and these are said to be successive; hence the string is fixed at only one end. (c) 25 Hz; (d) 3rd, 5th, 7th; (e) 2 m.
16. (a) 8.5 m, 8.5 mm; (b) 4.25 m, 4.25 mm.
18. (a) 70.8 Hz; (b) 4888 Hz; (c) 35.

PROBLEMS:

2. (a) 433 Hz; (b) 78.5 cm; (c) 32, f = 13,856 Hz.
4. (a) 450/375 = 6/5 so $f_1 = 75$ Hz; (b) 5th and 6th; (c) 2 m.
6. (a) 1834/1310 = 7/5, 2358/1834 = 9/7, so these are a succession of odd harmonics. The pipe is closed at one end.
(b) $f_1 = 262$ Hz; (c) 1.30 m is the fundamental wavelength; pipelength = 0.324 m.
8. (a) 85 Hz; (b) 34 m/sec; (c) 28.9 N.
10. $f = 60$ Hz, $\lambda_n = 5.0/n$ m, $\lambda_n f = v = \sqrt{T/\mu}$, so $T = 8 \times 10^{-3}(300/n)^2$.
$T_1 = 720$ N, $T_2 = 180$ N, $T_3 = 80$ N, $T_4 = 45$ N.
12. (a) $y = .03 \sin (\frac{3\pi}{4} x) \cos (200\pi t)$, x,y in m, t in sec.
(b) $dKE = \frac{1}{2} \mu \, dx \, (\frac{\partial y}{\partial t})^2$; this is a maximum whenever the transverse velocity is an extremum, which occurs at $[\sin (200\pi t)]^2 = 1$ or $200\pi t = n\pi/2$ or $t = n/400$, n = 0, 1, 2, ... . At these times y = 0, so the string is flat.
(c) $KE_{max} = \frac{1}{2} \mu [.03(200\pi)]^2$.
(d) $dPE = \frac{1}{2} \mu \, dx \, [.03(200\pi)]^2 \sin^2 (\frac{3\pi}{4} x) \cos^2 (200\pi t)$ and
$PE = \frac{1}{2} \mu [.03(200\pi)]^2 \cos^2 (200\pi t)$ whose maximum value is the same as the maximum KE.
14. $v = \sqrt{YRT/M}$ and $\lambda f = v$. But, $\lambda$ is fixed by the pipe length and mode of vibration so

$$f = \frac{1}{\lambda} \sqrt{\frac{YRT}{M}} .$$

Thus $df/f = \frac{1}{2} dT/T$. For small changes $\Delta f/f \approx \frac{1}{2} \Delta T/T$.
Data: f = 200 Hz when T = 293 K. $\Delta T = 12.2$ K.

$$\frac{\Delta f}{200} = \frac{1}{2} \frac{12.2}{293} = .021 .$$

$\Delta f = 4.2$ Hz so $f(98^\circ F) = 204.2$ Hz.

## Chapter 23

EXERCISES:

2. (a) 0.6 mm; (b) $0.006 \cos (0.1x - 10t) \cos (7.9x - 390t)$; 49.4 m/sec;

(c) 100 m/sec; (d) 62.8 m; (e) dispersive.
4. 4 Hz
6. (a) 496, or 504 Hz; (b) Wax on 500 Hz fork: If $f_2 = 496$ Hz, $f_{beat} < 4$, but if $f_2 = 504$ Hz, $f_{beat} > 4$. Wax on second fork: If $f_2 = 496$ Hz, $f_{beat} > 4$, but if $f_2 = 504$ Hz, $f_{beat} < 4$.
8. (a) $N = f_0 \Delta t$; (b) $\lambda = \Delta x/N$; (c) $k = 2\pi N/\Delta x$;
(d) Due to damping effects in starting and stopping the fork. At those times, $f \neq f_0$.
(e) $\Delta f = \Delta N/\Delta t = \pm 1/\Delta t$, usually given in magnitude only, i.e., $\Delta f = 1/\Delta t$.
(f) $\Delta k = 2\pi \Delta N/\Delta x = 2\pi/\Delta x$.
10. $\Delta k = 0.2\ m^{-1}$, 31.4 m
12. (a) $v_p = \sqrt{Tk/\rho}$; (b) $v_g = (3/2)\sqrt{Tk/\rho} = (3/2)v_p$; (c) $v_g > v_p$.

PROBLEMS:
2. Let the fork position be $y = A \sin \omega_o t$, $\omega_0 = 2\pi f_0$. Let the illumination frequency be $\omega = 2\pi f$; the illumination description will be $A \sin \omega t$. The illuminated fork then appears to have position $y = 2A \cos \frac{1}{2}(\omega_0 - \omega)t \sin \frac{1}{2}(\omega_0 + \omega)t$. The eye does not "see" the rapidly changing part, only the slower changing part at the frequency $(f_0 - f)/2$.
4. $f = \sqrt{T/\rho}$, $df/f = dT/2T$, thus $\Delta T/T_0 = 2f_B/f_0$. $\Delta T/T_0 \leq 1.53 \times 10^{-3} \approx 0.15\%$.
6. (a) For $x \gg 1$, $e^{2x} \gg 1$, so $\tanh x \approx 1$.
For $x \ll 1$, $e^{\pm x} \approx 1 \pm x$, so $\tanh x \approx \frac{1+x-1+x}{1+x+1-x} = x$.
Deep water: $\omega^2 \approx (gk + \frac{T}{\rho} k^3)$. Shallow water: $\omega^2 \approx (gk + \frac{T}{\rho} k^3)kH$.
(b) For shallow water, $\omega \approx [gH + \frac{T}{\rho} k^2 H]^{\frac{1}{2}} k$.
If $\frac{T}{\rho} k^2 H \ll gH$, i.e., if $4\pi^2 T/\rho\lambda^2 \ll g$, then $\omega \approx \sqrt{gH}\, k$ and $v_p \approx \sqrt{gH}$, $v_g \approx \sqrt{gH}$.
(c) For deep water $\omega \approx [gk + Tk^3/\rho]^{\frac{1}{2}}$ so $v_p = \omega/k = [g/k + Tk/\rho]^{\frac{1}{2}}$;
$v_g = [g/k + 3Tk/\rho]/2v_p$.
(d) For $\lambda = 1$ cm, $v_p = 0.250$ m/sec, $v_g = 0.313$ m/sec.
For $\lambda = 1$ m, $v_p = 1.25$ m/sec, $v_g = 0.625$ m/sec.
$v_p = v_g$ at $\lambda = 2\pi\sqrt{T/g\rho} = 1.74$ cm.

## Chapter 24

EXERCISES:
2. $P = 3.82 \times 10^{22}$ watts
4. (a) 50 ft, 20 $min^{-1}$; (b) 45 ft, 22.2 $min^{-1}$; (c) 50 ft, 22.0 $min^{-1}$.
6. (a) 1.30 m; (b) 262 Hz.
8. (a) 2.10 m; (b) 162 Hz.
10. (a) 80 m/sec toward the listener; (b) 420 m/sec; (c) 1.7 m; (d) 247 Hz.
12. 529 Hz, 474 Hz
14. 275 Hz, 825 Hz. Among other finite size effects, the listener has two ears which are not at the same location.
16. (a) 27.9 cm; (b) 1221 Hz; (c) 24.7°, 33.9°, 44.1°, 56.7°, 77.1°; (d) 3.99°.
20. (a) No change; (b) $\sin \theta$ = 1/12, 2/12, 3/12, 5/12, 6/12, 7/12, 9/12, 10/12, 11/12 or $\theta$ = 4.8°, 9.6°, 14.5°, 24.6°, 30.0°, 35.7°, 48.6°, 56.4°, 66.4° are minima.
22. No. The sources are not coherent.
24. (a) $4I_0$; (b) $2I_0$; (c) 0.

PROBLEMS:
2. (a) There is a 40 ft/sec wind toward the car so the velocity of sound is 1060 ft/sec into the wind and 1140 ft/sec with the wind. The frequency is 200 Hz and $\lambda = 1060/200 = 5.3$ ft. (b) At the wall f = 200(1100/1060) = 208 Hz. (c) From this frame the wall has velocity 40 ft/sec toward the observer so the frequency received back at the car is 208(1140/1100) = 215. (d) The beat frequency is 15 Hz.
4. (a) If source moves, $f' = f_0(1 \mp u/v)^{-1} \approx f_0(1 \pm u/v)$.
If observer moves, $f' = f_0(1 \pm u/v)$ is exact.
$\Delta f/f = \pm u/v$. From $\lambda f = v$, $\Delta\lambda/\lambda = -\Delta f/f = \mp u/v$.
(b) $f' = f_0[\frac{1 \pm u/v}{1 \mp u/v}]^{\frac{1}{2}} \approx f_0(1 \pm \frac{u}{v})$;
(c) $(\lambda' - \lambda)/\lambda = .01 = -u/c$ so $u = -.01c = -3.0 \times 10^6$ m/sec.

6. $5 \times 10^{-5}$ m; No; 0.5 mm.

8. For 4 sources, minima occur for a phase difference of $n\pi/2$, $n = 1, 2, 3, 5, 6, 7, \ldots$ . Thus $\frac{2\pi}{\lambda} d \sin\theta = n\pi/2$. For a distant screen $\sin\theta \approx \tan\theta = x/D$. Thus $x = n\frac{\lambda D}{4d}$. For two sources the width is $\lambda D/d = 1.2$ cm; for four sources the width is $\lambda D/2d = 0.6$ cm.

10. (a) $\tan\theta_1 = x/D$, $\tan\theta_2 = (x - d)/D = \tan(\theta_1) - d/D$. For small angles $\theta_2 \approx \theta_1 - d/D$ or $\theta_1 \approx \theta_2 + d/D$. Here $d/D = 10^{-4}$, so the difference is about $10^{-4}$ radians.

(b) In general,

$$\tan\theta_1 - \tan\theta_2 = \frac{d}{D} = \frac{\sin(\theta_1 - \theta_2)}{\cos\theta_1 \cos\theta_2} .$$

But $\cos\theta_1$ and $\cos\theta_2$ are each $\leq 1$, so

$$\sin(\theta_1 - \theta_2) = \cos\theta_1 \cos\theta_2 \frac{d}{D} \leq \frac{d}{D} << 1 .$$

Thus $\theta_1 - \theta_2 \lesssim d/D$.

12. (a) Let $y_1 = A_o \sin(kx_1 - \omega t)$, $y_2 = A_o \sin(kx_1 + k\Delta x - \omega t + \delta_0)$.
Then, $y = y_1 + y_2 = 2A_o \cos\frac{1}{2}(\delta + \delta_o) \sin(kx_1 - \omega t + \frac{1}{2}(\delta + \delta_0))$ where $\delta = \frac{2\pi}{\lambda}\Delta x$.

(b) For $\delta = 0$, the intensity is $I = 4I_0 \cos^2(Ct/2)$ is the equation of the desired curve.

(c) The equation is $I = 4I_0 \cos^2(\frac{\pi}{2} + \frac{Ct}{2}) = 4I_0 \sin^2(\frac{Ct}{2})$.
In both (b) and (c), the time average is $2I_0$.

14.

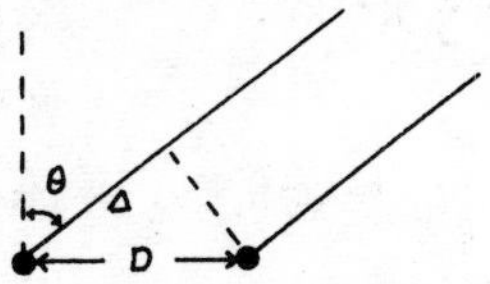


$\Delta = D\sin\theta$, so the phase difference is $\frac{2\pi}{\lambda}\Delta = \frac{2\pi}{\lambda} D\sin\theta$. The phase shift should then be $-\frac{2\pi}{\lambda} D\sin\theta$. Here $\lambda = 15$ m so the phase shift should have magnitude 14.55 radian.

Since a shift of $2\pi$ is equivalent to no shift, the effective phase shift would be $14.55 - 4\pi = 1.98$ rad $= 113.5^\circ$.

Chapter 25

EXERCISES:

2. (a) 110 Hz; (b) 11,000 Hz; 440 Hz, 44,000 Hz.
6. (a) .006 rad $= 0.34^\circ$; (b) $6.0 \times 10^{-4}$ rad $= 0.034^\circ$; (c) 0.06 rad $= 3.4^\circ$.
8. 3.01 cm
10. $\lambda_{light} << \lambda_{sound}$. The wavelength of light is always small on a macroscopic basis but for sound this is not the case, in general. For microwaves (ultrasonics) the smallness of $\lambda$ is satisfied, hence also the ray approximation, provided that the region of interest is suitably large.
12. $3.35 \times 10^{-10}$ m
14. $32.12^\circ$
16. $19.47^\circ$
18. $48.75^\circ$
20. 2.83 cm

PROBLEMS:

2.

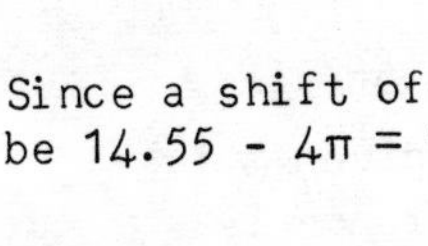

4.

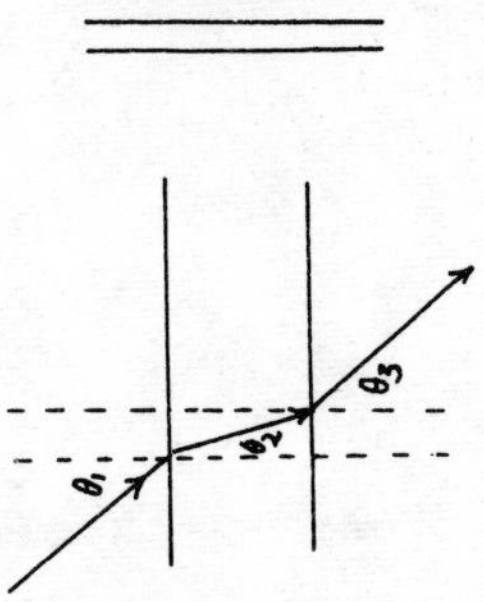


$n_1 \sin\theta_1 = n_2 \sin\theta_2 = n_3 \sin\theta_3$,

$n_1 = n_3$, so $\sin\theta_1 = \sin\theta_2$ or $\theta_1 = \theta_2$.

$d = t \tan \theta_1 - t \tan \theta_2$ where $t = 10$ cm, $\theta_1 = 60°$.
Since $n_1 \sin \theta_1 = n_2 \sin \theta_2$, $\theta_2 = \sin^{-1} (\frac{1}{1.5} \sin 60°) = 35.26°$. Thus $d = 10.25$ cm.

6. (b) $dI/d\alpha = 0$ when either $\sin \alpha = 0$ or when $\tan \alpha = \alpha$. The former corresponds to the minima so the secondary maxima occur at $\tan \alpha = \alpha$.
(c) Apart from $\alpha = 0$, the next root of $\tan \alpha = \alpha$ is $\alpha = 4.4934$ rad or $\alpha \approx 1.43\pi$, so $\varphi = 2.86\pi \approx 3\pi$.
(d) $I/I_0 = .05$.

## Chapter 26

EXERCISES:

2. 1.77 to 3.10 eV corresponding to $\lambda = 700$ nm to $\lambda = 400$ nm.
4. $1.0 \times 10^{10}$ Hz
6. For $f = 1000$ kHz, $\lambda = 300$ m; for $f = 100$ mega-Hz, $\lambda = 3.0$ m.
8. $I = k (\sin^2 \theta)/r^2$ so $I_1 = k/10^2$ or $k = 100 I_1$.
(a) $I = 100I_1 (\sin^2 90°)/30^2 = I_1/9$; (b) $I = 100I_1 (\sin^2 45°)/10^2 = I_1/2$;
(c) $I = 100I_1 (\sin^2 30°)/20^2 = I_1/16$.
10. (a) $5.88 \times 10^{12}$ miles; (b) $9.46 \times 10^{12}$ km is the exact result. Using the approximation that 1 yr = $3.16 \times 10^7$ sec, $9.48 \times 10^{12}$ km.
12. 500 sec, 8.33 light-min
14. 20.1 %
16. Yes.
18. In water, $v = 2.26 \times 10^8$ m/sec; in glass, $v = 2.00 \times 10^8$ m/sec.
20. 2.46
22. 7.0 mm
24. 8.54 cm
26. Use $\lambda = 600$ nm, headlight separation distance 4.5 ft. Then D = 5.8 miles.
28. $a = d/5 = 0.02$ mm; 9.
30. (a) 375 nm; (b) 5.33; (c) $\frac{16}{3} \cdot 2\pi - \pi = \frac{29}{3} \pi$ which is equivalent to $5\pi/3$.
32. $\varphi = \pi - \frac{2\pi}{\lambda'} 2t \approx \pi$ because the film is very thin at the top. For a given thickness t, the shortest wavelength which produces constructive interference is $\lambda = 4tn$. Since the film is thinnest at the top, the shorter wavelength will produce bright bands first. Thus blue shows first.
34. 434 nm at $8.68 \times 10^{-2}$ radian; 410 nm at $8.20 \times 10^{-2}$ radian.
36. 434 nm, 40.62°; 410 nm, 37.95°.
38. 500 nm
40. $27I_0/128 = 0.211I_0$.
42. $n = 1/\sin 45° = 1.414$; $\theta = \tan^{-1} n = 54.74°$.
44. $I_0 = I \cos^2 30°$, $I_e = I \sin^2 30°$, $I_e/I_0 = \tan^2 30° = 1/3$.

PROBLEMS:

2. (a) $n = \sqrt{2} = 1.414$; (b) $1.63 \leq n \leq 1.88$.
6. (a) 49.2 m; (b) blue.
8. 8
10. $1.09 \times 10^{-2}$ mm $< t < 1.15 \times 10^{-2}$ mm.
12. (a) 97.8 nm; (b) No; (c) 0.27 at 400 nm, 0.12 at 700 nm.
14. (a) 7200 nm; (b) 1.67.
16. (a) $\sin \theta = 1/1.66$ so $\theta = 37.04°$;
(b) $\sin \theta_{emergence} = 1.49 \sin 37.04° = 0.8976$, $\theta = 63.84°$. Thus this ray (extraordinary) emerges so the emerging light is plane-polarized.

## Chapter 27

EXERCISES:

2. (a) 20 cm, 40 cm, 80 cm, 100 cm; (b) 10 cm, 50 cm, 70 cm, 110 cm.
4.

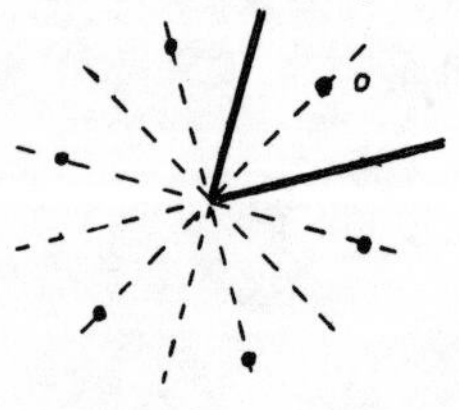

6. (a)

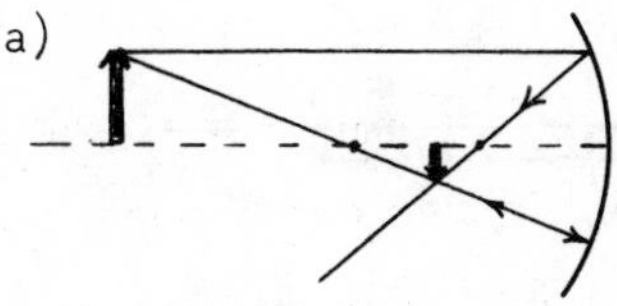

Real, inverted, reduced

(b) Image is at object position, but inverted. It is real and the same size.

(c)

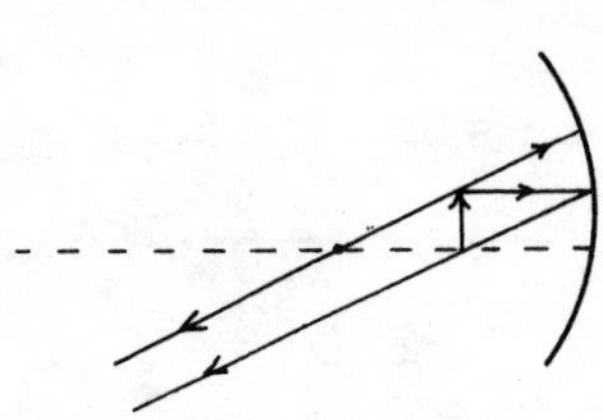

Virtual, enlarged image at ∞

(d) The actual rays diverge. There is a virtual, erect, enlarged image on the right of the mirror

8. In each case a virtual, erect, reduced image is formed. The image is successively closer to the back side of the mirror as the object is moved from 100 cm to 10 cm.

10. $f = -R/2$, so $s' = -\dfrac{\frac{R}{2}s}{\frac{R}{2}+s} = -Rs/(R+2s) < 0$ for any $s > 0$.

12. $s' \approx 4$ m and the image diameter is 3.68 cm.

14. (a) $s' = 30$ cm, image is real; (b) $s' = -15$ cm, that is, 15 cm toward the air side of the glass rod tip. This image is virtual. (c) $s' = 15$ cm, the image is real.

16. (a) $s' = -10$ cm, virtual; (b) $s' = -5$ cm, virtual; (c) $-15$ cm, virtual.

18. (a) $-14.49$ cm, virtual; (b) $-4.95$ cm, virtual; (c) $-40.54$ cm, virtual.

20. (a) 6 cm  (b) 6 cm 

22. (a) $s' = 40$ cm, real, inverted, $m = -1$; (b) $s' = -20$ cm, virtual, erect, $m = 2$; (c) $s' = -17.14$ cm, virtual, erect, $m = 0.43$; (d) $s' = -7.5$ cm, virtual, erect, $m = 0.75$.

24. $s' = 6.67$ cm, image is real, inverted and of height 1.0 cm.

26. $s' = -3.33$ cm, image is virtual, erect and of height 1.0 cm.

28. $\frac{1}{s'} = \frac{1}{f} - \frac{1}{s}$, with f negative the right side can never be positive.

30. $\frac{1}{s_1} + \frac{1}{s_1'} = \frac{1}{f_1}$ or $\frac{1}{s_1'} = \frac{1}{f_1} - \frac{1}{s_1}$ and $s_1' = -s_2$. Thus $\frac{1}{s_2} + \frac{1}{s_2'} = \frac{1}{f_2}$

or $-\frac{1}{s_1'} + \frac{1}{s_2'} = \frac{1}{f_2} = \frac{1}{s_2'} + \frac{1}{s_1} - \frac{1}{f_1}$. Thus $\frac{1}{s_1} + \frac{1}{s_2'} = \frac{1}{f_1} + \frac{1}{f_2} \equiv \frac{1}{f}$

so that $f = f_1f_2/(f_1 + f_2)$.

32. Spread is approximately 2 mm.

34. $f_{blue} = 9.43$ cm, $f_{red} = 10.64$ cm.

36. 2.0 cm

38. $1.22 \times 10^{-4}$ rad $= 6.99 \times 10^{-3}$ degrees $= 4.19 \times 10^{-1}$ minutes $= 25.2$ seconds.

40. (a) 5; (b) 6.

42. (a) The sum of the image distance for the objective lens plus the focal length of the ocular lens.
(b) 4.0; (c) 20; (d) 6.25 cm.

44. (a) 0.9 cm; (b) 0.18 radian.

PROBLEMS:

2. (a) 64 cm to the right of the 8 cm-radius end when the object is 20 cm to the left of this surface.
(b) 80 cm to the left of the right end (radius = 16 cm) or 16 cm to the right of the 8 cm-radius end.
(c) The image is virtual.

4. Take $s_1 = \infty$ so that $s_2' = f$. Then $s_1' = 60$ cm, so $s_2 = -56$ cm. Thus $f = 19.31$ cm.

6.

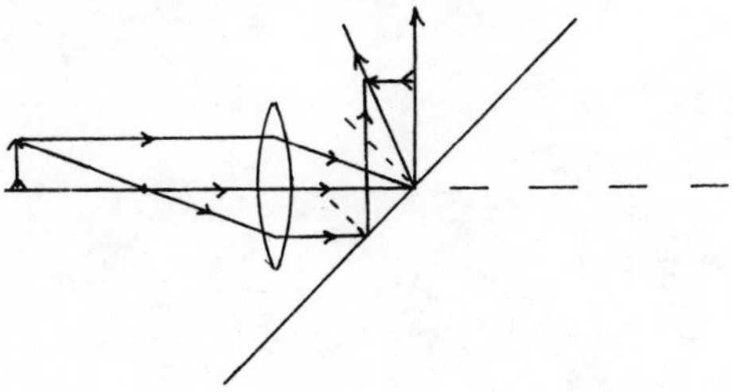

A real image is formed.

8. $s = x + f$, $s' = x' + f$.

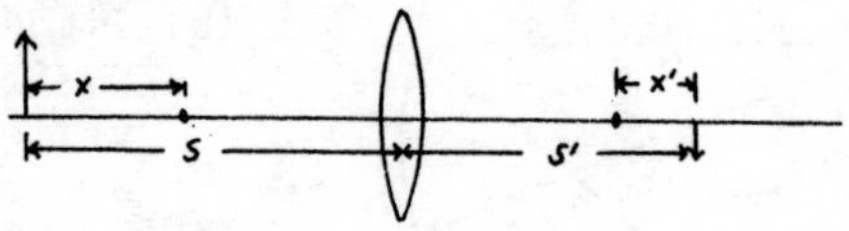


$$\frac{1}{x + f} + \frac{1}{x' + f} = \frac{1}{f}$$ leads directly

to $xx' = f^2$.

Then $m = -\frac{x' + f}{x + f} = -\frac{f(x + f)}{x(x + f)} = -\frac{f}{x} = -\frac{x'}{f}$.

12. (a) 103.45 cm from the objective; (b) $1/s - 1/25 = -1/5$ or $s = -6.25$; (c) 97.2 cm; (d) 13.8 cm, 1.62.

## Chapter 28

EXERCISES:

2. $t_{\parallel}/t_{\perp} = 1/\sqrt{1 - v^2/c^2}$.
4. $(\Delta t - \Delta t')/\Delta t = 1 - 1/\gamma \approx \frac{1}{2} v^2/c^2 = .01$, so $v \approx 0.1414c$.
6. (a) $(0.9c)(2.6 \times 10^{-8}$ sec$) = 7.02$ m; (b) 16.1 m.
8. (a) $4.5 \times 10^{-10}$ %; (b) $3.15 \times 10^7 - 1.42 \times 10^{-4}$ sec; $2.36 \times 10^{-6}$ min.
10. $0.6ct + ct = 40c$ so $t = 25$ min.
12. 60 min
16. $6.90 \times 10^{-2}$
18. (a) $t_2 - t_1 = \gamma(t_2' - t_1')$; (b) because $x_1$ and $x_2$ are not known.
20. (a) 0.994c; (b) 60,000 m/sec.
22. (a) 0.994c; (b) 0.9997c.
24. $$\frac{m^2u^2c^2}{(1 - u^2/c^2)} + m^2c^4 = \frac{m^2c^4}{(1 - u^2/c^2)} = E^2 .$$
26.

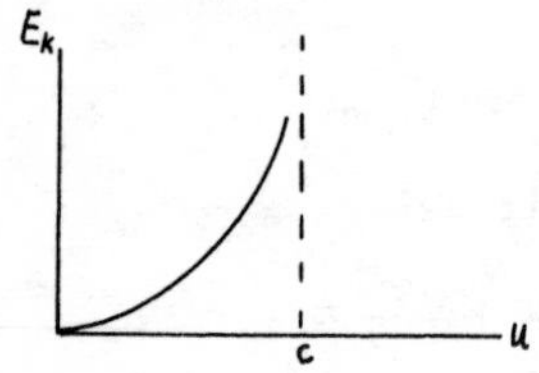


28. (a) $0.155E_0$; (b) $1.294E_0$; (c) $6.089E_0$.
30. $$\% \text{ error} = 100\,\frac{mu\gamma - mu}{mu\gamma} = \frac{100}{\gamma}(\gamma - 1) = (1 - \frac{1}{\gamma})100 .$$
    $E_k = E_0(\gamma - 1) = E_0$ so $\gamma = 2$, % error = 50 %.
32. (a) 2809.4 MeV; (b) 4.44 MeV.
34. (a) $2.56 \times 10^{-2}$; (b) 23.85 MeV; (c) $2.62 \times 10^{11}$.

PROBLEMS:

2. Time lost $= \Delta t(1 - \frac{1}{\gamma}) \approx \Delta t \frac{v^2}{2c^2} = 1$, $\Delta t \approx 9.01 \times 10^{11}$ sec.
4. $\%\text{ error} = 100[1 - \frac{v^2/c^2}{2(\gamma - 1)}]$. (a) 0.75 %; (b) 68.7 %.
6. $L_x' = (L\cos\theta)/\gamma$, $L_y' = L\sin\theta$, so $\tan\theta' = L_y'/L_x' = \gamma\tan\theta$.

$$L' = [L_x'^2 + L_y'^2]^{\frac{1}{2}} = [\frac{L^2\cos^2\theta}{\gamma^2} + L^2\sin^2\theta]^{\frac{1}{2}} = L[(\frac{\cos\theta}{\gamma})^2 + \sin^2\theta]^{\frac{1}{2}} .$$

8. First note: $\sqrt{1 - u'^2/c^2} = \sqrt{(1 - v^2/c^2)(1 - u^2/c^2)} = \frac{1}{\gamma}\sqrt{1 - u^2/c^2}$ for $u_x = 0$, $u_y = u$ and $u_x' = -v$, $u_y' = u/\gamma$.

Thus $$p_x' = \frac{mu_x'}{\sqrt{1 - u'^2/c^2}} = -\frac{mv\gamma}{\sqrt{1 - u^2/c^2}} = -\frac{v}{c^2}\gamma E = \gamma(p_x - \frac{v}{c^2}E) ;$$

$$p_y' = \frac{mu/\gamma}{\frac{1}{\gamma}\sqrt{1 - u^2/c^2}} = p_y \quad , \quad p_z' = p_z = 0 .$$

$$\frac{E'}{c} = \frac{mc}{\sqrt{1 - u'^2/c^2}} = \frac{mc\gamma}{\sqrt{1 - u^2/c^2}} = \gamma\frac{E}{c} = \gamma(\frac{E}{c} - \frac{v}{c}p_x) .$$

10. $p_x^2 + p_y^2 + p_z^2 - (E/c)^2 = \dfrac{m^2u_x^2 + m^2u_y^2 + m^2u_z^2}{1 - u^2/c^2} - \dfrac{m^2c^2}{1 - u^2/c^2}$

or $p^2 - (E/c)^2 = - m^2c^2$.

From Problem 8:

$$p_x'^2 + p_y'^2 + p_z'^2 - (E'/c)^2 = p_x^2\gamma^2(1 - \frac{v^2}{c^2}) + p_y^2 + p_z^2 - (\frac{E}{c})^2\gamma^2(1 - \frac{v^2}{c^2}) .$$

But $\gamma^2(1 - \frac{v^2}{c^2}) = 1$, so $p_x'^2 + p_y'^2 + p_z'^2 - (E'/c)^2 = - m^2c^2$.

12. For $m_2$: $\dfrac{\lambda'}{\lambda_0} = \dfrac{660}{656.3} = \sqrt{\dfrac{1 + \beta_2}{1 - \beta_2}}$, $\beta_2 = v_2/c$ .

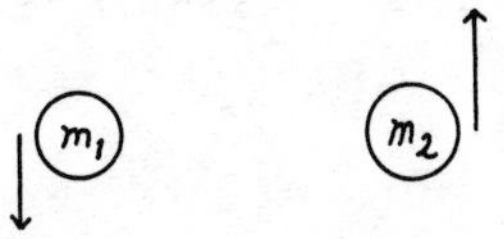


Thus $\beta_2 = .0056$.

For $m_1$: $\dfrac{\lambda'}{\lambda_0} = \dfrac{650}{656.3} = \sqrt{\dfrac{1 - \beta_1}{1 + \beta_1}}$ so $\beta_1 = .0097$.

Then $m_1v_1 = m_2v_2$, so $m_2/m_1 = v_1/v_2 = \beta_1/\beta_2 = 1.72$ .

14. For small $\beta = v/c$, $(f - f')/f = 1 - \sqrt{(1 - \beta)/(1 + \beta)} \approx \beta$ if motion is approach, and $- \beta$ if motion is away. Thus $\Delta f/f = \pm v/c$.
If $\Delta f/f = 8 \times 10^{-7}$, then $v = 240$ m/sec.

## Chapter 29

EXERCISES:

2. $9.65 \times 10^4$ C
4. (a) $2.4 \times 10^{-2}$ N away from $q_1$; (b) $2.4 \times 10^{-2}$ N away from $q_2$; (c) same magnitude but attractive.
6. $F_x = 1.28 \times 10^{-3}$ N, $F_y = - 3.24 \times 10^{-3}$ N.
8. (a) 1440 N/C, + x-direction; (b) 360 N/C, + x-direction; (c)

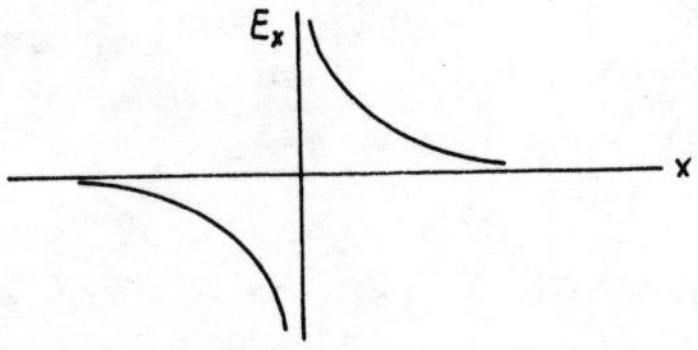


10. (a) $E_x = 3.46 \times 10^4$ N/C, $E_y = 0$; (b) $F_x = 6.91 \times 10^{-5}$ N, $F_y = 0$.
12. (a) $4 \times 10^5$ N/C, + y-direction; (b) $1.6 \times 10^{-3}$ N, - y-direction.
14.

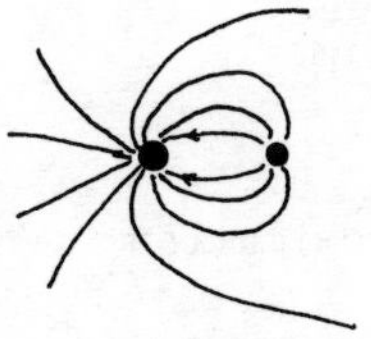

16. (a) 20 N-m$^2$/C; (b) $10\sqrt{3}$ N-m$^2$/C.
18. (a) $\pi$ m$^2$; (b) $7.2 \times 10^4$ N/C; (c) $7.2\pi \times 10^4$ N-m$^2$/C; (d) No; (e) $7.2\pi \times 10^4$ N-m$^2$/C.
20. (a) N; (b) N/6; (c) $4\pi kq$; (d) $4\pi kq/6$; (e) b and d.
22. (a) $\pi/2$ N-m$^2$/C; (b) 0; (c) $\pi$ N-m$^2$/C; (d) $2.78 \times 10^{-11}$ C.
24. (a) $9.58 \times 10^7$ C/kg, $a = 9.58 \times 10^9$ m/sec$^2$; (b) $3.13 \times 10^{-4}$ sec.
26. (a) $5.58 \times 10^{-11}$ N/C, downward; (b) $1.02 \times 10^{-7}$ N/C, upward; (c) $1.23 \times 10^6$ N/C, upward; (d) $2.45 \times 10^7$ N/C, upward.
28. (a) 639 nm; (b) 8.52 psec; (c) 4429 nm.
30. (a) 0; (b) $3.2 \times 10^{-24}$ N-m; (c) $1.6 \times 10^{-24}$ N-m.

PROBLEMS:

2. (a) $q_1/q_2 = - (D + L)^2/L^2$; (b) only at $\pm \infty$.
4. $F = kq(Q - q)/D^2$, $dF/dq = (k/D^2)(Q - 2q) = 0$ so $q_1 = q_2 = Q/2$.
6. (a) $dE_x/dx = [2kq/(x^2 + a^2)^{3/2}](a^2 - 2x^2) = 0$ implies $x = \pm a/\sqrt{2}$.

(b)

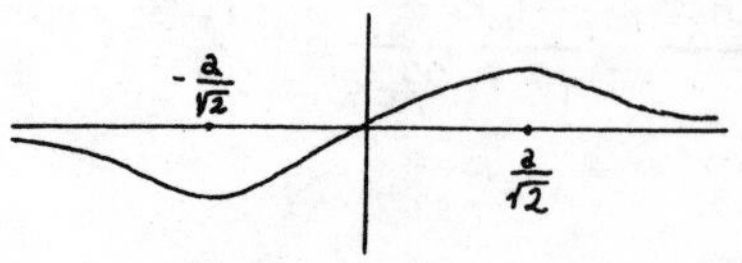


8. (a) $dW = \tau d\theta = pE \sin\theta \, d\theta$; (b) $W = \int_\theta^{\pi/2} dW = \int_0^{\pi/2} pE \sin\theta \, d\theta = pE \cos\theta$; (c) $U(\theta) = -W = -\underset{\sim}{p} \cdot \underset{\sim}{E}$.

10. (a) $\underset{\sim}{F} \approx \frac{dE_r}{dr} p\hat{\underset{\sim}{r}} = -\frac{2kQ}{r^3} p\hat{\underset{\sim}{r}}$; (b) $F_{\text{on } Q} \approx \frac{2kQ}{r^3} p = Q E_{\text{of dipole}}$.

Chapter 30

EXERCISES:

2. $E_x = kQ/[x^2(1 + a^2/x^2)^{3/2}] \rightarrow kQ/x^2$ when $a \ll x$.
4. $E_y = \frac{2k\lambda}{y} \sin\theta$; for large y, θ is small so $\sin\theta \approx \tan\theta = L/2y$.

   $E_y = \frac{2k\lambda}{y} \frac{L}{2y} = \frac{2kQ}{2y^2} = kQ/y^2$.
6. At y = 2 cm, $\sin\theta \approx 1$ so $E_y = 1.8 \times 10^6$ N/C.
   At y = 60 m, $E_y \approx k\lambda L/y^2 = 30$ N/C.
8. (a) $1.69 \times 10^6$ N/C; (b) $1.69 \times 10^6$ N/C; (c) $1.69 \times 10^6$ N/C; (d) 84.8 N/C.
10. (a) 0; (b) 0; (c) $1.80 \times 10^6$ N/C; (d) $4.50 \times 10^5$ N/C; (e) $1.13 \times 10^5$ N/C.
12. No, because there is not sufficient symmetry.
14. (a) Take as a Gaussian surface a concentric cylinder with radius r. Clearly E is radial, so

$$\oint E_n \, dA = E(2\pi rL) = Q_{\text{inside}}/\epsilon_0 = 0,$$

   so $E = 0$, $r < R$.

   (b) Take a cylindrical surface of radius $r > R$ and length L. Then

$$\oint E_n \, dA = E(2\pi rL) = \sigma(2\pi R)L/\epsilon_0,$$

   so $E = \sigma R/\epsilon_0 r$.

   (c) For a given length L the charge is $\lambda L = 2\pi R\sigma L$, so $\sigma R = \lambda/2\pi$ and $E = \lambda/(2\pi r\epsilon_0)$.

PROBLEMS:

2. (a) $dE_x/dx = kQ/a^3$; (b) $E_x = E_{x0} + \left.\frac{dE_x}{dx}\right|_0 x$ for small x,

   so $F = m\, d^2x/dt^2 = -q \frac{kQ}{a^3} x$. This is the equation for simple harmonic motion of angular frequency $\omega = (kQq/ma^3)^{\frac{1}{2}}$.
4. $E_x = 2\pi k\sigma\left[1 - \frac{x}{(x^2 + a^2)^{1/2}}\right] = \frac{\sigma}{2\epsilon_0}\left[1 - \frac{x}{(x^2 + a^2)^{1/2}}\right]$. With the approximation $E_x = \sigma/2\epsilon_0$, the neglected term is $\frac{\sigma}{2\epsilon_0}\left(\frac{x}{(x^2 + a^2)^{1/2}}\right)$ in magnitude. Thus the percent error is

$$100 \frac{x}{[(x^2 + a^2)^{1/2} - x]}.$$

| x | 0.1 cm | 0.2 cm | 3 cm | 0.3 cm |
|---|---|---|---|---|
| % error | 0.33 % | 0.67 % | 11.1 % | 1 % |

6. $dE_x = -(k\lambda/y) \sin\theta \, d\theta$,

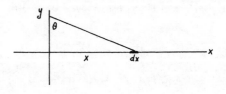

   $dE_y = (k\lambda/y) \cos\theta \, d\theta$.

   $E_x = -\int_0^{\pi/2} \frac{k\lambda}{y} \sin\theta \, d\theta = -\frac{k\lambda}{y}$,

   $E_y = \int_0^{\pi/2} \frac{k\lambda}{y} \cos\theta \, d\theta = \frac{k\lambda}{y}$.

For negative values of y, $E_y$ is downward, hence negative so the last expression is satisfactory. For negative y, $E_x$ is leftward, hence negative as it is for positive y. Thus, rewrite

$$E_x = -\frac{k\lambda}{|y|} \, .$$

8. (a) $E = 0$, $r < R_1$; $E = \sigma_1 R_1/\epsilon_0 r$, $R_1 < r < R_2$; and $E = (\sigma_1 R_1 + \sigma_2 R_2)/\epsilon_0 r$, $R_2 < r$. In each case $\underline{E}$ is radial, i.e., perpendicular to the cylinder axis.
(b) $\sigma_1 R_1 + \sigma_2 R_2 \simeq 0$ or $\sigma_1/\sigma_2 = -R_2/R_1$. Then for $R_1 < r < R_2$

$$E = \frac{\sigma_1 R_1}{\epsilon_0 r} = -\frac{\sigma_2 R_2}{\epsilon_0 r} \, .$$

(c) With $\sigma_1$ positive an end view is:

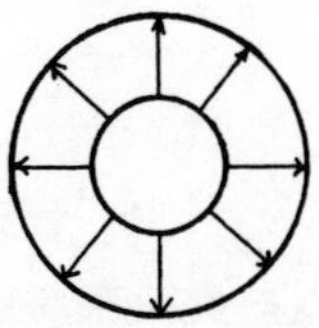

10. Consider a segment of arc of length $ds = R\,d\theta$ at an angle $\theta$ relative to the line OC. By symmetry its horizontal component is cancelled by a segment $ds = R\,d\theta$ at $-\theta$. Thus the component along OC is

$$dE = \frac{k\lambda \, ds}{R^2} \cos\theta = \frac{k\lambda}{R} \cos\theta \, d\theta \, .$$

Hence

$$E = \int_{-\theta_0}^{\theta_0} \frac{k\lambda}{R} \cos\theta \, d\theta = \frac{2k\lambda}{R} \sin\theta_0 \, .$$

## Chapter 31

EXERCISES:

2. (a) $8.85 \times 10^{-9}$ C/m$^2$; (b) $2.78 \times 10^{-12}$ C.
4. (a) $1.5 \times 10^{-7}$ C/m$^2$; (b) $8.48 \times 10^3$ N/C; (c) $7.5 \times 10^{-8}$ C/m$^2$; (d) $8.48 \times 10^3$ N/C.
6. (a) $1.13 \times 10^5$ N/C; (b) $1.13 \times 10^5$ N/C; (c) It is easiest to convince oneself that the answers are the same by considering a spherical shell in each case. Since $\sigma$ is the same, E will be the same. But E inside the metal is zero.
8. (a)

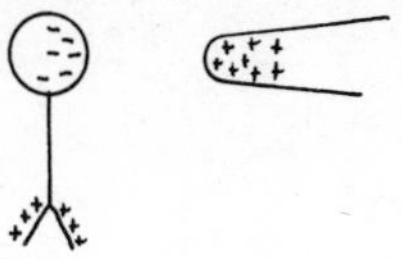

The rod induces negative charge on the ball which leaves positive charge on the electroscope leaves.

(b)

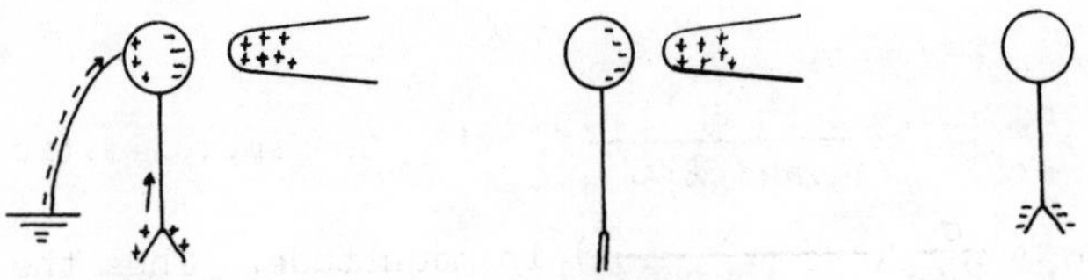

(c)

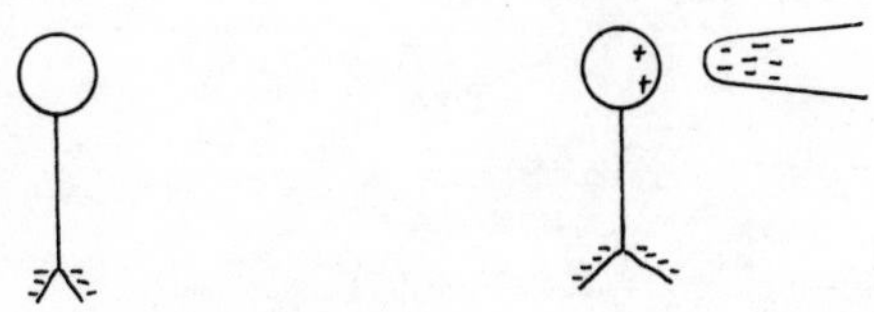

The leaves diverge further.

PROBLEMS:

2. (a) By symmetry E is radial. For $r < a$, Gauss' law yields $E 4\pi r^2 = q/\epsilon_0$ or $E = kq/r^2$, $k = 1/4\pi\epsilon_0$. For $a < r < b$, $E = 0$ because this is inside the metal. For $r > b$, $E = kq/r^2$.
(b)

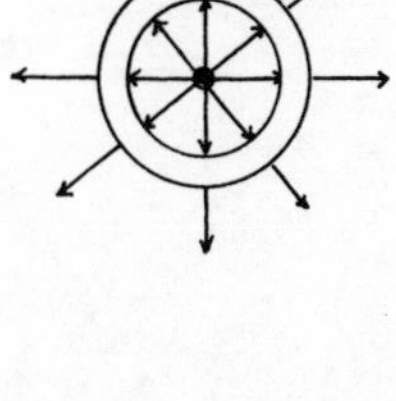

(c) $\sigma = q/4\pi b^2$ uniformly.

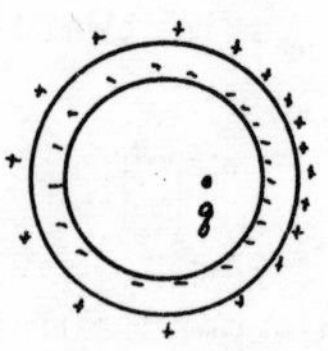


Charge distribution

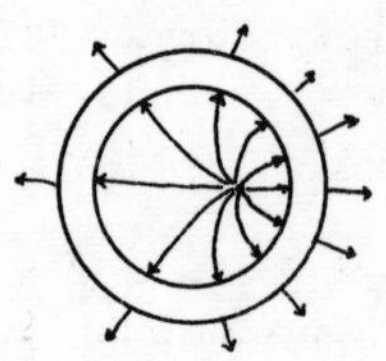

Force lines

## Chapter 32

EXERCISES:

2. (a) $5.65 \times 10^4$ N/C = $5.65 \times 10^4$ V/m, + x-direction;
 (b) 1.69 V; (c) $1.69 \times 10^{-5}$ J.
4. (a) 5000 V/m, positive plate is at the higher electric potential;
 (b) 5000 eV = $8.0 \times 10^{-16}$ J; (c) - 5000 eV, 5000 eV.
6. (a) - 3000 V/m; (b) - 3000 V/m; (c) 3000 V/m; (d) 0.
8. (a) V/m$^2$; (b) $\frac{1}{2} q_0 a x^2$; (c) $V(x) = -\frac{1}{2} a x^2$.
10. $E_r = -dV/dr$, $V = kq/r$, so $E_r = kq/r^2$.
12. (a) $3.6 \times 10^{-2}$ J; (b) - $1.2 \times 10^{-2}$ J.
14. (a) $1.2 \times 10^4$ V; (b) $6.0 \times 10^{-2}$ J; (c) Zero for both questions.
16.

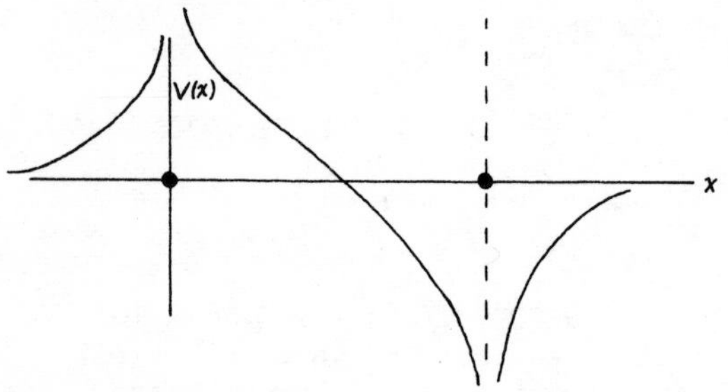


18.

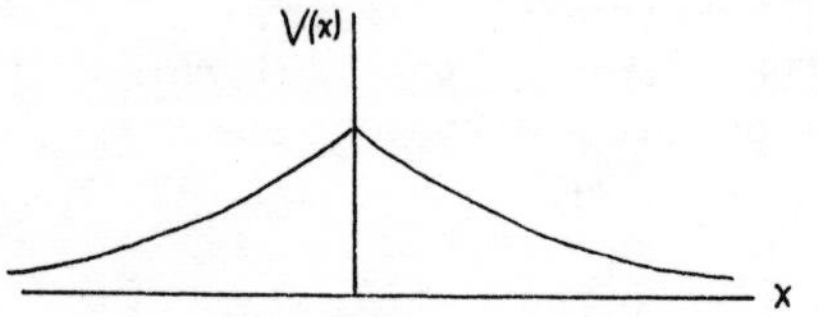


V(x) is a maximum at x = 0 and there, $E = kq/R^3$.

20. In general, $E = ke/r^2$, $r \geq R$ and $V = ke/r$;
 $E = ker/R^3$, $r \leq R$ and $V = -ker^2/2R^3 + 3ke/2R$.
 (a) At r = R, $E = ke/R^2 = 1.44 \times 10^{21}$ V/m and $V = 1.44 \times 10^6$ V.
 (b) At r = 0, E = 0 and $V = 2.16 \times 10^6$ V.
22. V = 10/r = n(20) where n = 1, 2, 3, 4, 5. Thus r = 1/2n meters locates the equipotentials.
24.

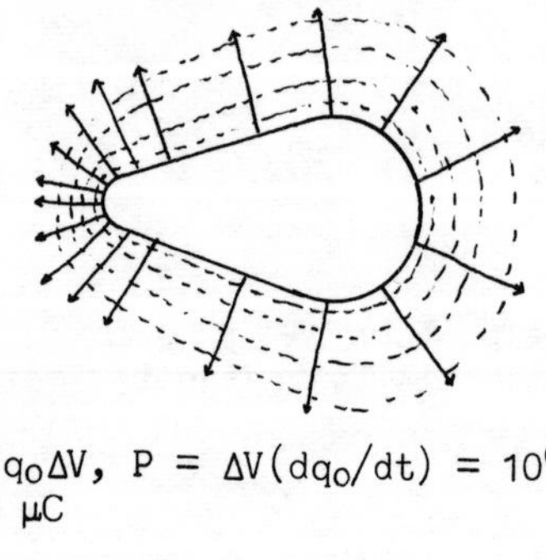

26. $W = q_0 \Delta V$, $P = \Delta V(dq_0/dt) = 10^6$ V$(2 \times 10^{-4}$ C/sec$)$ = 200 watts.
28. 3.33 μC

PROBLEMS:

2. $V = 2\pi k\sigma[(x^2 + R^2)^{1/2} - x] = 2\pi k\sigma[x(1 + R^2/x^2)^{1/2} - x]$

$$= 2\pi k\sigma[x + \frac{x}{2}(\frac{R}{x})^2 + \ldots - x] = \pi k\sigma \frac{R^2}{x} = \frac{kq}{x}.$$

4. (a) $3.75 \times 10^{-11}$ J = 234 MeV; (b) $2.67 \times 10^{16}$.

6. $V = -\frac{kq}{r} + \frac{kq}{r_1} = -\frac{kq}{r} + \frac{kq}{r[1 + \frac{a^2}{r^2} - 2\frac{a}{r}\cos\theta]^{1/2}}$, so

$$V \approx \frac{kaq\cos\theta}{r^2} = \frac{kpr\cos\theta}{r^3} = \frac{kpz}{r^3}.$$

8. For $a < r < b$, $E = kq/r^2$, thus $V_a - V_b = kq(1/a - 1/b)$.

10. For $r < a$: $E = kq/r^2$, $V = kq/r - kq(1/a - 1/b)$.
For $a < r < b$: $E = 0$, $V = kq/b$.
For $b < r$: $E = kq/r^2$, $V = kq/r$.
Thus, for $r > b$, $V = kq/r$. For $a < r < b$, $V$ = constant = $kq/b$. For $r < a$, $V = kq/r + C$. To determine C, V at $r = a$ is $kq/a + C = kq/b$. Thus the above values are found.

12. (a) $dq = \rho\, dV = 4\pi r^2\rho\, dr = 4\pi r^3\rho_0\, dr/R$;
(b) $q = \int_0^r 4\pi r^3\rho_0\, dr/R$ for $r < R$, $q = \rho_0\pi r^4/R$;

$q = \int_0^R 4\pi r^3\rho_0\, dr/R$ for $r > R$, $q = Q = \pi R^3\rho_0$.

(c) $4\pi Er^2 = \rho_0\pi r^4/R\epsilon_0$ for $r < R$ or $E = \rho_0 r^2/4R\epsilon_0$;
$4\pi Er^2 = \pi R^3\rho_0/\epsilon_0$ for $r > R$ or $E = \rho_0 R^3/4\epsilon_0 r^2$.
For $r > R$, $V = \rho_0 R^3/4\epsilon_0 r$. For $r < R$, $V = -\rho_0 r^3/12R\epsilon_0 + C$. To determine C use the fact that V at $r = R$ is continuous. Thus $C = \rho_0 R^2/3\epsilon_0$.
Notice that by using $\rho_0 = Q/\pi R^3$ these may be written as:
$E = kQ/r^2$, $V = kQ/r$ for $r > R$;
$E = kQr^2/R^4$, $V = -kQr^3/3R^4 + 4kQ/3R$ for $r < R$.

## Chapter 33

EXERCISES:

2. 711 μF
4. $8.85 \times 10^{-10}$ F
6. (a) 3000 V; (b) $6.0 \times 10^{-3}$ C.
8. (a) 1.54 pF; (b) 15.4 pC/m.
10. (a) 20.0 μF; (b) 6.0 V; (c) 60 μC, 120 μC.
12. (a) 24 μC; (b) 4.0 μF.
14. 2.0 μF
16. (a) 15.0 mJ; (b) 45.0 mJ.
18. (a) 0.8 μJ; (b) 0.2 μJ.
20. (a) $V_\infty = 0$, $V_R = kq/R$, so $dW = kq\, dq/R$; (b) $W = \int_0^Q \frac{k}{R} q\, dq = kQ^2/2R$.
22. 39.8 J/m$^3$
24. 2.71 nF
26. (a) 5; (b) 1.25; (c) 50.

PROBLEMS:

2. $\frac{1}{c} = \frac{1}{c_1} + \frac{1}{c_2} + \frac{1}{c_3} = \frac{c_2c_3 + c_1c_3 + c_1c_2}{c_1c_2c_3}$.

4. (a) For $r < R_1$, $E = 0$, $u = 0$.

For $R_1 < r < R_2$, $E = \frac{kQ}{r^2}$, $u = \frac{\epsilon_0}{2}\frac{k^2Q^2}{r^4}$.

For $R_2 < r$, $E = 0$, $u = 0$.

(b) $dU = \frac{\epsilon_0}{2}\frac{k^2Q^2}{r^4}(4\pi r^2)\, dr = \frac{1}{2} k \frac{Q^2}{r^2} dr$.

(c) $U = \frac{1}{2} kQ^2(\frac{1}{R_1} - \frac{1}{R_2})$; $V = kQ\int_{R_2}^{R_1}\frac{dr}{r^2} = kQ(\frac{1}{R_1} - \frac{1}{R_2})$, so $U = \frac{1}{2} QV$.

6. i) Parallel: 7.0 μF.
   ii) Series: 4/7 μF.
   iii) Two in series, other in parallel: 4 2/3 μF, 2 4/5 μF, 2 1/3 μF.
   iv) Two in parallel then series: 1 5/7 μF, 1 3/7 μF, 6/7 μF.

8. (a) Because the potential difference must be the same in order that the upper plate is at one common potential and similarly, the lower plate is an equipotential.
   (b) On the left side, $E = (\sigma_1 - \sigma_b)/\epsilon_0 = \sigma_1/2\epsilon_0$.
   On the right side, $E = \sigma_2/\epsilon_0$, so $\sigma_1 = 2\sigma_2$.
   (c) Before: $Q = \sigma_0 A$ which remains constant. Now we may also write $Q = \sigma_2 A/2 + \sigma_1 A/2$ so $\sigma_0 = (\sigma_1 + \sigma_2)/2 = 3\sigma_2/2$.
   Before: $V_b = Ed = \sigma_0 d/\epsilon_0 \equiv V$.
   After: $V_a = Ed = \sigma_2 d/\epsilon_0$, so $V_a = \frac{2}{3} V$.
   Before: $C_b = Q/V$.
   After: $C_a = Q/\frac{2}{3}V = \frac{3}{2} C_b = \frac{3}{2} \frac{\epsilon_0 A}{d}$.
   Note that regarded as a parallel combination one has $C = \frac{\epsilon_0 A}{2d} + \frac{\kappa\epsilon_0 A}{2d} = \frac{3\epsilon_0 A}{2d}$.

10. Proceed as in Problem 8 or regard as a parallel combination of two capacitors of area A/2, viz.,

$$C = \frac{\kappa_1 \epsilon_0 A}{2d} + \frac{\kappa_2 \epsilon_0 A}{2d} = \left(\frac{\kappa_1 + \kappa_2}{2}\right) \frac{\epsilon_0 A}{d}.$$

12. (a) $U = \frac{1}{2} CV^2 = \frac{1}{2} \frac{\epsilon_0 A}{x} \left(\frac{Qx}{A\epsilon_0}\right)^2 = \frac{1}{2} \frac{Q^2 x}{A\epsilon_0}$; (b) $dU = \frac{1}{2} \frac{Q^2}{A\epsilon_0} dx$;
   (c) $F\,dx = \frac{1}{2} \frac{Q^2}{A\epsilon_0} dx$, so $F = Q^2/2\epsilon_0 A$;
   (d) $E = Q/A\epsilon_0$, so $F = \frac{1}{2} QE$. The $\frac{1}{2}$ occurs because each plate contributes $Q/2A\epsilon_0$ to the electric field E. This is the field that exerts the force on the charge Q on the opposite plate.

14. The charge remains constant, so $U_i = \frac{1}{2} Q^2/\kappa C_0$ and $U_f = \frac{1}{2} Q^2/C_0$.
   Thus the work done is $U_f - U_i = \frac{1}{2} \frac{Q^2}{C_0} (1 - \frac{1}{\kappa}) = \frac{1}{2} \frac{\kappa^2 C_0^2 V^2}{C_0} (1 - \frac{1}{\kappa})$
   or Work $= \frac{1}{2} \frac{\epsilon_0 A}{d} V^2(\kappa^2 - \kappa) = 2.55$ μJ.

16. For $r < R$, $E = \frac{\rho r}{3\epsilon_0}$; for $r > R$, $E = \frac{\rho}{3\epsilon_0} \frac{R^3}{r^2}$.
   (a) $U = \frac{\rho^2 r^2}{18\epsilon_0}$ for $r < R$ and $U = \frac{\rho^2}{18\epsilon_0} \frac{R^6}{r^4}$ for $r > R$.
   (b) $dU = \frac{4\pi\rho^2 r^4}{18\epsilon_0} dr$ for $r < R$ and $dU = \frac{4\pi\rho^2}{18\epsilon_0} \frac{R^6}{r^2} dr$ for $r > R$.
   (c) Direct integration yields $\frac{4\pi\rho^2 R^5}{15\epsilon_0} = \frac{3}{5} k \frac{Q^2}{R}$.
   (d) For a spherical conductor, all the charge is on the surface whereas here the charge is also inside the surface. Hence on the average, the charges are closer together here, hence the higher energy. From a field point of view, E outside is the same as for the spherical conductor but in contrast to that case E inside is not zero. The excess over the $\frac{1}{2} k Q^2/R$ for the spherical conductor is just the energy stored inside the ball of charge.

## Chapter 34

EXERCISES:

2. $2.79 \times 10^{-2}$ cm/sec
4. (a) $5.93 \times 10^7$ m/sec; (b) $4.74 \times 10^{-3}$ A/cm$^2$; (c) 37.7 μA.
6. $\lambda R\omega$
8. (a) 10-gauge wire: 285 A/cm$^2$; 14-gauge wire: 719 A/cm$^2$;
   (b) 10-gauge wire: $2.10 \times 10^{-2}$ cm/sec; 14-gauge wire: $5.29 \times 10^{-2}$ cm/sec.
10. (a) 33.3 Ω; (b) 0.75 A.
12. (a) $4.2 \times 10^{-2}$ Ω; (b) 200 A; (c) $8.0 \times 10^6$ A/m$^2$.
14. 0.53 Ω
16. 1.96 V

18. 246 m
20. (a) $5.0 \times 10^{-3}$ A/m$^2$; (b) $3.68 \times 10^{-11}$ cm/sec; (c) $4.93 \times 10^{-14}$ sec;
(d) $4.93 \times 10^{-9}$ m.
22. (a) $4.50 \times 10^5$ N/C; (b) $\approx 0$.
24. 250 W
26. (a) 8.23 min; (b) 52.3 min.
28. (a) $\sqrt{2}/2$ A; (b) 7.07 V.
30. 180 J

PROBLEMS:
2. (a) 50 $\mu$A; (b) 5.0 W.
4. (a) 100 $\Omega$, 1.0 A; (b) $P = V^2/R$, so $dP/P = 2\,dV/V$; (c) 130 W.
6. (a) $R_1 = \rho_1 \frac{L}{A_1}$, $R_2 = \rho_2 \frac{L}{A_2}$ so $I_1 = \frac{V}{R_1}$ and $I_2 = \frac{V}{R_2}$; $I = V(\frac{1}{R_1} + \frac{1}{R_2})$.
(b) $R_{eq} = \dfrac{R_1 R_2}{R_1 + R_2} = \dfrac{\rho_1 \rho_2}{\rho_1 A_2 + \rho_2 A_1} L$.
8. (a) $e^{\alpha(t - 20^\circ C)} \approx 1 + \alpha(t - 20^\circ C)$, so $\rho \approx \rho_{20}[1 + \alpha(t - 20^\circ C)]$.
(b) $e^{\alpha(t - 20^\circ C)} \approx 1 + \alpha(t - 20^\circ C) + \frac{1}{2}\alpha^2(t - 20^\circ C)^2$ or $\rho = \rho_{20}[1 + x + \frac{1}{2}x^2]$
where $x = \alpha(t - 20^\circ C)$. Thus, $\rho - \rho_{20} \approx \rho_{20} x(1 + \frac{1}{2}x)$.
(c) $-.02 \leqslant x \leqslant .02$;
(d) 14.9° to 25.1°C.

Chapter 35

EXERCISES:
2. (a) 240 W, 228 W; (b) $4.32 \times 10^4$ J; (c) $2.16 \times 10^3$ J.
4. (a) 5.0 $\Omega$; (b) 30 V.
6. (a) 4.0 A; (b) 2.0 V; (c) 1.0 $\Omega$.
8. (a) Graph $18/(3 + R)$; (b) Graph $18^2R/(3 + R)^2$; (c) 3.0 $\Omega$, 27 W.
10. (a) In 4 ohm, 2/3 A; in 3 ohm, 8/9 A; in 6 ohm, 14/9 A;
(b) 84/9 = 9.33 V; (c) 32/3 W, 8 W.
12. (a) 1.0 $\Omega$; (b) 6 A, 4 A, 2 A.
14. (a) 18/5 = 3.6 $\Omega$; (b) 2 and 7 ohm resistors, 4/3 A; 6 ohm resistor, 2 A.
16. (a) 18 V; (b) 2 A.
18. (a) Path acb: $R_{eq} = 2R$; path adb: $R_{eq} = 2R$; thus $R_{eq} = R$.
(b) None, there is no potential difference between c and d.
20. (a) $R_{eq} = R_1R_2/(R_1 + R_2) = R_1x/(1 + x)$.
(b)

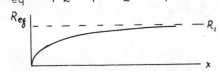

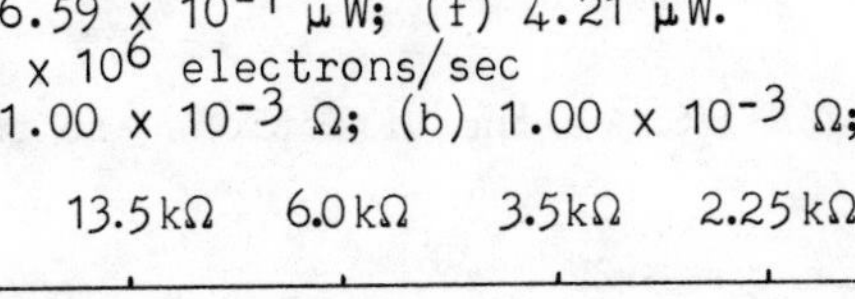


22. (a) $3.0 \times 10^{-2}$ J; (b) $U = Q^2/2C = \frac{Q_0^2}{2C}(e^{-t/t_c})^2 = U_0 e^{-2t/t_c}$.
24. (a) 5.0 $\mu$C; (b) $4.61 \times 10^{-2}$ sec.
26. (a) 5.19 $\mu$C; (b) $8.12 \times 10^{-1}$ $\mu$A; (c) $8.12 \times 10^{-1}$ $\mu$A; (d) 4.87 $\mu$W;
(e) $6.59 \times 10^{-1}$ $\mu$W; (f) 4.21 $\mu$W.
28. $6.25 \times 10^6$ electrons/sec
30. (a) $1.00 \times 10^{-3}$ $\Omega$; (b) $1.00 \times 10^{-3}$ $\Omega$; (c) 31 cm.
32.

∞  13.5 kΩ  6.0 kΩ  3.5 kΩ  2.25 kΩ  1.5 kΩ  1.0 kΩ  640 Ω  375 Ω  167 Ω  0

34. $R_1 = .001\ \Omega$, $R_2 = .009\ \Omega$, $R_3 = .090\ \Omega$.
36. (a) 9800 $\Omega$; (b) $dR_x/R_x = 100\,dL/[L(100 - L)]$, then $dL/L \approx 0.2\%$, so
$dR_x/R_x = 0.10 = 10\%$. Thus $dR_x \approx 980\ \Omega$. (c) Choose $R_4 \approx 10{,}000\ \Omega$.

PROBLEMS:
2. $P = \mathcal{E}^2R/(r + R)^2$, $dP/dR = \mathcal{E}^2(r - R)/(r + R)^3 = 0$ yields $R = r$. Then $P = \mathcal{E}^2/4r$.
4. (a) Parallel; (b) series.
6. (a) $t_c = RC = K\epsilon_0 \frac{A}{d} \rho \frac{d}{A} = K\epsilon_0\rho$; (b) $t_c = 7965$ sec $\approx 8000$ sec.

8. (a) Parallel; (b) series; (c) series; (d) series.

10. (a) $R_{ab} = .09\ \Omega$, $R_{bc} = 0.81\ \Omega$, $R_{cd} = 8.1\ \Omega$, $R_{de} = 81\ \Omega$; (b) 0.9 mA.

12. (a) $I = \mathcal{E}/\bar{R}$, $\bar{R} = R_a + \dfrac{RR_v}{R + R_v}$, $V = (\mathcal{E}/\bar{R})\ \dfrac{RR_v}{R + R_v}$.

$$\therefore\ R_c = \frac{RR_v}{R + R_v} \quad \text{or} \quad \frac{1}{R_c} = \frac{1}{R_v} + \frac{1}{R}.$$

(b) $I = \mathcal{E}/(R + R_a)$, $V = \mathcal{E}$, so $R_c = R + R_a$.

(c) Using (a), $R_c$ is always $\le R$, so $R_c \ge 0.95R$ leads to $R \le \frac{1}{0.95} R_v - R_v$ or $R \le 526\ \Omega$. Using (b), $R_c$ is always $\ge R$ so we want $R_c \le 1.05\ R$ or $R \ge 20R_a = 0.2\ \Omega$.

14. $I = I_1 + I_2 + I_3$ so $\dfrac{1}{R_{eq}} = \dfrac{1}{R_1} + \dfrac{1}{R_2} + \dfrac{1}{R_3}$.

## Chapter 36

EXERCISES:

2. (a) $3.6\,\underset{\sim}{k}$ mN; (b) $3.6\,\underset{\sim}{k}$ mN; (c) 0; (d) $(3.6\,\underset{\sim}{k} - 3.6\,\underset{\sim}{j})$ mN.
4. $-1.04 \times 10^{-12}\,\underset{\sim}{k}$ N
6. 0.27 N
8. $(0.08\,\underset{\sim}{i} - 0.06\,\underset{\sim}{j})$ N
10. $\text{A-m}^2 = \dfrac{\text{C}}{\text{sec}}\ \text{m}^2 = \dfrac{\text{N-m}}{(\text{N/C})(\text{sec/m})} = \dfrac{\text{J}}{\text{T}}$.
12. (a) $2.83 \times 10^{-1}$ A-m$^2$; (b) 5.66 A-m.
14. A-m$^2$ = J/T so T = J/A-m$^2$ = N-m/A-m$^2$ = N/A-m.
16. (a) $0.96\,\underset{\sim}{k}$ N-m; (b) 0; (c) 0; (d) $0.679\,\underset{\sim}{k}$ N-m.
18. (a) $I = q/T = q/(2\pi/\omega) = q\omega/2\pi$; $m = q\omega\pi r^2/2\pi = q\omega r^2/2$;
    (b) $L = Mvr = M\omega r^2$ so $m = qL/2M$ and since the directions are the same, $\underset{\sim}{m} = q\underset{\sim}{L}/2M$.
20. (a) $mv^2/r = qvB$ so $mv = qBr = p$; (b) $E_k = p^2/2m = B^2q^2r^2/2m$.
22. From Exercise 20, $r = \sqrt{2mE_k}/Bq$ so $r_d/r_p = (\sqrt{m_d/m_p})(q_p/q_d) = \sqrt{2}$.
    $r_\alpha/r_p = (\sqrt{m_\alpha/m_p})(q_p/q_\alpha) = 1$.
24. $\omega = qB/m$ so $\omega_1/\omega_2 = (q_1/q_2)(m_2/m_1) = (q_1m_2)/(q_2m_1)$. Thus $\omega_d/\omega_\alpha = 1$ and $\omega_d/\omega_p = \frac{1}{2}$.
26. (a) $2 \times 10^6$ m/sec; (b) 20.9 keV; (c) 11.4 eV.
28. (a) 63.1 cm; (b) $r_{26}/r_{24} = \sqrt{26/24} = 1.041$ so the difference is (.041)(63.1 cm) = 2.58 cm.
30. (a) $\omega = qB/m = 1.92 \times 10^8\ \text{sec}^{-1}$, so f = 30.5 MHz; (b) 32.3 cm; (c) 200.
32. (a) a; (b) b.
34. $v_d = 7.35 \times 10^{-5}$ m/sec and $B = \mathcal{E}_H/(v_dW) = 6.8 \times 10^5\,\mathcal{E}_H$ T.
    (a) 1.36 T; (b) 3.57 T; (c) 5.44 T.

PROBLEMS:

2. (a) $F = Ma = ILB$ so $a = BIL/M$ and $v = (BIL/M)t$; (b) to the right;
   (c) $B \ge \mu_s Mg/IL$.
4. $d\underset{\sim}{F} = I\ d\underset{\sim}{\ell} \times \underset{\sim}{B}$ so $\underset{\sim}{F} = \int_{\substack{\text{along}\\\text{wire}}} I\ d\underset{\sim}{\ell} \times \underset{\sim}{B} = I(\int d\underset{\sim}{\ell}) \times \underset{\sim}{B}$ or $\underset{\sim}{F} = I\underset{\sim}{L} \times \underset{\sim}{B}$.
6. (a) $dm = A\ dI = (\pi x^2)(\lambda\ dx/T) = (\pi x^2)(\lambda\ dx\,\omega/2\pi) = \frac{1}{2}\lambda\omega x^2\ dx$;
   (b) $m = \int dm = \frac{1}{6}\lambda\omega\ell^3 = \frac{1}{6}Q\omega\ell^2$;
   (c) $L = I\omega = \omega M\ell^2/3$, so $m = \frac{1}{2}\frac{Q}{M}(\frac{1}{3}M\omega\ell^2) = \frac{1}{2}\frac{Q}{M}L$. Since the directions are the same, $\underset{\sim}{m} = \frac{1}{2}\frac{Q}{M}\underset{\sim}{L}$.
8. $\frac{1}{2}mv^2 = qV$ so $v = \sqrt{2qV/m}$ and $mv^2/r = qvB$. Thus $q/m = 2V/B^2r^2$.
10. (a) $dW = \tau\ d\theta = mB \sin\theta\ d\theta$;
    (b) $W = \int_\theta^{90^\circ} mB \sin\theta\ d\theta = mB\cos\theta$;
    (c) $U(\theta) - U(90^\circ) = -\int_\theta^{90^\circ} \tau\ d\theta = -mB\cos\theta$. So with $U(90^\circ) = 0$, $U(\theta) = -\underset{\sim}{m} \cdot \underset{\sim}{B}$.
    (d) No, merely write m = NIA.

## Chapter 37

EXERCISES:

2. $-9.6 \times 10^{-12} \underset{\sim}{i}$ T
4. (a) $1.50 \times 10^{-4}$ T; (b) $3.0 \times 10^{-5}$ T; (c) $7.5 \times 10^{-6}$ T.
6.

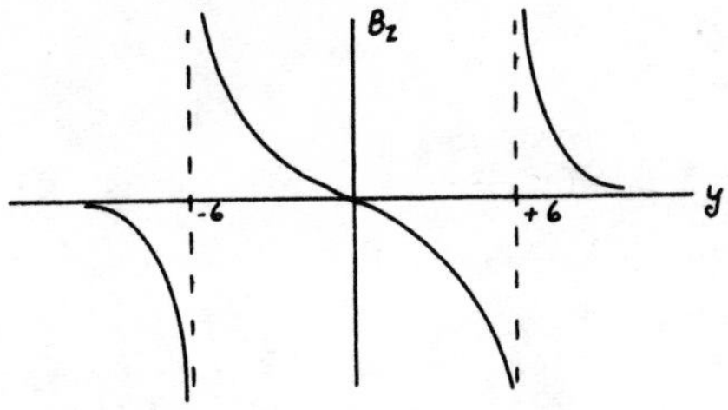


8.

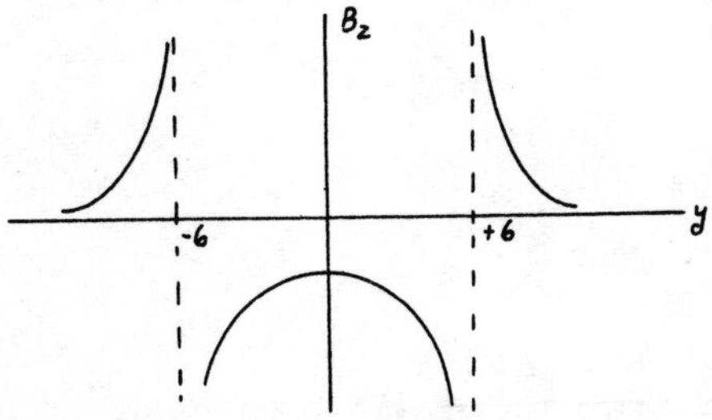


10. $6.67 \times 10^{-4}$ N/m
12.

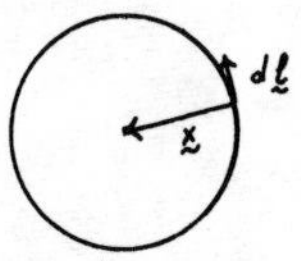


$$\underset{\sim}{x} = -\hat{\underset{\sim}{r}}, \quad |d\underset{\sim}{B}| = k_m \frac{I|d\underset{\sim}{\ell} \times \underset{\sim}{x}|}{x^2} \quad \text{so} \quad dB = k_m \frac{I\,d\ell}{R^2}.$$

$$\text{Then } B = \int_0^{2\pi} k_m \frac{IR\,d\theta}{R^2} = \frac{\mu_o I}{2R}.$$

14. 11.1 A
16. $\frac{\mu_o I}{4}\left(\frac{1}{R_1} - \frac{1}{R_2}\right)$
18. 78.3 A
20. (a) $7.79 \times 10^{-4}$ N/m, up; (b) $5.20 \times 10^{-5}$ T, right.
22. For $r < R$, $\underset{\sim}{B} = 0$; for $r > R$, $B = \mu_o I/2\pi r$ where the lines of $\underset{\sim}{B}$ circle the cylinder according to the right-hand rule.
24. (a) Inside, $B = \mu_o I/2\pi r$; (b) outside, $B = 0$.
26. $\oint \underset{\sim}{B} \cdot d\underset{\sim}{\ell} = BL$ where L is the vertical length of the path. But $BL = \mu_o I = 0$ which implies $B = 0$ just inside. Move the path to the left so that the right side is along this line where $B = 0$ and repeat. Ultimately, $B = 0$ everywhere.
28. (a) $6.70 \times 10^{-3}$ T; (b) 2.01 A-m$^2$; (c) 6.70 A-m; (d) $4.08 \times 10^{-8}$ T.
30. $3.98 \times 10^5$ A/m
32. (a) 0.25 T; (b) 6.0 A-m; (c) 0.9 A-m$^2$.
34. $\varphi_m = (5.0 \times 10^{-4} \text{ weber}) \cos\theta$.

| θ | 0° | 30° | 60° | 90° |
|---|---|---|---|---|
| $\varphi_m$ | $5 \times 10^{-4}$ | $4.33 \times 10^{-4}$ | $2.5 \times 10^{-4}$ | 0 |

36. $1.89 \times 10^{-6}$ weber
38. $\varphi_m = 3.02 \times 10^{-2}\, \underset{\sim}{i} \cdot \hat{\underset{\sim}{n}}$.
    (a) $3.02 \times 10^{-2}$ weber; (b) 0; (c) $2.13 \times 10^{-2}$ weber; (d) 0; (e) $1.81 \times 10^{-2}$ weber.
40. $\oint \underset{\sim}{B} \cdot d\underset{\sim}{\ell} = B\,2\pi r = \mu_o(I + I_d) = \mu_o I_d = \mu_o J_d A = \mu_o J_d \pi r^2$ so $B = \mu_o J_d r/2$.

PROBLEMS:

2. (a) .2 x $10^{-16}$ N, opposite the current; (b) $3.2 \times 10^{-16}$ N, away from the wire;
   (c) [illegible]
4. (a)

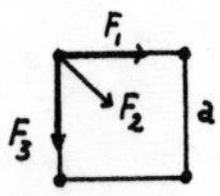


$$F_1 = F_3 = \frac{2k_m I^2}{a}, \quad F_2 = \frac{2k_m I^2}{a\sqrt{2}}.$$

$$F = \frac{3\sqrt{2}\,k_m I^2}{a} \text{ directed toward the center.}$$

(b)

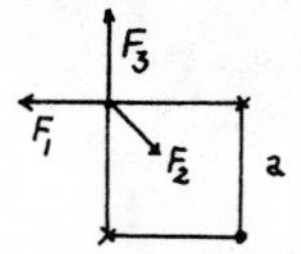


$$F_1 = F_3 = \frac{2k_m I^2}{a}, \quad F_2 = \frac{2k_m I^2}{a\sqrt{2}}.$$

$$F = \frac{\sqrt{2}\,k_m I^2}{a} \text{ directed away from the center.}$$

6. (a) $F = q^* \dfrac{\mu_0 I}{2r}$ directed from N toward S pole of magnet;

(b) $F' = (2\pi r I)B$ directed along S to N magnet direction;

(c) $2\pi r I B = \dfrac{q^* \mu_0 I}{2r}$ or $B = \dfrac{\mu_0}{4\pi}\dfrac{q^*}{r^2}$.

8.

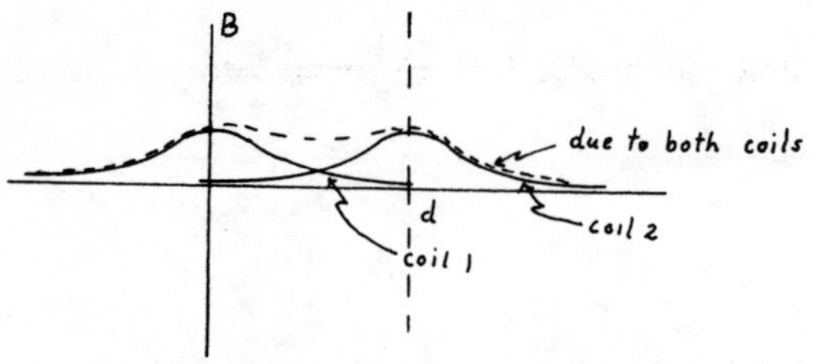


10.

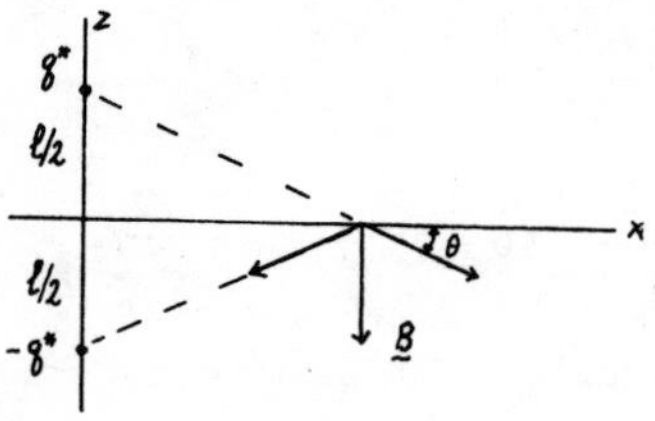


$$\underset{\sim}{B} = -2\,\frac{\mu_0}{4\pi}\,\frac{q^*}{(x^2 + \ell^2/4)}\sin\theta\,\underset{\sim}{k}$$

$$= -\frac{\mu_0}{4\pi}\,\frac{q^*}{(x^2 + \ell^2/4)}\,\frac{2(\ell/2)}{\sqrt{x^2 + \ell^2/4}}\,\underset{\sim}{k}$$

$$\approx -\frac{\mu_0}{4\pi}\,\frac{IA}{x^3}\,\underset{\sim}{k}.$$

12. (a) $dB_x = \dfrac{2k_m I' A}{(x^2 + R^2)^{3/2}} = \dfrac{2k_m A n I\,dx}{(x^2 + R^2)^{3/2}}$.

$$B = 2k_m(\pi R^2) n I \int_{-x_1}^{x_2} \frac{dx}{(x^2 + R^2)^{3/2}} = \frac{\mu_0}{2} R^2 n I \left. \frac{x}{R^2\sqrt{x^2 + R^2}} \right|_{-x_1}^{x_2}$$

$$= \frac{\mu_0}{2} n I \left[ \frac{x_2}{\sqrt{x_2^2 + R^2}} + \frac{x_1}{\sqrt{x_1^2 + R^2}} \right].$$

(b) With $\cos\theta_1 = x_1/\sqrt{x_1^2 + R^2}$ and $\cos\theta_2 = x_2/\sqrt{x_2^2 + R^2}$,

$$B = \frac{\mu_0}{2} n I[\cos\theta_1 + \cos\theta_2].$$

(c) For $x_1$ and $x_2$ each much greater than R, $\cos\theta_1 \approx 1$ and $\cos\theta_2 \approx 1$, so $B \approx \mu_0 n I$.

At each end either $\cos\theta_1 = 1$, $\cos\theta_2 \approx 0$ or vice-versa, so $B \approx \dfrac{\mu_0}{2} n I$.

14. (a) $\varphi_m = N(\mu_0 n I)\pi R_1^2$; (b) $\varphi_m = (\mu_0 n I)\pi R_3^2$.

16. (a) $B = \dfrac{k_m I}{y}(\sin\theta_1 + \sin\theta_2) = \dfrac{\mu_0}{4\pi}\dfrac{I}{R}\left(\dfrac{a}{\sqrt{a^2 + R^2}} + \dfrac{a}{\sqrt{a^2 + R^2}}\right)$ or

$$B = \frac{\mu_0}{2\pi}\frac{I}{R}\frac{a}{\sqrt{a^2 + R^2}}.$$

(b) By symmetry, $E_y = 0$. Then

$$E_x = \frac{1}{4\pi\epsilon_0}\left[\frac{Q}{(y^2 + a^2)}\frac{a}{\sqrt{y^2 + a^2}} + \frac{Q}{(y^2 + a^2)}\frac{a}{\sqrt{y^2 + a^2}}\right] = \frac{1}{2\pi\epsilon_0}\frac{Qa}{(y^2 + a^2)^{3/2}}.$$

(c) $d\varphi_E = \dfrac{1}{2\pi\epsilon_0}\dfrac{Qa}{(r^2 + a^2)^{3/2}}(2\pi r\,dr) = \dfrac{Q}{\epsilon_0}\dfrac{a r\,dr}{(r^2 + a^2)^{3/2}}$.

(d) $\epsilon_0 \varphi_E = Qa \int_0^R \frac{r\,dr}{(r^2 + a^2)^{3/2}} = Qa \left[ - \frac{1}{(r^2 + a^2)^{1/2}} \right]_0^R$

$$= Qa \left[ \frac{1}{a} - \frac{1}{(R^2 + a^2)^{1/2}} \right] = Q \left[ 1 - \frac{a}{(R^2 + a^2)^{1/2}} \right].$$

(e) $I_d = \epsilon_0 \frac{d\varphi_E}{dt} = \frac{dQ}{dt} \left[ 1 - \frac{a}{\sqrt{R^2 + a^2}} \right]$, so $I + I_d = - \frac{dQ}{dt} \frac{a}{\sqrt{R^2 + a^2}}$ since $I = - dQ/dt$. (The $+Q$ must decrease for the current to be moving to the right.) Hence $I + I_d = Ia/\sqrt{R^2 + a^2}$.

$$\oint \underset{\sim}{B} \cdot d\underset{\sim}{\ell} = \mu_0 (I + I_d) = \frac{\mu_0 Ia}{\sqrt{a^2 + R^2}} = B\,2\pi R \text{ so that } B = \frac{\mu_0 I}{2\pi R} \frac{a}{\sqrt{a^2 + R^2}}.$$

## Chapter 38

EXERCISES:

2. $v = V/BL = (6.0)/(5.0 \times 10^{-2} \times 0.3) = 400$ m/sec.
4. (a) $\mathcal{E} = 3.6$ V; (b) 3.0 A; (c) 1.8 N; (d) 10.8 W; (e) 10.8 W.
6.

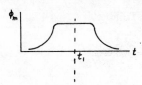

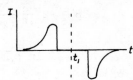

8. (a) $\pi \times 10^{-4}$ V; (b) $7.85 \times 10^{-4}$ A; (c) $2.47 \times 10^{-7}$ W.
10. $Q = \int_{t_1}^{t_2} I\,dt$, but $I = \frac{\mathcal{E}}{R} = \frac{N}{R} \frac{d\varphi_m}{dt}$ so $Q = \frac{N}{R} \int_1^2 d\varphi = \frac{N}{R} [\varphi_{m_2} - \varphi_{m_1}]$.
12. (a) $\varphi_m$ has maximum magnitude at $t = 2$ sec at which time $\mathcal{E} = 0$;
    (b) $\varphi_m = 0$ at $t = 0$ and at $t = 4$ sec. At the former $\mathcal{E} = -0.4$ V while at $t = 4$ sec, $\mathcal{E} = +0.4$ V.
14. $\varphi_{m_2} = (0.7\text{ G})A$ and $\varphi_{m_1} = -(0.7\text{ G})A$, so (see Exercise 10)
    $Q = \frac{1000}{15} [7 \times 10^{-5} - (-7 \times 10^{-5})](3.0 \times 10^{-2}) = 2.80 \times 10^{-4}$ C.
16. $\oint \underset{\sim}{E} \cdot d\underset{\sim}{\ell} = E(2\pi r) = -\pi r^2\, dB/dt$, so in magnitude $E = \frac{r}{2} \frac{dB}{dt}$ for $r < R$.
    $\oint \underset{\sim}{E} \cdot d\underset{\sim}{\ell} = E(2\pi r) = -\pi R^2\, dB/dt$ or $E = \frac{R^2}{2r} \frac{dB}{dt}$ for $r > R$.
18. $\varphi_m = LI_0 \sin(2\pi ft)$, $\mathcal{E} = -LI_0\, 2\pi f \cos(2\pi ft)$.
20. (a) $\varphi_{m_1} = N_1 (\frac{\mu_0 N_2 I_2}{\ell_2}) A_2 = \mu_0 N_1 (\frac{N_2}{\ell_2}) A_2 I_2$;
    (b) $B = 0$ in the region between the solenoid and coil;
    (c) $\varphi_{m_1} = MI_2$ so $M = \frac{N_1 N_2 \mu_0 A_2}{\ell_2}$;
    (d) One would need to evaluate B everywhere along the long solenoid which is somewhat difficult.
22. (a) $I/2 = I(1 - e^{-4/t_c})$, so $t_c = 5.77$ sec; (b) $L = Rt_c = 28.85$ H.
24. $t = t_c \ln \frac{1}{[1 - I/I_f]}$.

| $I/I_f$ | 90 % | 99 % | 99.9 % |
|---|---|---|---|
| $t/t_c$ | 2.30 | 4.61 | 6.91 |

26. $I = I_0 e^{-t/t_c}$ so $dI/dt|_{t=0} = -I_0/t_c$. If one had $I = I_0 - (I_0/t_c)t$, then $I = 0$ at $t = t_c$.
28. (a) $5.36 \times 10^{-2}$ J; (b) $4.47 \times 10^2$ J/m$^3$; (c) $3.35 \times 10^{-2}$ T; (d) $4.47 \times 10^2$ J/m$^3$.
30. (a) At t = 1 sec: 47.7 W, and at t = 100 sec: 48.0 W;
    (b) At t = 1 sec: 47.4 W, and at t = 100 sec: 48.0 W;
    (c) At t = 1 sec: 0.3 W, and at t = 100 sec: 0 W.

32. Magnetic energy density, $\eta_m = \frac{1}{2} B^2/\mu_0$ and $c = 1/\sqrt{\epsilon_0\mu_0}$.
Electric energy density, $\eta_e = \frac{1}{2} \epsilon_0 E^2 = \frac{1}{2} \epsilon_0 c^2 B^2 = \frac{1}{2} B^2/\mu_0$.

34. Henry $= \frac{N}{A^2}$ m $= \frac{J}{A^2}$; farad $= \frac{C}{V} = \frac{C^2}{J}$.

So $\frac{1}{\sqrt{LC}} = \left[\frac{\text{joule}}{\text{coul}^2} \frac{\text{amp}^2}{\text{joule}}\right]^{\frac{1}{2}} = \left[\frac{1}{\text{coul}^2} \frac{\text{coul}^2}{\text{sec}^2}\right]^{\frac{1}{2}} = \text{sec}^{-1}$.

36. $\omega = 2\pi \cdot 60 = 1/\sqrt{8 \times 10^{-5} L}$ so $L = 8.80 \times 10^{-2}$ H = 88 mH.

PROBLEMS:

2. (a) At some point a distance r from the long wire the magnetic field is $B = \mu_0 I/2\pi r$ directed into the paper. When the charges in the short wire have reached equilibrium there will exist an electric field $E = v\mu_0 I/2\pi r$ directed to the right. Thus

$$V_a - V_b = -\int_b^a \underset{\sim}{E} \cdot d\underset{\sim}{\ell} = \frac{v\mu_0 I}{2\pi} \int_d^{d+\ell} dr/r$$

or

$$V = \frac{v\mu_0 I}{2\pi} \ln \left(\frac{d+\ell}{d}\right).$$

(b) $d\varphi_m = B\,dA = Bvt\,dr$

$$= \frac{\mu_0 I}{2\pi r} vt\,dr.$$

$$\varphi_m = \frac{\mu_0 I}{2\pi} vt \ln \left(\frac{d+\ell}{d}\right).$$

Thus $\mathcal{E} = \frac{d\varphi_m}{dt} = \frac{\mu_0 I v}{2\pi} \ln \left(\frac{d+\ell}{d}\right)$.

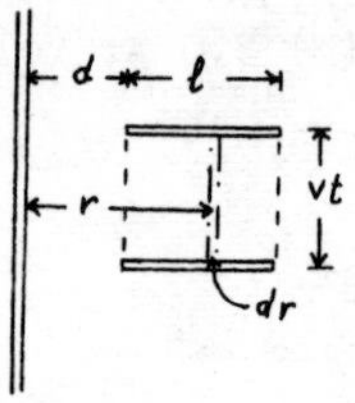


4. $\mathcal{E}_1 = L_1\, dI/dt$ and $\mathcal{E}_2 = L_2\, dI/dt$ since neither coil affects the other by direct flux. Then $\mathcal{E} = \mathcal{E}_1 + \mathcal{E}_2 = (L_1 + L_2)\, dI/dt$ or $\mathcal{E} = L\, dI/dt$ so that $L = L_1 + L_2$.

6. $\mathcal{E} = \mathcal{E}_1 = \mathcal{E}_2$ because of the parallel connection. Then $I = I_1 + I_2$ and so $dI/dt = dI_1/dt + dI_2/dt$. Thus

$$\frac{\mathcal{E}}{L} = \frac{dI}{dt} = \frac{\mathcal{E}_1}{L_1} + \frac{\mathcal{E}_2}{L_2} = \frac{\mathcal{E}}{L_1} + \frac{\mathcal{E}}{L_2} \quad \text{or} \quad \frac{1}{L} = \frac{1}{L_1} + \frac{1}{L_2}.$$

8. (a) $\oint \underset{\sim}{B} \cdot d\underset{\sim}{\ell} = B\,2\pi r = \mu_0 I_{inside}$, so $B = \mu_0 I/2\pi r$, $r_1 < r < r_2$; $B = 0$ for $r < r_1$ and $r > r_2$.

(b) $\eta_m = \frac{1}{2}\frac{B^2}{\mu_0} = \frac{1}{2\mu_0}\left(\frac{\mu_0^2 I^2}{4\pi^2 r^2}\right) = \frac{\mu_0 I^2}{8\pi^2 r^2}$;

(c) $dU_m = \frac{\mu_0 I^2 \ell\, dr}{4\pi r}$, so $U_m = \frac{\mu_0 I^2 \ell}{4\pi} \ln \frac{r_2}{r_1}$;

(d) $U_m = \frac{1}{2} LI^2$ so $\frac{L}{\ell} = \frac{\mu_0}{2\pi} \ln \frac{r_2}{r_1}$.

10. $B = \mu_0 I/2\pi r$ so $\varphi_m = (\mu_0 I\ell/2\pi) \ln (r_2/r_1) = LI$.

12. (a) $\varphi_m = NBA \cos\theta$ where $\theta$ is the angle between $\underset{\sim}{B}$ and the normal to the coil and $\theta = \omega t$. Thus, in magnitude, $\mathcal{E} = NBab\omega \sin \omega t$.
(b) 275 $\text{sec}^{-1}$.

14. (a) $F = B\ell\left(\frac{\mathcal{E} - Bv\ell}{R}\right) = m\frac{dv}{dt}$;
(b) $v = v_0(1 - e^{-t/\tau})$ is the correct solution with $v_0 = \mathcal{E}/B\ell$ and $\tau = mR/(B\ell)^2$. The terminal velocity is $v_0$.
(c) When $v = v_0$ = a constant, $F = 0$, so $\mathcal{E} = Bv_0\ell$ and thus the induced emf has the same value as the applied potential but the opposite sense. Thus the current is zero.

16. $\oint \underset{\sim}{E} \cdot d\underset{\sim}{\ell} = EL$ where L is the path length along the left side of the path. But since there is no magnetic field, this yields $E = 0$. One can repeat the argument moving leftward across the gap and conclude that $E = 0$, contrary to hypothesis.

18. (a) $Q = Q_o e^{-Rt/2L} \cos \omega' t$, so

$$I = \frac{dQ}{dt} = -Q_o \frac{R}{2L} e^{-Rt/2L} \cos \omega' t - \omega' Q_o e^{-Rt/2L} \sin \omega' t$$

$$= -I_o[\sin \omega' t + (\frac{R}{2L\omega'}) \cos \omega' t] e^{-Rt/2L}, \quad I_o = \omega' Q_o .$$

(b) The form $A \sin x + B \cos x = R \sin (x + \alpha)$ yields $R = \sqrt{A^2 + B^2}$ and $\tan \alpha = B/A$. Thus here

$$I = -I_o[1 + (\frac{R}{2L\omega'})^2]^{\frac{1}{2}} \sin (\omega' t + \delta) e^{-Rt/2L}$$

where $\tan \delta = R/2L\omega'$. Since $\cos \delta = [1 + (R/2L\omega')^2]^{-\frac{1}{2}}$ one has

$$I = -\frac{I_o}{\cos \delta} \sin (\omega' t + \delta) e^{-Rt/2L} .$$

## Chapter 39

EXERCISES:

2. Because of assumed spherical symmetry, $\oint \underset{\sim}{H} \cdot d\underset{\sim}{A} = H 4\pi r^2 = q^*$.
4. (a) Treat near pole as a disc of pole density $\sigma^* = M$, then $\underset{\sim}{H}$ due to this disc is $(\sigma^*/2)(-\hat{\underset{\sim}{k}})$ since the right pole is positive. This yields $-\underset{\sim}{M}/2$ to $\underset{\sim}{H}$. Treat the far pole as an isolated point pole a distance L away. This yields $(1/4\pi)(q^*/L^2)(-\hat{\underset{\sim}{k}}) = -(1/4\pi)(\pi a^2/L^2)\underset{\sim}{M}$. Thus,
$$\underset{\sim}{H} = -\frac{\underset{\sim}{M}}{2}[1 + \frac{a^2}{2L^2}].$$
(b) $\underset{\sim}{B} = \mu_o(\underset{\sim}{H} + \underset{\sim}{M}) = \frac{\mu_o \underset{\sim}{M}}{2}[1 - \frac{a^2}{2L^2}]$.

(c) $\underset{\sim}{H}_{interior} = \frac{\underset{\sim}{M}}{2}[1 - \frac{a^2}{2L^2}]$ and $\underset{\sim}{B}_{interior} = \frac{\mu_o \underset{\sim}{M}}{2}[1 - \frac{a^2}{L^2}]$.

Thus, there is a discontinuity in $\underset{\sim}{H}$ (due to the pole) but none in $\underset{\sim}{B}$.
6. $\underset{\sim}{H} = 8.0 \times 10^3 \hat{\underset{\sim}{k}}$ A/m, $\underset{\sim}{M} = 1.84 \times 10^{-1} \hat{\underset{\sim}{k}}$ A/m, $\underset{\sim}{B} = 1.01 \times 10^{-2}$ T.
8. $m = M_s/n = 0.61/n$, $n = 8.92 \times 10^{28}$, so $\chi = M_s/\mu_B n = 0.585$. Thus $m = 0.585\ m_b$.
10. $M = \frac{1}{3}\frac{mB}{kT} M_s$. For paramagnetic materials, $\chi_m \ll 1$ and $B \approx \mu_o H$, so $M = \chi_m B/\mu_o = \frac{1}{3}\frac{mB}{kT} M_s$. Hence $\chi_m = m\mu_o M_s/3kT$.
12. (a) $M = fM_s = \frac{1}{3}\frac{mB}{kT} M_s$ so $f = mB/3kT$. (b) $f = 7.46 \times 10^{-4}$.
14. $B = 8.66 \times 10^{-1}$ T, $M = 6.87 \times 10^5$ A/m.
16. (a) $10^4$ A/m; (b) $1.36 \times 10^6$ A/m; (c) 137.

PROBLEMS:

2. 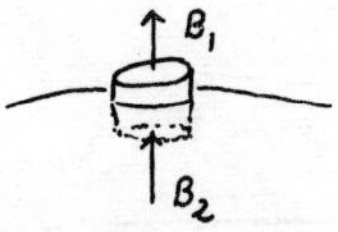


$$\oint \underset{\sim}{B} \cdot \hat{\underset{\sim}{n}}\, dA = B_1 A - B_2 A = 0 \text{ so } B_1 = B_2.$$

4. (a) $H = 500$ A/m, $M = 1.11 \times 10^6$ A/m; (b) 2200;
(c) $B_{gap} = B_{inside} = 1.40$ T;
$H_{gap} = H_{ring} + \sigma^* = 500 + 1.11 \times 10^6 \approx 1.11 \times 10^6$ A/m.
6. $\chi_m = M/H = \frac{n}{3}[-\frac{Zq^2r^2}{4m_e}B]/H = -\frac{nZq^2r^2}{12m_e}$. For the given data, $\chi_m = -17.6$.
8. $L = N\Phi/I$, $\Phi = BA = \mu_o(1 + \chi_m)HA$ and $H = nI$, so
$L = n\ell\mu_o(1 + \chi_m)nIA/I = \mu_o n^2 \kappa_m \ell A = \mu n^2 \ell A$.

## Chapter 40

EXERCISES:

2. 3300 G
4. $I = \frac{\mathcal{E}_m}{R} \sin \omega t$, $P = \frac{\mathcal{E}_m^2}{R} \sin^2 \omega t$, $P_{ave} = \frac{R}{T}\int_0^T I^2\, dt = I_{rms}^2 R$.

6. (a) $2.65 \times 10^6\ \Omega$; (b) $2.65 \times 10^4\ \Omega$; (c) $2.65 \times 10^1\ \Omega$.

8.

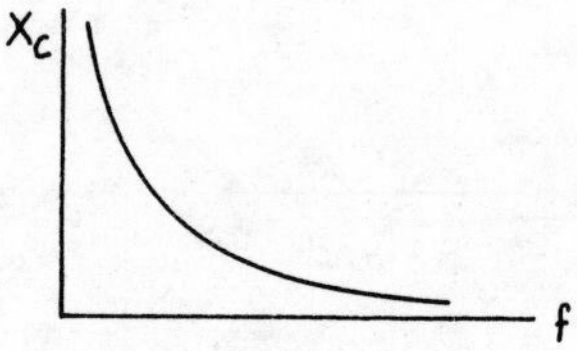


10. $P = (I_m \cos \omega t)(\mathcal{E}_m \sin \omega t) = \omega C \mathcal{E}_m^2 \sin \omega t \cos \omega t = \frac{\mathcal{E}_m^2 \omega C}{2} \sin 2\omega t$.

$$P_{ave} = \frac{\omega}{2\pi} \int_0^{\omega/2\pi} \frac{\mathcal{E}_m^2 \omega C}{2} \sin 2\omega t\, dt = -\frac{\omega C \mathcal{E}_m^2}{8\pi} \cos 2\omega t \Big]_0^{\omega/2\pi} = 0 .$$

12. $P = (-I_m \cos \omega t)(\mathcal{E}_m \sin \omega t) = -\frac{\mathcal{E}_m^2}{2\omega L} \sin 2\omega t$.

$$P_{ave} = \frac{\omega}{2\pi} \int_0^{\omega/2\pi} \left(-\frac{\mathcal{E}_m^2}{2\omega L}\right) \sin 2\omega t\, dt = 0 .$$

14. (a) $L = X_L/\omega = 100/(2\pi \cdot 80) = 0.20$ H; (b) 200 $\Omega$.

16. $$I_m = \frac{\mathcal{E}_m}{\sqrt{(X_C - X_L)^2 + R^2}} = \frac{\mathcal{E}_m}{\sqrt{(\frac{1}{\omega C} - \omega L)^2 + R^2}} = \frac{\omega \mathcal{E}_m}{\sqrt{(\frac{1}{C} - \omega^2 L)^2 + \omega^2 R^2}}$$

$$= \frac{\omega \mathcal{E}_m}{\sqrt{L^2(\frac{1}{LC} - \omega^2) + \omega^2 R^2}} = \frac{\omega \mathcal{E}_m}{\sqrt{L^2(\omega_0^2 - \omega^2)^2 + \omega^2 R^2}} .$$

18. (a) $\tan \varphi = \frac{X_C - X_L}{R} = \frac{(1/C) - \omega^2 L}{\omega R} = \frac{L(\omega_0^2 - \omega^2)}{\omega R}$ .

(b) $\tan \varphi \approx L\omega_0^2/R\omega$ for $\omega \ll \omega_0$. Now $\tan(\frac{\pi}{2} - \theta) = 1/\tan \theta$ and for small $\theta$, $\tan \theta \approx \theta$, so $\varphi \approx (\pi/2) - (R\omega/L\omega_0^2)$. As a check, for very low $\omega$, $X_C$ dominates and $\varphi$ is nearly $\pi/2$.

(c) For $\omega \gg \omega_0$, $X_L$ dominates Z and $\varphi \approx -\pi/2$. One has $\tan \varphi \approx -\frac{L}{R}\omega$ which is large. Then $\tan(-\frac{\pi}{2} + \theta) = -1/\tan \theta$, so $\varphi \approx -\frac{\pi}{2} + \frac{R}{L\omega}$.

20. $C = 1/(L\omega_0^2)$, so at $f_0 = 500$ kHz, $C = 0.101\ \mu$F while at $f_0 = 1600$ kHz, $C = 9.90$ nF. Thus C varies between these limits.

22. In general, for $\tan \varphi = (X_C - X_L)/R$ fixed, the frequencies at which $\cos \varphi$ is the power factor are $\omega = \frac{1}{2}\{\pm \frac{R}{L} \tan \varphi + [(\frac{R}{L} \tan \varphi)^2 + \omega_0^2]^{\frac{1}{2}}\}$.

24. $\cos \varphi = R/Z$ and for $X_L = 0$, $Z = \sqrt{X_C^2 + R^2}$, so

$$\cos \varphi = \frac{R}{\sqrt{(\frac{1}{\omega C})^2 + R^2}} = \frac{R\omega C}{\sqrt{1 + (R\omega C)^2}} .$$

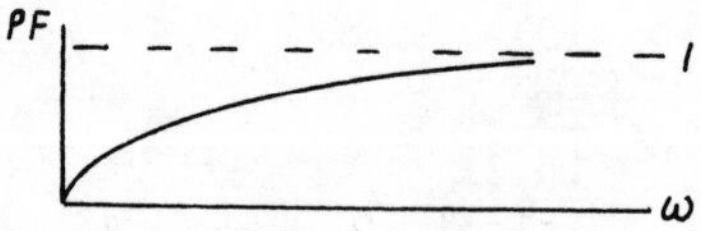


26. For no capacitance, $PF = R/\sqrt{(\omega L)^2 + R^2}$.

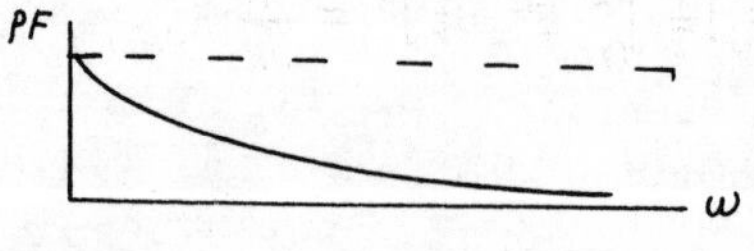


28.

| f (Hz) | $X_C$ ($\Omega$) | $X_L$ ($\Omega$) | $\tan \varphi$ | $\varphi$ (deg) | $\cos \varphi$ |
|---|---|---|---|---|---|
| 900 | 88.4 | 56.6 | 6.37 | 81.08 | 0.155 |
| 1100 | 72.3 | 69.1 | 0.65 | 32.85 | 0.840 |
| 1300 | 61.2 | 81.7 | -4.09 | -76.27 | 0.237 |

PROBLEMS:

2. (a) $\cos \varphi = 60/(120)(1.5) = 1/3$.

(b) $R = \frac{1}{3} Z$ and $P_{ave} = \frac{\mathcal{E}_{rms}^2}{Z} \cos \varphi = 60$ so $Z = 80\ \Omega$ and $R = 26\ 2/3\ \Omega$.

(c) $Z = \sqrt{X_L^2 + R^2}$ so $X_L = \sqrt{(80)^2 - (80/3)^2} = \frac{160}{3}\sqrt{2}\ \Omega$ and $X_L = \omega L$ so $L = 0.20$ H.

(d) $\tan\varphi = -X_L/R = -2.83$, so $\varphi = -70.5^\circ$, the current lags.

4. $L < 8.5$ mH or $L > 32$ mH and $I_m < 3.0$ A.

6. (a) $\tan\varphi = \dfrac{X_C - X_L}{R} = \dfrac{(1/\omega C) - \omega L}{R} = \dfrac{1}{\omega}\left[\dfrac{(1/C) - \omega^2 L}{R}\right]$

$$= \frac{L}{R}\,\frac{\omega_0^2 - \omega^2}{\omega} = \frac{L\omega_0}{R}\,\frac{\omega_0^2 - \omega^2}{\omega\omega_0} = Q\,\frac{\omega_0^2 - \omega^2}{\omega\omega_0}.$$

(b) $\tan\varphi = Q\,\dfrac{(\omega_0 - \omega)(\omega_0 + \omega)}{\omega\omega_0} \approx Q\,\dfrac{(\omega_0 - \omega)(2\omega_0)}{\omega_0^2} = 2Q\,\dfrac{(\omega_0 - \omega)}{\omega_0}.$

(c) Graph is of $\tan^{-1}\dfrac{Q(1 - x^2)}{x}$.

8. Use Kirchhoff's laws.

(a) $\mathcal{E} - I_R R = 0$ or $I_R = \dfrac{\mathcal{E}_m \sin\omega t}{R}$.

(b) $-L\dfrac{dI_L}{dt} + I_R R = 0$ or $-L\dfrac{dI_L}{dt} = -\mathcal{E}_m \sin\omega t$ so

$$I_L = \frac{\mathcal{E}_m}{X_L}\sin(\omega t - 90^\circ) = -\frac{\mathcal{E}_m}{X_L}\cos\omega t.$$

(c) $I = I_R + I_L = \dfrac{\mathcal{E}_R}{R}\sin\omega t - \dfrac{\mathcal{E}_m}{X_L}\cos\omega t \equiv I_m \sin(\omega t - \varphi)$.

Expand and equate coefficients of $\sin\omega t$, $\cos\omega t$ to find $I_m\cos\varphi = \mathcal{E}_m/R$ and $I_m\sin\varphi = \mathcal{E}_m/X_L$. Thus $I_m^2 = \mathcal{E}_m^2\left(\dfrac{1}{R^2} + \dfrac{1}{X_L^2}\right)$ or $I_m = \mathcal{E}_m/Z$ and

$Z^{-2} = R^{-2} + X_L^{-2}$. $\tan\varphi = R/X_L$.

10. $P = \dfrac{\mathcal{E}_m^2}{Z}\left[\sin^2\omega t\cos\varphi + \sin\omega t\cos\omega t\sin\varphi\right]$, so

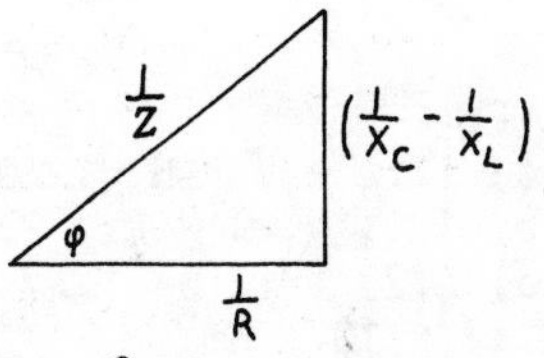


$P_{ave} = \frac{1}{2}\dfrac{\mathcal{E}_m^2}{Z}\cos\varphi$ and the power factor is $\cos\varphi$.

$\tan\varphi = R\left(\dfrac{1}{X_C} - \dfrac{1}{X_L}\right)$ so one has $\cos\varphi = Z/R$ and

$\dfrac{1}{Z^2} = \dfrac{1}{R^2} + \left(\dfrac{1}{X_C} - \dfrac{1}{X_L}\right)^2$. When $X_C = X_L$, $Z = R$ and $\cos\varphi = 1$ or $\varphi = 0^\circ$.

12. $L = 1/\omega_0^2 C = 4.0$ mH, $I_m = 10/100 = 100$ mA. Note that $I_{rms} = 70.7$ mA is the current measured by the ac ammeter.

## Chapter 41

EXERCISES:

2. (a) $E_{rms} = \left[\frac{1}{T}\int_0^T E^2\,dt\right]^{\frac{1}{2}} = \dfrac{1}{\sqrt{2}}E_0$.

$$I_{ave} = \frac{c}{T}\int_0^T \frac{W}{Vol}\,dt = \frac{c}{T}\,\frac{E_0^2}{\mu_o c^2}\int_0^T \sin^2(kr - \omega t) = \frac{E_0^2}{2\mu_0 c}.$$

So $E_{rms} = \dfrac{1}{\sqrt{2}}E_0 = \left[\dfrac{E_0^2}{2}\right]^{\frac{1}{2}} = \sqrt{\mu_0 c I_{ave}}$.

(b) $B_{rms} = \left[\frac{1}{T}\int_0^T B^2\,dt\right]^{\frac{1}{2}} = \left[\dfrac{E_0^2}{c^2}\,\frac{1}{T}\int_0^T \sin^2(kx - \omega t)\right]^{\frac{1}{2}} = \dfrac{1}{\sqrt{2}}\,\dfrac{E_0}{c}$

or $B_{rms} = E_{rms}/c$.

4. $[S] = [E][H] = \dfrac{N}{C}\,\dfrac{A}{m} = \dfrac{N}{A\text{-sec}}\,\dfrac{A}{m} = \dfrac{N\text{-m}}{sec}\,\dfrac{1}{m^2} = \dfrac{W}{m^2}$.

PROBLEMS:

2. (a) $\oint_c \underset{\sim}{B}\cdot d\underset{\sim}{\ell} = \mu_0\epsilon_0 \dfrac{d}{dt}\int \underset{\sim}{E}\cdot\hat{n}\,dA = \mu_0\epsilon_0 \dfrac{dE_y}{dt}\,\Delta x\,\Delta z$ and

$$\oint_c \underset{\sim}{B} \cdot d\underset{\sim}{\ell} = B_z(x_1)\Delta z - B_z(x_2)\Delta z = -\frac{\partial B_z}{\partial x}\Delta x\,\Delta z \quad \text{where } x_2 - x_1 = \Delta x.$$

Thus $\frac{\partial B_z}{\partial x} = -\mu_0\epsilon_0 \frac{\partial E_y}{\partial t}$ .

(b) $\frac{\partial E_y}{\partial x} = -\frac{\partial B_z}{\partial t}$ so $\frac{\partial^2 E_y}{\partial t \partial x} = -\frac{\partial^2 B_z}{\partial t^2}$ , but

$$\frac{\partial^2 E_y}{\partial t\partial x} = \frac{\partial^2 E_y}{\partial x\partial t} = \frac{\partial}{\partial x}\left[\frac{\partial E_y}{\partial t}\right] = -\frac{1}{\mu_0\epsilon_0}\frac{\partial}{\partial x}\left(\frac{\partial B_z}{\partial x}\right) .$$

Thus $\frac{\partial^2 B_z}{\partial t^2} - \frac{1}{\mu_0\epsilon_0}\frac{\partial^2 B_z}{\partial x^2} = 0$ .

4. Use small areas as shown.

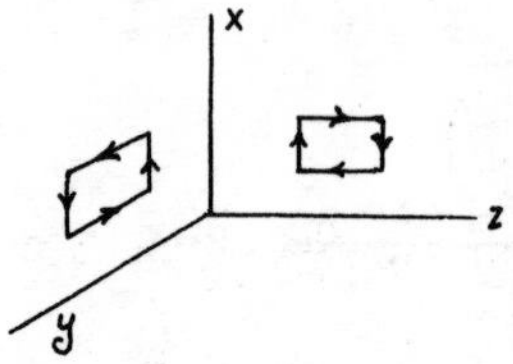


6. (a) $R = V/I = E\ell/I = \rho\,\ell/A$ , so $E = \rho I/\pi a^2$ and $\underset{\sim}{E}$ is in the direction of the current.

(b) $\oint \underset{\sim}{B} \cdot d\underset{\sim}{\ell} = B(2\pi r) = \mu_0 I + \mu_0\epsilon_0 \frac{d}{dt}\int \underset{\sim}{E} \cdot \underset{\sim}{\hat{n}}\, dA$ or $2\pi r B = \mu_0 I + 0$ .

The last term vanishes because E and I are steady. Thus $|\underset{\sim}{B}| = \mu_0 I/2\pi r$ and the direction of $\underset{\sim}{B}$ is given by the right hand rule.

(c) $S = \frac{1}{\mu_0} EB = \frac{1}{\mu_0}\frac{\rho I}{\pi a^2}\frac{\mu_0 I}{2\pi a} = \frac{\rho I^2}{2\pi^2 a^3}$ and the direction of $\underset{\sim}{S}$ is radially inward.

(d) $\Phi = \frac{\rho I^2}{2\pi^2 a^3} 2\pi a L = I^2\left(\frac{\rho L}{\pi a^2}\right) = I^2 R$ .

## Chapter 42

EXERCISES:

2. (a) 12.4 keV; (b) 1240 Mev.
4. (a) $1.11 \times 10^{15}$ Hz, 271 nm; (b) 1.62 V; (c) 0.388 V.
6. (a) 4.73 eV; (b) 1.47 V.
8. $2.43 \times 10^{-1}$ nm
10. $$r_0 = \frac{\hbar^2}{mke^2} = \frac{(6.625 \times 10^{-19})^2(1/2\pi)^2}{(9.11 \times 10^{-31})(8.988 \times 10^9)(1.602 \times 10^{-19})^2} .$$

    $r_0 = 5.29 \times 10^{-11}$ m = 0.529 Å.
12. (a) 6562.1 Å, 4860.8 Å, 4340.0 Å; (b) 1.890 eV, 2.551 eV, 2.857 eV.
14. 4052.3 nm, 2625.9 nm, 2166.1 nm; series limit 1458.8 nm.
16. (a) For the electron $\lambda_e = h/p_e \approx ch/E_e$; for the photon $\lambda = c/f = c/(E/h) = ch/E$. If $E = E_e$, $\lambda_e = \lambda$.

    (b) $\lambda \approx ch/E = 1240$ eV-nm/$10^8$ eV $= 1.24 \times 10^{-5}$ nm.
18. $\lambda = h/p = hc/[2(mc^2)(KE)]^{\frac{1}{2}} = 1240$ eV-nm/$[2(938 \text{ MeV})(1 \text{ MeV})]^{\frac{1}{2}}$

    or $\lambda = 2.86 \times 10^{-14}$ m.
20. (a) $\Delta x\,\Delta p \geq h/4\pi = hc/4\pi c = 1240$ eV-nm/$4\pi c = 98.7$ eV-nm/c.

    So $\Delta p \geq 987$ eV/c $= 5.26 \times 10^{-25}$ kg-m/sec.

    (b) Use $KE = p^2/2m = (987 \text{ eV/c})^2/2m = (987)^2(\text{eV})^2/2mc^2$

    or $KE = \frac{(987)^2(\text{eV})^2}{2(5.12 \times 10^5 \text{ eV})} = 9.51 \times 10^{-1}$ eV .

PROBLEMS:

2. (a) 7.96 W/m$^2$; (b) $2.40 \times 10^{15}$ photons/sec.
4. (a) $p_1c + mc^2 = p_2c + \sqrt{(mc^2)^2 + p_e^2c^2}$, so $\sqrt{(mc^2)^2 + p_e^2c^2} = (p_1 - p_2)c + mc^2$ .

    Square each side and divide by $c^2$.

    $$p_e^2 = (p_1 - p_2)^2 + 2mc(p_1 - p_2)$$

$$= p_1^2 + p_2^2 - 2p_1p_2 + 2mc(p_1 - p_2).$$

(b) $p_e^2 = p_1^2 + p_2^2 - 2p_1p_2 \cos\theta$. Thus $mc(p_1 - p_2) = p_1p_2(1 - \cos\theta)$.

(c) $\frac{h}{p_1p_2}(p_1 - p_2) = \frac{h}{mc}(1 - \cos\theta)$, so $\frac{h}{p_1} - \frac{h}{p_2} = \frac{h}{mc}(1 - \cos\theta)$

or $\lambda_1 - \lambda_2 = \frac{h}{mc}(1 - \cos\theta)$.

6. $f(\lambda) = \dfrac{8\pi hc\lambda^{-5}}{e^{hc/\lambda kT} - 1} = \dfrac{8\pi(kT)^5x^5}{(hc)^4(e^x - 1)}$, $x = \dfrac{hc}{\lambda kT}$.

As $\lambda$ runs 0 to $\infty$, $x$ runs $\infty$ to 0, and $d\lambda = -\frac{hc}{kTx^2}\,dx$, so

$\eta = \int_0^\infty f(\lambda)\,d\lambda = \dfrac{8\pi(kT)^5}{(hc)^4}\dfrac{(hc)}{kT}\int_0^\infty \dfrac{x^3\,dx}{e^x - 1}$ or $\eta = \alpha T^4$

where $\alpha = \dfrac{8\pi k^4}{(hc)^3}\int_0^\infty \dfrac{x^3\,dx}{e^x - 1}$.

8. (a) $f_{rev} = \dfrac{v}{2\pi r} = (\dfrac{n\hbar}{mr})/(2\pi r) = \dfrac{n\hbar}{2\pi m}\dfrac{1}{r^2}$, so $f_{rev} = \dfrac{n\hbar}{2\pi m}(\dfrac{mkZe^2}{n^2\hbar^2})^2 = \dfrac{k^2Z^2e^4m}{2\pi\hbar^3n^3}$.

(b) $\dfrac{1}{n_2^2} - \dfrac{1}{n_1^2} = \dfrac{1}{(n-1)^2} - \dfrac{1}{n^2} = \dfrac{n^2 - n^2 + 2n - 1}{n^2(n-1)^2} \approx \dfrac{2}{n^3}$ for $n \gg 1$.

(c) $f_{rad} = \dfrac{k^2Z^2e^4m}{4\pi\hbar^3}\left[\dfrac{1}{n_2^2} - \dfrac{1}{n_1^2}\right] \approx \dfrac{k^2Z^2e^4m}{4\pi\hbar^3}\dfrac{2}{n^3} = f_{rev}$.

10. (a) $E_n = \dfrac{p_n^2}{2m} = (\dfrac{h}{\lambda_n})^2/2m$, and $\lambda_n = 2L/n$, so $E_n = \dfrac{n^2h^2}{8mL^2} = n^2[\dfrac{h^2}{8mL^2}] = n^2E_1$.

(b) $E_1 = \dfrac{h^2}{8mL^2} = \dfrac{(hc)^2}{8(mc^2)L^2} = \dfrac{[1240 \text{ eV-nm}]^2}{8(0.511 \times 10^6 \text{ eV})(10^{-10} \text{ m})^2} = 37.6$ eV.

(c) 205 MeV.

## SAMPLE EXAMINATIONS

Granvil C. Kyker, Jr.

In this section several sample one-hour examinations are presented, such as might be used in a typical two-semester course using Tipler's PHYSICS. They are meant to illustrate one of the many ways in which you might arrange such a course and write one-hour tests for it. I don't mean for you to regard them, as they stand, as a very specific model; your students, the kind of test questions you prefer, and your choice of what material to cover would surely be different from mine. Some of the various ways in which material for a two-semester course might be selected are also discussed in the Preface to this Instructor's Manual.

I conceive of the course as occupying two full-length semesters, in a lecture format, for more or less average first-year physics, chemistry, and engineering majors in a four-year college. The students have either taken, or are taking concurrently, their first course in calculus. I give three one-hour examinations, spaced about evenly through each semester. I imagine choosing material as follows:

Semester I. Cover Chapters 2 through 13 fairly thoroughly, except for skimping on collision theory in Chapter 11 and on the last few sections of Chapter 13. The sections on fluids from Chapters 5 and 7, and a brief treatment of simple harmonic motion from Chapter 14, are covered together after talking about conservation of energy, and Chapter 16 briefly at the end of the "mechanics" segment. Cover Chapters 17 through 19 pretty thoroughly in about the last four weeks or so of the term.

Semester II. Cover the basic conceptual development of wave motion fairly well, omitting almost all of Chapter 23 as well as the last section or two of Chapters 24 and 25 and skipping Chapter 27 entirely except for a brief discussion, in lecture, of image formation. Electricity and magnetism are covered through Chapter 39, omitting Chapter 31 and the last half of Chapter 35; electromagnetic radiation is given about one lecture, but students aren't assigned Chapter 41. Chapters 28 and 42 are skipped altogether, because most of these students take a Modern Physics course next.

This has the students reading the equivalent of just a touch over one chapter a week; in my own experience, this is about what you can get away with. This particular selection follows my own prejudices - again, there are many different ways to choose two semesters' worth of material.

A few words about the way I write tests might be in order. I usually intend them to be only moderately difficult; if most of the scores are bunched around zero - or for that matter, around 100 - I really haven't learned anything. I tend always to include some verbal questions of the one-or-two-sentence answer type, and a derivation question if appropriate to the material; but the largest part of an exam is always numerical problems. At least one of the latter should be difficult enough so that most students won't answer it fully.

On the problem of exactly what reference material to include on the quiz paper: I think I have tried every possibility at one time or another - giving just necessary numbers, giving a selection of formulas, and so forth. In my experience, open-book tests in elementary courses haven't worked well, and yet memorization for its own sake doesn't appeal to me at all. What seems to me to have worked best is the "crib card" system: I let each student make up for himself, and use on the exam, as much reference material as he can get on one face of a 3" x 5" file card. The need to make his own selection sometimes turns out to be of substantial help to the student in reviewing material. It also teaches them to write small.

At the end of each semester of the course, I would give a comprehensive final exam. This would be selected from the whole semester's material, but the kinds of questions would be just about the same as on the hour quizzes.

Semester I

TEST NO. 1

Tipler, Chapters 2 to 7 Name: ______________________

Show all your work on the test paper; scratch paper may be used but will not be taken in. Take the time to make whatever you do as clear as possible, circle answers, etc. Each of you may use one face of a 3" x 5" file card of notes, formulas, or whatever, and slide rules or pocket calculators may be used freely. Otherwise no reference materials of any kind are allowed.

Time allowed: 1 hour

---

1. (22 pts) A boy standing on the roof of a building, 24 ft above the ground, throws a ball straight up at a speed of 18 ft/sec. When does it hit the ground?

2. (16 pts) In no more than a sentence or two each, give a clear explanation or definition of each of the following:

   (a) Inertia

   (b) Vector quantity

   (c) Centripetal acceleration

   (d) Fictitious force

3. (15 pts) In the sketch at right, the pulley can be considered frictionless; if the weight is being hauled upward with an acceleration of 4 ft/sec$^2$, what must be the tension in the rope?

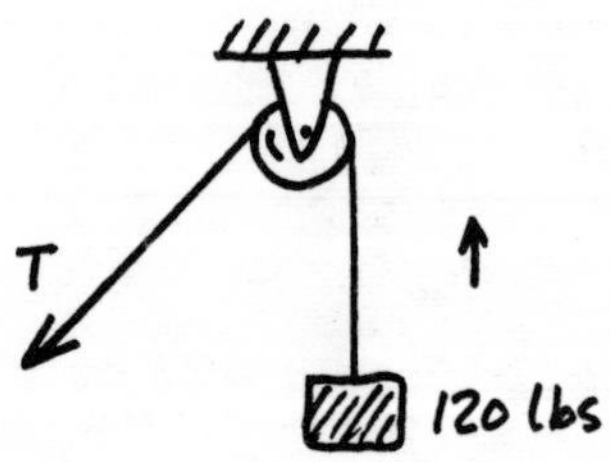

4. (25 pts) In the situation sketched at right, find an expression for the acceleration of mass M. Friction in the pulley can be ignored.

5. (22 pts) A crate with a mass of 190 kg is slid across a floor with an initial speed of 8 m/sec. If the crate comes to rest after sliding 3.3 m, what is the coefficient of friction between it and the floor?

Semester I

TEST NO. 2

Tipler, Chapters 8 to 12 Name: ______________________

Show all your work on the test paper; no scratch paper will be handed in. Take your time and make what you do as clear and legible as possible. Each of you may use his own list of formulas, numbers, etc. - whatever you can fit on one side of a 3" x 5" file card - and a calculator or slide rule if you wish. No other notes, papers, or references of any kind are allowed.

Time allowed: 1 hour

---

1. (8 pts) Define each of the following in a sentence or two, no more:

   (a) Conservative force

   (b) Coefficient of restitution

2. (26 pts) In the sketch at right, the pendulum is 1.5 m long and has a mass of 6.0 kg. A 15-gm bullet is fired into it (and stopped in it) and the pendulum, initially at rest, swings back to a maximum angle of $26^{\circ}$.

   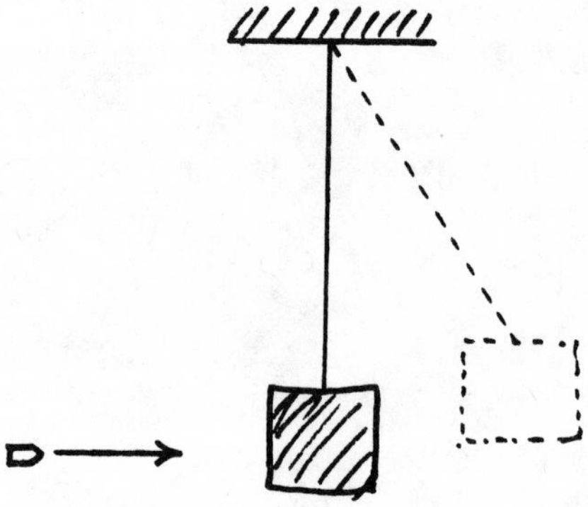

   (a) Briefly but carefully, comment on whether and how conservation of energy and conservation of momentum can be applied to this situation.

   (b) What was the initial speed of the bullet?

   $\cos(26^{\circ}) = 0.8988 \quad \sin(26^{\circ}) = 0.4383$

3. (20 pts) The position of a particle undergoing simple harmonic motion is given by

$$x = A \sin(\omega t + \phi)$$

where $\omega$ is the angular frequency. Show that the total energy of the oscillating particle is

$$E = \frac{1}{2} kA^2$$

4. (8 pts) An ice cube floating in a glass of water slowly melts. As it does, how does the water level in the glass change?

5. (20 pts) A cylinder rolls, without slipping, a distance of 2.2 m down a $25^\circ$ incline. If it started from rest, what is its speed at the bottom?

$\cos(25^\circ) = 0.9063$ $\sin(25^\circ) = 0.4225$

6. (18 pts) In the sketch at right, the board is 20 ft long and weighs 100 lb; the supports are 6 ft from either end. How far toward the end can the 160-lb man walk before the board starts to tip up?

Semester I

TEST NO. 3

Tipler, Chapters 13 to 19 Name: ______________________________

Show all your work on the quiz paper: no scratch paper will be accepted when you hand in your test. Make your work as clear as possible, circle answers, etc. The usual 3" x 5" card reference rule applies.

Time limit: 1 hour

---

1. (24 pts) Define, explain, or otherwise identify

   (a) Vector product

   (b) Cavendish experiment

   (c) State variable

   And distinguish between

   (d) Adiabatic and diathermic walls

   (e) Reversible and irreversible processes

2. (18 pts) Show that Kepler's law of areas follows from conservation of angular momentum.

3. (14 points) In conditions typical of the centers of stars, the average kinetic energy of particles is around 1000 electron volts. What is the corresponding temperature?

4. (20 pts) 50 gm of ice at $0^{o}C$ are dropped into 120 gm of water at $30^{o}C$. Assuming no heat loss to the surroundings, the system comes to equilibrium at what temperature? Take the specific heats of ice and water as 0.50 and 1.0 cal/gm-$^{o}C$, respectively.

5. (24 pts) A certain steam engine runs between reservoir temperatures of $90^{o}C$ and $370^{o}C$ at a rated power of $10^5$ watts. It achieves 82% of the ideal Carnot efficiency. By how much is the entropy of the universe increased in running this engine for 1 hour?

Semester II

TEST NO. 1

Tipler, Chapters 20 to 25 Name: ______________________________

Scratch paper may be used but will not be taken in, so show all your work on the test paper. Take the trouble to make clear what you are doing, write legibly, indicate answers clearly, etc.

You may use whatever notes, numbers, formulas, or whatever, that you can fit on one face of a standard 3" x 5" file card. No other reference materials may be used, but you may bring a slide rule or calculator if you want.

Time allowed: 1 hour

---

1. (24 pts) In no more than a sentence or two, define or explain each of the following:

   (a) Superposition

   (b) Dispersion

   (c) Polarization

   (d) Harmonic series

   (e) Wavefront

   (f) Diffraction

2. (14 pts) In a certain wave motion, each particle of the medium is undergoing simple harmonic motion. Write the expression for the wave function, and define all the quantities involved in it.

3. (20 pts) In an experiment, waves of frequency 140 Hz are propagating along a stretched string. The string is 3.2 m long, has a mass of 28 gm, and is under a tension of 660 N. What is the wavelength of the waves?

4. (20 pts) The fundamental and first few overtones of a certain organ pipe are 44, 131, 219, and 307 Hz. If the speed of sound in air is 1080 ft/sec,

(a) How long is the pipe?

(b) Is it open or closed at the ends?

5. (22 pts) A car passes by you blowing its horn. If its speed is V and it is going in a straight line whose closest approach to you is a distance b, find an expression for the frequency of the sound you hear as a function of time.

Semester II

TEST NO. 2

Tipler, Chapters 26 to 33 Name: ______________________

Show all your work on the test paper; no scratch paper will be taken in. Make your work as clear as possible - it's worth your time; if I can't read it, I can't grade it. Each of you may use whatever numbers, formulas, notes, etc., that you can fit on one face of a 3" x 5" file card, and you may use slide rules or calculators if you need them. No other reference materials are allowed.

Time allowed: 1 hour

---

1. (8 pts) In no more than a sentence or two, define

   (a) Huygens' principle

   (b) Polarization of a dielectric

2. (24 pts) Imagine that you are setting up Young's experiment for red light, as a demonstration for an elementary physics class. You want the separation between interference fringes to be of a reasonable viewing size on a wall 25 ft from the slits. What should be the separation of the slits? Be particularly careful to make clear any assumptions you are making.

3. (10 pts) Sketch, approximately - don't take a lot of time to be artistic, but make it clear - what a lines-of-force diagram for two point charges would look like, if they have opposite signs and magnitudes in the ratio 2:1.

4. (20 pts) The electric field due to a long straight line of charge is

$$E = \frac{\lambda}{2\pi\varepsilon_0 r}$$

where $\lambda$ is the charge per unit length. On a cylindrical surface centered on the line of charge, calculate the flux of the electric field and show explicitly that Gauss's law holds.

5. (14 pts) What is the magnitude of a point charge if the electric field due to it is 0.7 V/m at a distance of 2.5 m from the charge?

6. (24 pts) A parallel-plate capacitor has a capacitance of 400 F and plate area of 180 $cm^2$. It is filled with a dielectric whose dielectric constant is 2.40. If the potential difference across it is 100 V,

(a) What is the electric field in the dielectric?

(b) What is the energy stored in the field?

Semester II

TEST NO. 3

Tipler, Chapters 34 to 39 Name: ______________________

Scratch paper may be used but not handed in; do all your work on the test paper. Take the trouble to make clear what you are doing; if I can't read it, I won't grade it. The usual 3" x 5" card system applies, no other references are to be used, but you may use a slide rule or pocket calculator if you need it.

Time: 1 hour

---

1. (24 pts) In no more than a sentence or two, define, explain, or otherwise identify each of the following:

   (a) Drift velocity

   (b) Joule heating

   (c) Magnetic pole strength

   (d) Cyclotron frequency

   (e) Amperean currents

   (f) Ferromagnetism

2. (24 pts) For the circuit sketched at right

   (a) Write out the equations that follow from Kirchhoff's rules.

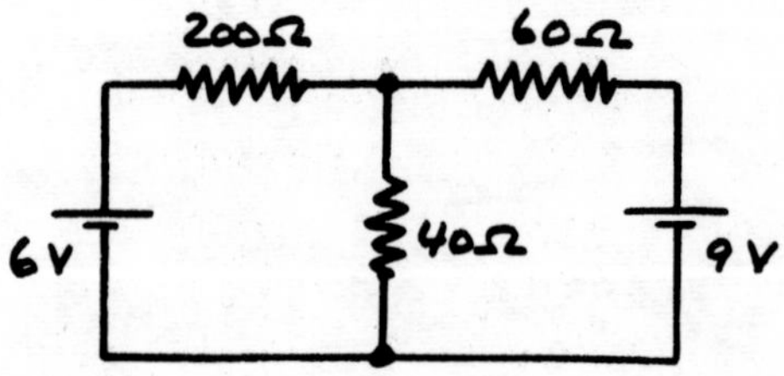

(b) Solve for the currents in the three branches.

3. (14 pts) A bar magnet is in a magnetic field. Explain carefully under what circumstances there is (a) a force, (b) a torque on it due to the field.

4. (18 pts) Neglecting end effects, find an expression for the total energy stored in the magnetic field of a solenoid of length L and N turns, carrying a current I.

5. (20 pts) A small search coil (5 cm square, 25 turns, resistance 12 ohms) is drawn out of the region between the poles of a large electromagnet at a speed of 3.0 m/sec. If the current in the coil while it is being drawn out is 0.21 A, what is the magnetic field of the magnet?

## SUGGESTIONS FOR FURTHER READING

Granvil C. Kyker, Jr.

What follows is a collection of books, texts, and articles which you may find useful in teaching elementary physics, using Tipler's PHYSICS. It is not a systematic bibliography of physics; that would require several volumes, in itself. Instead, I have set down items I have come across and in large part have used, in the course of teaching undergraduate physics.

I use such materials in several ways: to aid in organizing and preparing both specific lectures and whole segments of a course, to suggest related topics that would be interesting to bring in, and to assign or suggest to students for supplementary reading.

Your choice of materials, no doubt, would be different from mine. But even if you don't find what you're looking for in the references I've listed, most of them are thoroughly footnoted; you will at least find where to find it.

The list is not broken down chapter-by-chapter to correspond to Tipler's text. No such one-to-one correspondence exists. Most of the entries relate to topics discussed in several chapters and could be used at a number of different points. Instead, they are divided under eight subject headings, as follows:

A. Physics in General
B. Mechanics (Chapters 2 to 16 in Tipler)
C. Thermodynamics (Chapters 17 to 19)
D. Waves and Optics (Chapters 20 to 27)
E. Relativity (Chapter 28)
F. Electricity and Magnetism (Chapters 29 to 41)
G. Quantization (Chapter 42)
H. Reference and Teaching Aids

Within each subject heading, entries are subdivided by type and use:

1. Textbooks
2. General Articles and Books
3. History, Biography, Source Readings, etc.
4. Sidelines and Applications
5. Miscellaneous

Occasionally, this subdivision makes for some odd bedfellows in Procrustes' bed; but so would any other with more than one entry per category.

Most of the entries under "Textbooks," in the subject headings relating to specific areas of physics, are intermediate-level texts; many of them are not suitable for undirected reading by first-year students, although I find them useful for reference. I've tried in places to indicate the most readable ones. Other than this, almost all the books and articles may be assigned to students as supplementary reading.

Most of the articles were taken from Scientific American, Physics Today, or The Physics Teacher. Another extremely rich source of brief articles on teaching topics, of course, is the American Journal of Physics. Very many articles, most of them quite specific, may be found there; just because of this, I've included very few. The American Journal of Physics is very thoroughly indexed, however, and half an hour's prowling through back volumes will locate several helpful items on any topic you can think of. A number of other periodicals will occur to you that have occasional useful pieces, but these are the four that I have found by far the most helpful.

There is relatively little annotation. Here and there I have thrown in a note as to which of several books I find most useful for a particular purpose. By and large, however, the nature of an entry is pretty clear from its location in the list, its title, and perhaps its source; and I've preferred to use the space available for variety rather than extensive description.

## A. Physics in General

### 1. Textbooks

a. Feynman, R., R.B. Leighton, and M. Sands, The Feynman Lectures in Physics (Addison-Wesley, Reading, Mass., 1963), 3 vols.

b. The Berkeley Physics Course (McGraw-Hill, New York, 1962-69), 5 vols.

Both of these sets are enormously useful for reference by either teacher or student. Each covers the whole of introductory physics, including "modern" physics as the last volume. Several other first-year textbooks, roughly comparable to Tipler in scope and treatment, are:

c. Alonzo, M., and E.J. Finn, Physics (Addison-Wesley, Reading, Mass., 1970).

d. Bueche, F., Introduction to Physics for Scientists and Engineers (McGraw-Hill, New York, 1969).

e. Ford, K.W., Classical and Modern Physics (Xerox College Publishing, Lexington, Mass., 1972). The first two volumes are classical physics.

f. Resnick, R., and D. Halliday, Physics (Wiley, New York, 1966).

g. Sears, F.W., and M.W. Zemansky, University Physics (Addison-Wesley, Reading, Mass., 3rd edition 1964).

h. Weidner, R.T., and R.L. Sells, Elementary Classical Physics (Allyn and Bacon, Boston, Mass., 2nd edition 1973).

Very similar to the above, and including modern physics, are:

i. Bergmann, P.G., Basic Theories of Physics: Mechanics and Electricity (Prentice-Hall, Englewood Cliffs, N.J., 1949); Basic Theories of Physics: Heat and Quanta (1951).

j. Blanpied, W., Physics - Its Structure and Evolution (Blaisdell Publishing Co., Waltham, Mass., 1969).

k. Young, H.D., Fundamentals of Mechanics and Heat (McGraw-Hill, New York, 2nd edition 1973); Fundamentals of Optics and Modern Physics (1968).

There are also a number of texts for the first-year survey course, without calculus, which sometimes make useful references. That by Cooper is especially entertaining reading. Several of these are:

l. Bueche, F., Principles of Physics (McGraw-Hill, New York, 1965).

m. Cooper, L., Introduction to the Meaning and Structure of Physics (Harper & Row, New York, 1968).

n. McCormick, W.W., Fundamentals of College Physics (Macmillan, New York, 1965).

o. Stephenson, R., and R.B. Moore, Theory of Physics (Saunders, Philadelphia, 1967).

p. Atkins, K.R., Physics (Wiley, New York, 1965).

2. General Articles and Books

a. Amaldi, E., "The Unity of Physics" Phys. Today 26 (Sept. 1973), p. 23.

b. Astin, A.V., "Standards of Measurement" Sci. Am. 218 (June 1968), p. 50.

c. Bauman, R.F., "The Meaning of Conservation Laws" Phys. Teacher 9 (April 1971), p. 186.

d. Butterfield, H., "The Scientific Revolution" Sci. Am. 203 (Sept. 1960), p. 173.

e. Goldhaber, M., and G. Feinberg, "The Conservation Laws of Physics" Sci. Am. 209 (Oct. 1963), p. 36.

f. Schrödinger, E., "What Is Matter?" Sci. Am. 189 (Sept. 1953), p. 52.

g. Wheeler, J.A., "Our Universe, Known and Unknown" Phys. Teacher 7 (Jan. 1969), p. 24.

h. Wigner, E.P., "Symmetry and Conservation Laws" Phys. Today 17 (March 1964), p. 34.

Two important series of paperbound books, widely varied and suitable for general reading by introductory students, are:

i. The "Science Study Series" of Anchor Books, Doubleday, Garden City, N.Y.

j. The "Momentum Books" of Van Nostrand Reinhold, New York.

Several examples of both series appear in this list.

Several interesting books on the nature, meaning, and laws of physics in general follow. The lectures by Feynman are a gem.

k. Bridgman, P.W., The Nature of Physical Theory (Wiley, New York, 1936, 1964).

l. Feynman, R., The Character of Physical Law (M.I.T., Cambridge, Mass., 1967).

m. Karplus, R., Physics and Man (W.A. Benjamin, Inc., Menlo Park, Calif., 1970).

n. Lindsay, R.B., and H. Margenau, Foundations of Physics (Dover, New York, 1957).

o. Peierls, R., Laws of Nature (Scribner, New York, 1956).

p. Rothman, M.A., Discovering the Natural Laws (Anchor Books Science Study Series) (Doubleday, Garden City, N.Y., 1972).

q. Weyl, H., Space, Time, and Matter (Dover, New York, 4th edition 1952).

## 3. History, Biography, Source Readings, etc.

The history of physics, of course, is a field all to itself. A few scattered items that have been of use or interest to me are given below.

a. Butterfield, H., The Origins of Modern Science (Collier Books, Macmillan, New York, 1962).

b. Casper, B.M., and R.J. Noer, Revolutions in Physics (Norton, New York, 1972).

c. Cajori, F., A History of Physics (Dover, New York, 1962; original 1929).

d. D'Abro, A., Rise of the New Physics: Its Mathematical and Physical Theories (Dover, New York, 1951), 2 vols.

e. Dirac, P.A.M., "Evolution of the Physicist's Picture of Nature" Sci. Am. 209 (May 1963), p. 45.

f. Einstein, A., and L. Infeld, The Evolution of Physics (Simon and Schuster, New York, 1938).

g. Gamow, G., Biography of Physics (Harper & Row, New York, 1961).

h. Holliday, L., "Early Views on Forces Between Atoms" Sci. Am. 222 (May 1970), p. 116.

i. Koyré, A., From the Closed World to the Infinite Universe (Harper & Row, New York, 1958), Torchbook #TB-31.

j. Lemon, H.B., From Galileo to the Nuclear Age (University of Chicago Press, Chicago, revised edition 1946).

k. Phys. Today 21 (May 1968) is a special issue devoted to "Twenty Years of Physics."

Several scientific biographies are to be found in other sections of this listing. Two works containing brief biographical entries on many physicists and other scientists are

l. Asimov, I., Asimov's Biographical Encyclopedia of Science and Technology (Doubleday, Garden City, N.Y., 1964).

m. Howard, A.V., Chambers' Dictionary of Scientists (Dutton, New York, 1951).

Selections from original writings, lectures, and the like are in the books listed below. Magie's Sourcebook is the standard, and most extensive, work; shorter, but especially entertaining, selections are in the books by Marion and by Shamos.

n. Beiser, A., The World of Physics (McGraw-Hill, New York, 1960).

o. Knickerbocker, W., Classics of Modern Science: Copernicus to Pasteur (Knopf, New York, 1927).

p. Magie, W.F., A Sourcebook in Physics (Harvard University Press, Cambridge, Mass., 1964).

q. Marion, J.B., A Universe of Physics (Wiley, New York, 1970).

r. Rapport, S., and H. Wright, Physics (Washington Square Press, Pocket Books, Inc., New York, 1965).

s. Shamos, M.H., Great Experiments in Physics (Holt, New York, 1962).

t. The Nobel Lectures in Physics (Elsevier, Amsterdam, 1964), 3 vols.

u. Turning Points in Physics (Oxford University Lecture Series) (Harper & Row, New York, 1961), Torchbook #TB-535.

v. ter Haar, D., ed., Selected Readings in Physics (Pergamon Press, New York, 1965- ). This is a series of books, including, for example, S.C. Brown, Benjamin Thomson, Count Rumford, 1967; S.G. Brush, Kinetic Theory, 1965; and several others.

4. Sidelines, Applications, and Miscellany

a. DiLavore, P., and J.R. Weyland, "Pulsars for the Beginner" Phys. Teacher 9 (May 1971), p. 232.

b. Dyson, F.J., "Mathematics in the Physical Sciences" Sci. Am. 211 (Sept. 1964), p. 128.

c. Haworth, L.J., "Scientists and Society" Phys. Today 16 (July 1963), p. 19.

d. Harrison, E.R., "The Cosmic Numbers" Phys. Today 25 (Dec. 1972), p. 30.

e. Lindsay, R.B., "Arbitrariness in Physics" Phys. Today 20 (Dec. 1967), p. 23.

f. Pippard, A.B., "The Cat and the Cream" Phys. Today 14 (Nov. 1961), p. 38.

g. Rose, D.J., J.H. Gibbons, and W. Fulkerson, "Physics Looks at Waste Management" Phys. Today 25 (Feb. 1972), p. 32.

h. Sartor, J.D., "Clouds and Precipitation" Phys. Today 25 (Oct. 1972), p. 32.

i. Sartor, J.D., "Electricity and Rain" Phys. Today 22 (Aug. 1969), p. 45.

j. Stephens, W.E., "Origin of the Elements" Phys. Teacher 7 (Nov. 1969), p. 431.

k. Weisskopf, V.F., "The Privilege of Being a Physicist" Phys. Today 22 (Aug. 1969), p. 39.

l. Benedek, G.B., and F.M.H. Villars, Physics, with Applications from Biology and Medicine (Addison-Wesley, Reading, Mass., 1973), 3 vols. A rich source of illustrations of basic physics as it operates in living systems.

## B. Mechanics

In Tipler's PHYSICS, this section includes newtonian mechanics of a particle (Chapters 2 to 6), the conservation of energy and momentum (Chapters 7 to 11), rotation and angular momentum (Chapters 12 and 13), oscillations (Chapters 14 and 15), and gravity (Chapter 16).

### 1. Textbooks

These are intermediate-level texts on mechanics and on a few of the specialized areas of mechanics. The most generally readable by first-year students would probably be those by French and by Kittel, Knight, and Ruderman.

a. Danby, J.M.A., Fundamentals of Celestial Mechanics (Macmillan, New York, 1962).

b. Fowles, G.R., Analytical Mechanics (Holt, New York 2nd edition 1970).

c. French, A.P., Newtonian Mechanics (Norton, New York, 1971).

d. Hauser, W., Introduction to the Principles of Mechanics (Addison-Wesley, Reading, Mass., 1965).

e. Kittel, C., W.D. Knight, and M.A. Ruderman, Mechanics (Berkeley Physics Course, vol. 1)(McGraw-Hill, New York, 1962).

f. Maxwell, J.C., Matter and Motion (Dover, New York, 1952). Original 1877; still a fine treatment of fundamental classical mechanics.

g. Slater, J.C., and N.H. Frank, Mechanics (McGraw-Hill, New York, 1947).

h. Symon, K.R., Mechanics (Addison-Wesley, Reading, Mass., 2nd edition 1960).

i. Synge, J.L., and B.A. Griffith, Principles of Mechanics (McGraw-Hill, New York, 3rd edition 1959).

j. Tabor, D., and F.P. Bowden, Friction and Lubrication (Methuen Monograph series)(Wiley, New York, 1961).

k. Vennard, J.K., Elementary Fluid Mechanics (Wiley, New York, 4th edition 1961).

## 2. General Articles and Books

a. Eisenbud, L., "On the Classical Laws of Motion" Am. J. Phys. 26 (1958), p. 114.

b. Gamow, G., "Gravity" Sci. Am. 205 (March 1961), p. 94.

c. Gardner, M., "Can Time Go Backward?" Sci. Am. 216 (Jan. 1967), p. 98.

d. Gribbin, J.E., "Not-So-Free Fall" Phys. Teacher 10 (March 1972), p. 122.

e. Hart, J.B., "Great Ellipsoids of Inertia and Space Physics" Phys. Teacher 6 (March 1968), p. 118.

f. Kearsley, E.A., and M.S. Green, "The Foundations of Mechanics and Thermodynamics" Phys. Today 13 (July 1960), p. 22.

g. MacDonald, J.E., "The Coriolis Effect" Sci. Am. 186 (May 1952), p. 72.

h. Macklin, P.A., "Inverse-Square Law from Kepler's First and Second Laws" Am. J. Phys. 39 (1971), p. 1088.

i. Maor, E., "A Repertoire of S.H.M." Phys. Teacher 10 (Oct. 1972), p. 377.

j. Marshak, R.E., "The Fourth Force in Nature" Phys. Teacher 9 (Nov. 1971), p. 435 (part I); 9 (Dec. 1971), p. 516 (part II).

k. Marton, L., "The Law of Gravitation" Phys. Teacher 4 (Jan. 1966), p. 10.

l. Raman, V.V., "The Second Law of Motion and Newton's Equations" Phys. Teacher 10 (March 1972), p. 136.

m. Schurr, G.H., "Energy" Sci. Am. 218 (Sept. 1963), p. 110.

n. Sciama, D.W., "Inertia" Sci. Am. 196 (Feb. 1957), p. 71.

o. Whitrow, G.J. "Time" Phys. Teacher 4 (Feb. 1966), p. 58.

p. Chalmers, B., Energy (Academic Press, New York, 1963).

q. Feather, N., Introduction to the Physics of Mass, Length, and Time (Pelican Books, 1959). Discussion and illustration of the fundamental mechanical quantities.

r. Holton, G., and D.H. D. Roller, Foundations of Modern Physical Science (Addison-Wesley, Reading, Mass., 1958).

s. Jammer, M., Concepts of Force (Harvard University Press, Cambridge, Mass., 1957).

t. Jammer, M., Concepts of Space (Harper & Row, New York, 1960), Torchbook #TB-533.

u. Mach, E., The Science of Mechanics (Open Court Publishing Co., Lasalle, Ill., 1960).

## 3. History, Biography, Source Readings, etc.

The original works of Galileo and Newton, which laid the foundation for all our present ideas of mechanics, are available in

a. Galilei, Galileo, Dialogues Concerning Two New Sciences, translated by H. Crew and A. de Salvio (Northwestern University Press, Evanston, Ill., 1939).

b. Newton, Sir Isaac, Mathematical Principles of Natural Philosophy, translation by A. Motte, revised by F. Cajori (University of California Press, Berkeley, 1934).

Some other books and articles in this general category are

c. Boyer, C.B., "Aristotle's Physics" Sci. Am. 182 (May 1960), p. 48.

d. Drake, S., "Galileo's Discovery of the Law of Free Fall" Sci. Am. 228 (May 1973), p. 17.

e. Mayfield, M.R., "The Rise of Gravity in the Seventeenth Century, or a Day in the Life of Isaac Newton" Phys. Today 21 (June 1968), p. 42.

f. Sherman, P.D., "Galileo and the Inclined Plane Controversy" Phys. Teacher 12 (June 1974), p. 343.

g. Wilson, C., "How Did Kepler Discover His First Two Laws?" Sci. Am. 226 (March 1972), p. 92.

h. Cohen, I.B., The Birth of a New Physics (Anchor Books Science Study Series) (Doubleday, Garden City, N.Y., 1960).

i. Hesse, M.B., Forces and Fields, the Concept of Action at a Distance in the History of Physics (Philosophical Library, Inc., New York, 1962).

j. Koestler, A., The Watershed - A Biography of Johannes Kepler (Doubleday, Garden City, N.Y., 1960).

k. Toulmin, R., and J. Goodfield, The Architecture of Matter (Harper & Row, New York, 1962).

l. Toulmin, R., and J. Goodfield, The Fabric of the Heavens (Harper & Row, New York, 1961).

4. Sidelines and Applications

a. Beams, J.W., "Ultra High Speed Rotation" Sci. Am. 105 (April 1961), p. 134.

b. Bernal, J.D., "The Structure of Liquids" Sci. Am. 203 (Aug. 1960), p. 124.

c. Dennis, J., and L. Choate, "Some Problems with Artificial Gravity" Phys. Teacher 8 (Nov. 1970), p. 441.

d. Edwards, L.K., "High-Speed Tube Transportation" Sci. Am. 213 (Aug. 1965), p. 30.

e. Heinrich, B., "The Energetics of the Bumblebee" Sci. Am. 228 (April 1973), p. 96.

f. Keller, J.B., "A Theory of Competitive Ruhning" Phys. Today 26 (Sept. 1973), p. 42.

g. Kemeny, J.G., "Man Viewed as a Machine" Sci. Am. 192 (April 1955), p. 58.

h. Leondes, C.T., "Inertial Navigation for Aircraft" Sci. Am. 222 (March 1970), p. 80.

i. Merchant, M.E., "The Mechanism of Static Friction" J. Appl. Phys. 11 (1940), p. 230.

j. Palmer, F.J., "What about Friction?" Am. J. Phys. 17 (1949), pp. 181, 327.

k. Penrose, R., "Black Holes" Sci. Am. 226 (May 1972), p. 38.

l. Sci. Am. 225 (Sept. 1971) is a special issue devoted to "Energy and Power."

m. Shonle, J.I., and D.L. Nordick, "The Physics of Ski Turns" Phys. Teacher 10 (Dec. 1972), p. 491.

n. Smith, N.F., "Bernoulli and Newton in Fluid Motion" Phys. Teacher 10 (Nov. 1972), p. 451.

o. Starr, V.P., "The General Circulation of the Atmosphere" Sci. Am. 195 (Dec. 1956), p. 40.

p. Sterne, T.E., "Celestial Mechanics of Artificial Satellites" Sky and Telescope 17 (1957), p. 66.

q. Thorne, K.S., "Gravitational Collapse" Sci. Am. 217 (Nov. 1967), p. 88.

r. Weber, J., "The Detection of Gravitational Waves" Sci. Am. 224 (May 1971), p. 22.

5. Miscellany

a. Beams, J.W., "Finding a Better Value for G" Phys. Today 24 (May 1971), p. 34.

b. Dicke, R.H., "The Eötvos Experiment" Sci. Am. 205 (Dec. 1961), p. 84.

c. Essen, L., "Accurate Measurement of Time" Phys. Today 13 (Aug. 1960), p. 26.

d. King-Hele, D., "The Shape of the Earth" Sci. Am. 217 (Oct. 1967), p. 67.

e. Steinherz, H.A., and P.A. Redhead, "Ultrahigh Vacuum" Sci. Am. 206 (March 1962), p. 38.

f. Weinberg, A.M., "Energy as an Ultimate Raw Material" Phys. Today 12 (Nov. 1959), p. 18.

g. Sutton, R.M., The Physics of Space (Holt, New York, 1965).

## C. Thermodynamics

Chapters 17 to 19 in Tipler's text define heat, temperature, internal energy, and entropy, discuss the kinetic theory of gases, and introduce the laws of thermodynamics.

### 1. Textbooks

Again, these are mostly intermediate-level textbooks. The first few chapters of Reif, and Zemansky, are perfectly accessible to the average first-year student. Fermi's book is something between text and commentary. Also to be recommended are the appropriate sections of the Feynman Lectures (A.1.a above), as well as other introductory texts (A.1).

a. Fast, J.D., Entropy, translated by M. Mulder-Woolcock (Philips Technical Library, Holland, 1962).

b. Fermi, E., Thermodynamics (Dover, New York, 1936).

c. Jackson, L.C., Low-Temperature Physics (Methuen & Co., London, 5th edition 1962).

d. Jeans, Sir J.H., An Introduction to the Kinetic Theory of Gases (Macmillan, New York, 1940).

e. Kittel, C., Thermal Physics (Wiley, New York, 1969).

f. Reif, F., Statistical Physics (Berkeley Physics Course, vol. 5) (McGraw-Hill, New York, 1964).

g. Pippard, A.B. Classical Thermodynamics (Cambridge University Press, New York, 1957).

h. Zemansky, M.W., Heat and Thermodynamics: an Introductory Textbook for Students of Physics, Chemistry, and Engineering (McGraw-Hill, New York, 4th edition 1957).

### 2. General Articles and Books

a. Ehrenburg, W., "Maxwell's Demon" Sci. Am. 217 (Nov. 1967), p. 103.

b. Ford, K., "Probability and Entropy in Thermodynamics" Phys. Teacher 5 (Feb. 1967), p. 77.

c. Schurr, G.H., "Energy" Sci. Am. 209 (Sept. 1963), p. 110.

d. Sci. Am. 181 (Sept. 1954) is a special issue devoted to "Heat."

e. Zemansky, M.W., "The Use and Misuse of the Word 'Heat' in Physics Teaching" Phys. Teacher 8 (June 1970), p. 294.

f. Angrist, S.W., and L.G. Hepler, Order and Chaos (Basic Books, Inc., Publishers, New York, 1967).

g. Born, M., The Restless Universe (Dover, New York, 1951).

h. Bridgman, P.W., The Nature of Thermodynamics (Harper & Row, New York, 1961).

i. Sandfort, J.F., Heat Engines (Anchor Books Science Study Series) (Doubleday, Garden City, N.Y., 1962).

j. Mendelssohn, K., The Quest for Absolute Zero (McGraw-Hill, New York, 1966).

k. Zemansky, M.W., Temperatures Very Low and Very High (Momentum Books)(Van Nostrand, Princeton, N.J., 1964).

3. History, Biography, Source Readings, etc.

a. Barr, E.S., "James Prescott Joule and the Quiet Revolution" Phys. Teacher 7 (April 1969), p. 199.

b. Dutta, M., "A Hundred Years of Entropy" Phys. Today 21 (Jan. 1968), p. 75.

c. Mendoza, E., "Sketch for a History of Early Thermodynamics" Phys. Today 14 (Feb. 1961), p. 36.

d. Mendoza, E., "Sketch for a History of the Kinetic Theory of Gases" Phys. Today 14 (March 1961), p. 36.

e. Carnot, S., and others, Reflections on the Motive Power of Fire and Other Papers on the Second Law of Thermodynamics (Dover, New York, 1960).

f. The Scientific Papers of Prescott Joule (Dawsons, Ltd., London, 1963).

g. Roller, D., "The Development of the Concepts of Temperature and Heat" Harvard Case Histories in Experimental Science No. 3 (Harvard University Press, Cambridge, Mass., 1966).

4. Sidelines and Applications

a. Angrist, S.W., "Perpetual Motion Machines" Sci. Am. 218 (Jan. 1968), p. 114.

b. Barnea, J., "Geothermal Power" Sci. Am. 226 (Jan. 1972), p. 70.

c. Burwell, C.C., "Desalting and Nuclear Energy" Phys. Teacher 9 (Feb. 1971), p. 67.

d. Gray, W.T., and D.I. Finch, "How Accurately Can T Be Measured?" Phys. Today 24 (Sept. 1971), p. 32.

e. Little, W.A., "Superconductivity at Room Temperature" Sci. Am. 213 (Feb. 1965), p. 21.

f. Meinel, A.B., and M.P. Meinel, "Physics Looks at Solar Energy" Phys. Today 25 (Feb. 1972), p. 44.

g. Phys. Today 24 (Aug. 1971) is a special issue devoted to "Physics at Low Temperatures."

h. Phys. Today 26 (Aug. 1973) is a special issue devoted to "Report on Nuclear Energy."

i. Sci. Am. 225 (Sept. 1971) is a special issue devoted to "Energy and Power."

j. Wheatley, J.C., and H.J. Van Till, "Attaining Low Temperatures" Phys. Teacher 8 (Feb. 1970), p. 70.

k. Weinberg, A.M., "Energy as an Ultimate Raw Material" Phys. Today 12 (Nov. 1959), p. 18.

l. Woodruff, A.E., "The Radiometer and How It Does Not Work" Phys. Teacher 6 (Oct. 1968), p. 358.

m. Efron, A., Liquids and Gases (Rider Publications, John F. Rider, Publisher, Inc., New York, 1959).

## D. Waves and Optics

Wave motion, its description, and assorted wave phenomena are treated in Tipler's text in Chapters 20 to 25. Optics is discussed in Chapters 26 and 27.

### 1. Textbooks

The majority of intermediate-level texts are "Optics" - and are weighted more heavily toward light, and less to wave phenomena in general, than introductory texts usually are. A variety is given below. R.W. Wood is the standard for phenomena of physical optics. Crawford (Berkeley Physics Course, vol. 3), Coulson, and the appropriate sections of Feynman (A.l.a. above) should be readable by introductory students.

a. Crawford, F.S., Waves (Berkeley Physics Course, vol. 3)(McGraw-Hill, New York, 1965).

b. Coulson, C.A., Waves (Oliver & Boyd, London, 1949).

c. Fowles, G.R., Introduction to Modern Optics (Holt, New York, 1968).

d. Hastings, R.V., The Physics of Sound (Bruce Publishing Co., St. Paul, Minn., 1960).

e. Jenkins, F.A., and H.E. White, Fundamentals of Optics (McGraw-Hill, New York, 3rd edition 1957).

f. Pearson, J.M., Theory of Waves (Allyn & Bacon, Boston, Mass., 1966).

g. Shurcliff, W.A., and S.S. Ballard, Polarized Light (Momentum Books)(Van Nostrand, Princeton, N.J., 1964).

h. Stroke, G.W., Introduction to Coherent Optics and Holography (Academic, New York, 1969).

i. Waldron, R.A., Waves and Oscillations (Momentum Books)(Van Nostrand, Princeton, N.J., 1964).

j. Wood, R.W., Physical Optics (Macmillan, New York, 3rd edition 1934).

2. General Articles and Books

a. Bascom, W., "Ocean Waves" Sci. Am. 201 (Aug. 1959), p. 74.

b. Rush, J.H., "The Speed of Light" Sci. Am. 193 (Aug. 1955), p. 62.

c. Sci. Am. 219 (Sept. 1968) is a special issue devoted to "Light."

d. Bragg, Sir W., The Universe of Light (Dover, New York, 1959).

e. Johnson, B.K., Optics and Optical Instruments (Dover, New York, 1960).

f. Kock, W., Sound Waves and Light Waves (Anchor Books Science Study Series #S-40)(Doubleday, Garden City, N.Y., 1965).

g. Michelson, A.A., Light Waves and Their Uses (Phoenix Books, The University of Chicago Press, Chicago, 1961). Original 1902; summarizes two decades of research in optics.

h. Optical Society of America, The Science of Color (Crowell and Optical Society of America, Washington, D.C., 1963).

i. Schawlow, A., ed., Lasers and Light: Readings from Scientific American (Freeman, San Francisco, Calif., 1969).

j. Simon, I., Infrared Radiation (Momentum Books)(Van Nostrand, Princeton, N.J., 1966).

k. Van Bergeijk, W., J.R. Pierce, and E.E. David, Jr., Waves and the Ear (Anchor Books Science Study Series)(Doubleday, Garden City, N.Y., 1960).

3. History, Biography, Source Readings, etc.

a. Helm, E.E., "The Vibrating String of the Pythagoreans" Sci. Am. 217 (Dec. 1967), p. 92.

b. Newton, Sir Isaac, Opticks (Dover, New York, 1952; based on the 4th edition, London, 1730).

4. Sidelines, Applications, and Miscellany

a. Baranek, Leo N., "Noise" Sci. Am. 215 (Dec. 1966), p. 66.

b. Baumeister, P., and G. Pincus, "Optical Interference Coatings" Sci. Am. 223 (Dec. 1970), p. 58.

c. Beyer, R.T., "Acoustics as a Physical Science" Phys. Today 26 (Feb. 1973), p. 40.

d. Bullard, Sir E., "The Detection of Underground Explosions" Sci. Am. 215 (July 1966), p. 19.

e. Faller, J.E., and E.J. Wampler, "The Lunar Laser Reflector" Sci. Am. 222 (March 1970), p. 38.

f. Hutchins, C.M., "The Physics of Violins" Sci. Am. 207 (Nov. 1962), p. 78.

g. Land, E.H., "Experiments in Color Vision" Sci. Am. 200 (May 1959), p. 84.

h. MacDonald, R.K., "Optics and Information Theory" Phys. Today 14 (July 1961), p. 36.

i. Miller, S.E., "Communication by Laser" Sci. Am. 214 (Jan. 1966), p. 19.

j. Hubbard, H.H., "Sonic Booms" Phys. Today 21 (Feb. 1968), p. 31.

k. Oliver, J., "Long Earthquake Waves" Sci. Am. 200 (March 1959), p. 131.

l. Wald, G., "Eye and Camera" Sci. Am. 183 (Aug. 1950), p. 32.

m. Risset, J.C., and M.V. Matthews, "Analysis of Musical Instrument Tones" Phys. Today 22 (Feb. 1969), p. 23.

n. Tucker, V.A., "Waves and Water Beetles" Phys. Teacher 10 (Jan. 1971), p. 9.

o. Whitaker, R.J., "Physics of the Rainbow" Phys. Teacher 12 (May 1974), p. 283.

p. Benade, A.H., Horns, Strings, and Harmony (Anchor Books Science Study Series #S-11)(Doubleday, Garden City, N.Y., 1960).

q. Wood, E.A., Crystals and Light, an Introduction to Optical Crystallography (Momentum Books)(Van Nostrand, Princeton, N.J., 1964).

## E. Relativity

The special theory of relativity is treated in Chapter 28 of Tipler.

### 1. Textbooks

To my mind, the best of the modern, short relativity books are those by Kacser and Smith. There are a number of others, besides what is given here. The classic expositions are those of Einstein and of Eddington; these should not be missed. Of the ones listed below, Synge is somewhat harder reading than the rest.

a. Bohm, D., Relativity (Routledge & Kegan Paul, Ltd., London, 1957).

b. Eddington, A.S., The Mathematical Theory of Relativity (Cambridge University Press, New York, 3d edition 1960).

c. Einstein, A., Relativity: the Special and General Theories (H. Holt & Co., New York, 1920).

d. Kacser, C., Introduction to the Special Theory of Relativity (Prentice-Hall, Englewood Cliffs, N.J., 1967).

e. Synge, J.L., Relativity: The Special Theory (North-Holland Publishing Company, Amsterdam, 1965).

f. Taylor, E.F., and J.A. Wheeler, Spacetime Physics (Freeman, San Francisco, Calif., 1966).

g. Smith, J.H., Introduction to Special Relativity (W. A. Benjamin, Inc., Menlo Park, Calif., 1965).

2. General Articles and Books

a. Bronowski, J., "The Clock Paradox" Sci. Am. 208 (Feb. 1963), p. 134.

b. Sachs, M., "A Resolution of the Clock Paradox" Phys. Today 24 (Sept. 1971), p. 23.

c. Weisskopf, V.F., "The Visual Appearance of Rapidly Moving Objects" Phys. Today 13 (Sept. 1960), p. 24.

d. Born, M., The Restless Universe (Dover, New York, 1951).

e. Bridgman, P.W., A Sophisticate's Primer of Relativity (Wesleyan University Press, Middletown, Conn., 1962).

f. Einstein, A., The Meaning of Relativity (Princeton University Press, Princeton, N.J., 5th edition 1956).

g. Einstein, A., and L. Infeld, The Evolution of Physics (Simon and Schuster, Inc., New York, 1938).

3. History, Biography, Source Readings, etc.

The Clark item is probably one of the best scientific biographies around. In addition to the items below, see also various listings in section A.3, especially those by Marion and by Shamos.

a. Clark, R.W., Einstein: the Life and Times (World Publishing Co., Cleveland, Ohio, 1971).

b. Williams, L.P., ed., Relativity Theory: Its Origin and Impact on Modern Thought (Wiley, New York, 1968).

4. Sidelines, Applications, and Miscellany

a. Feinberg, G., "Particles that Go Faster than Light" Sci. Am. 222 (Feb. 1970), p. 68.

b. Ginzburg, V.L., "Artificial Satellites and the Theory of Relativity" Sci. Am. 200 (May 1959), p. 159.

c. Hewitt, P.G., "On Teaching about Twins and Time" Phys. Teacher 11 (Dec. 1973), p. 519.

d. Sandage, A.R., "The Red Shift" Sci. Am. 195 (Sept. 1956), p. 170.

e. Weber, J., General Relativity and Gravitational Waves (Interscience Publishers, Inc., New York, 1961).

## F. Electricity and Magnetism

The material in Tipler's text includes electrostatics (Chapters 29 to 32), dielectrics and capacitance (Chapter 33), conduction and dc circuits (Chapters 34 and 35), magnetism (Chapters 36 to 39), ac circuits (Chapter 40), and electromagnetic waves (Chapter 41).

## 1. Textbooks

Intermediate-level textbooks on electromagnetism abound; a random selection is given below, including a few on special topics. As on most subjects, insights and approaches beyond the standard introductory treatment are to be found in the Berkeley volume and in the Feynman Lectures (A.l.a. above).


a. Barnes, T.G., Foundations of Electricity and Magnetism (Heath, Boston, Mass., 1965).

b. Bernumof, R., Concepts in Electricity and Magnetism (Holt, New York, 1961).

c. Guillemin, E.A., Introductory Circuit Theory (Wiley, New York, 1960).

d. Holdren, A., Conductors and Semiconductors (Bell Telephone Laboratories, Murray Hill, N.J., 1964).

e. Malmstadt, H.V., C.G. Enke, and E.C. Toren, Electronics for Scientists: Principles and Experiments for Those Who Use Instruments (W.A. Benjamin, Inc., Menlo Park, Calif., 1962).

f. Purcell, E.M., Electricity and Magnetism (Addison-Wesley, Reading, Mass., 1958).

g. Reitz, J.R., and F.J. Milford, Foundations of Electromagnetic Theory (Addison-Wesley, Reading, Mass., 1960).

h. Sears, F.W., Electricty and Magnetism (Berkeley Physics Course, vol. 2)(McGraw-Hill, New York, 1963).

i. Smyth, C.P., Dielectric Behavior and Structure (McGraw-Hill, New York, 1955).

j. Stoner, E.C., Magnetism and Matter (Methuen & Co. Ltd., London, 1934).

k. Whitmer, R.M. Electromagnetics (Prentice-Hall, Englewood Cliffs, N.J., 2nd edition 1962).


## 2. General Articles and Books


a. Azbel, M. Ya., M.I. Kaganov, and I.M. Lifschitz, "Conduction Electrons in Metals" Sci. Am. 228 (Jan. 1973), p. 88.

b. Becker, J.J., "Permanent Magnets" Sci. Am. 223 (Dec. 1970), p. 92.

c. Derjaguin, B.V., "The Force between Molecules" Sci. Am. 203 (July 1960), p. 47.

d. Ford, K.W., "Magnetic Monopoles" Sci. Am. 209 (Dec. 1963), p. 122.

e. Hamman, J.W., "Characteristics and Nature of Dielectrics" Phys. Teacher 3 (Nov. 1965), p. 354.

f. Karioris, F.G., and J.B. Green, "Force on a Magnetic Dipole" Am. J. Phys. 39 (1971), p. 172.

g. Keffer, F., "Magnetic Properties of Materials" Sci. Am. 217 (Sept. 1967), p. 222.

h. Long, D., "Electrical Conduction in Solids" Phys. Teacher 7 (May 1969), p. 264.

i. Moore, A.D., "Electrostatics" Sci. Am. 226 (March 1972), p. 46.

j. Rohrlich, F., "The Classical Description of Charged Particles" Phys. Today 15 (March 1962), p. 19.

k. Bitter, F., Magnets: The Education of a Physicist (Doubleday, Garden City, N.Y., 1959).

l. Efron, A., Magnetic and Electric Fundamentals (Rider Publications, John F. Rider, Publisher, Inc., New York, 1958).

3. History, Biography, Source Readings, etc.

a. Frank, N.H., "Faraday and the Field Concept in Physics" Phys. Teacher 6 (May 1968), p. 210.

b. Priestley, H., "Maxwell: Models to Mathematics" Phys. Teacher 9 (Dec. 1971), p. 497.

c. Anderson, D.L., The Discovery of the Electron (Momentum Books) (Van Nostrand, Princeton, N.J.).

d. Cohen, I.B., ed., Benjamin Franklin's Experiments (Harvard University Press, Cambridge, Mass., 1941).

e. Dibner, B., Oersted and the Discovery of Electromagnetism (Dover, New York).

f. Faraday, Michael, Experimental Researches in Electricity (Dover, New York, 1964), 2 vols., original 1838. Original research records of one of the greatest experimenters of the nineteenth century.

g. Gilbert, W., De Magnete (Dover, New York, 1958). The experiments of the first great investigator of magnetic phenomena; original 1600.

h. Hertz, H.R., Electric Waves, translated by D.E. Jones (Macmillan, London, 2nd edition 1900; Dover, New York, 1962).

i. Maxwell, J.C., Treatise on Electricity and Magnetism (Oxford University Press, Oxford, 3rd edition 1904; Dover, New York, 1962), 2 vols.

j. Roller, D., and D.H.D. Roller, "Development of the Concept of Electric Charge" Harvard Case Histories in Experimental Science, No. 8 (Harvard University Press, Cambridge, Mass., 1954).

k. Tricker, R.A.R., The Contributions of Maxwell and Faraday to Electrical Science (Selected Readings in Physics, ed. D. ter Haar) (Pergamon Press, New York, 1966).

l. Whitaker, Sir E., A History of Theories of the Aether and Electricity, vol. 1 (Harper & Row, New York, 1960).

4. Sidelines and Applications

a. Alley, R.E., "Semiconductors and Semiconductor Devices" Phys. Teacher 3 (Feb. 1965), p. 55.

b. Barthold, L.O., and H.G. Pfeiffer, "High-Voltage Power Transmission" Sci. Am. 211 (May 1964), p. 38.

c. Barschall, H.H., "Electrostatic Accelerators" Phys. Teacher 8 (June 1970), p. 316.

d. Cox, A., "Reversals of the Earth's Magnetic Field" Sci. Am. 216 (Feb. 1967), p. 44.

e. Elsasser, W.M., "The Earth as Dynamo" Sci. Am. 198 (May 1958), p. 44.

f. Henry, G.E., "Radiation Pressure" Sci. Am. 196 (June 1957), p. 99.

g. Jefimenko, O., and D.K. Walter, "Electrostatic Motors" Phys. Teacher 9 (March 1971), p. 121.

h. Kolm, H.H., and R.D. Thornton, "Electromagnetic Flight" Sci. Am. 229 (Oct. 1973), p. 17.

i. Meinel, A.B., and M.P. Meinel, "Physics Looks at Solar Energy" Phys. Today 25 (Feb. 1972), p. 44.

j. Pake, G.E., "Magnetic Resonance" Sci. Am. 199 (Aug. 1958), p. 58.

k. Sears, F.W., "Magnetic Fields and Relativity" Phys. Teacher 3 (June 1965), p. 265.

l. Shiers, G., "The Induction Coil" Sci. Am. 224 (May 1971), p. 80.

m. Smith, F.A., and J.D. Wilson, "Electric Circuits and Water Analogies" Phys. Teacher 12 (Oct. 1974), p. 396.

n. Van Allen, J.A., "Radiation Belts around the Earth," Sci. Am. 200 (March 1959), p. 39.

o. Wilson, R.R., "Particle Accelerators" Sci. Am. 198 (March 1958), p. 64.

p. Putley, E.H., The Hall Effect and Related Phenomena (Butterworths, Ltd., London, 1960).

q. Moore, A.D., ed., Electrostatics and Its Applications (Interscience Publishers, John Wiley and Sons, New York, 1973).

5. Miscellany

a. Bitter, F., "Ultrastrong Magnetic Fields" Sci. Am. 213 (July 1965), p. 64.

b. Gordy, W., "The Shortest Radio Waves" Sci. Am. 196 (May 1957), p. 46.

c. Harper, W.R., "Electrification Following Contact of Solids" Contemp. Phys. 2 (1961), p. 345.

## G. Quantization

Chapter 42 in Tipler.

1. Textbooks

a. Beiser, A., Concepts of Modern Physics (McGraw-Hill, New York, 1968).

b. Wichmann, E.H., Quantum Physics (Berkeley Physics Course, vol. 4) (McGraw-Hill, New York, 1967). Highly interesting, like the rest of the series, but mostly too hard for first-year students to read.

c. Tipler, P.A., Foundations of Modern Physics (Worth Publishers, Inc., New York, 1969). Obviously this one is highly recommended.

2. Other Articles and Books

a. Darrow, K.K., "The Quantum Theory" Sci. Am. 186 (March 1952), p. 47.

b. Gamow, G., "The Exclusion Principle" Sci. Am. 201 (July 1959), p. 74.

c. Andrade, E.N. da C., "The Birth of the Nuclear Atom" Sci. Am. 195 (Nov. 1956), p. 93.

d. Alberghotti, J.C., "Uncertainty Principle - Limited Experiments" Phys. Teacher 11 (Jan. 1973), p. 19.

e. Germer, L.H., "Low-Energy Electron Diffraction" Phys. Today 17 (July 1964), p. 19.

f. Kendall, H.W., and W.K. Panofsky, "The Structure of Proton and Neutron" Sci. Am. 224 (June 1971), p. 60.

g. Lyons, H., "Atomic Clocks" Sci. Am. 196 (Feb. 1957), p. 71.

h. Andrade, E.N. da C., Rutherford and the Nature of the Atom (Anchor Books Science Study Series)(Doubleday, Garden City, N.Y.).

i. Boorse, H.A., and L. Motz, The World of the Atom (Basic Books, Inc., New York, 1966), 3 vols. Selected source readings bearing on the history, nature, and structure of the atom.

j. Cline, B., The Questioners (Thomas Y. Crowell Co., New York, 1965). The development of quantum ideas, emphasizing Bohr. A nice book.

k. Cropper, W.H., The Quantum Physicists and an Introduction to Their Physics (Oxford University Press, London, 1968). Combines exposition and history of the quantum theory.

l. Gamow, G., Thirty Years that Shook Physics (Anchor Books Science Study Series)(Doubleday, Garden City, N.Y.).

m. Jammer, M., The Conceptual Development of Quantum Mechanics (McGraw-Hill, New York, 1966).

## H. Reference and Teaching Aids

One of the most important resources for the teacher of introductory physics is the American Journal of Physics. Articles regularly appear there not only on physics topics but on teaching aids and strategies, course design, visual aids, computer-assisted instruction, and literally anything else you can think of; a prime piece of reference matreial is the index to each volume. Also appearing regularly there are "Resource Letters" prepared by the American Institute of Physics. Around 40 of these have come out in the last dozen years, including:

ERPEE-1 on Energy: Resources, Production, Environmental Effects, by R.H. Romer; 40 (1972) 805.
Scy-2 on Superconductivity, by D.M. Ginsberg; 38 (1970) 849.
PL-1 on Polarized Light, by W.A. Shurcliff; 30 (1962) 227.
SRT-1 on Special Relativity Theory, by G. Holton; 30 (1962) 462.
SO-1 on Satellite Orbits, Kinematics, and Dynamics, by L. Blitzer; 31 (1963) 233.

FC-1 on Evolution of the Electromagnetic Field Concept, by W.T. Scott; 31 (1963) 819.
Scr-1 on Semiconductors, by P. Handler; 32 (1964) 329.
PhM-1 on Philosophical Foundations of Classical Mechanics, by M.B. Hesse; 32 (1964) 905.
EEC-1 on Evolution of the Energy Concept from Galileo to Helmholtz, by T.M. Brown; 33 (1965) 759.
CM-1 on Teaching of Angular Momentum and Rigid-Body Motion, by J.I. Shonle; 33 (1965) 879.
ECAN-1 on Electronic Charge and Avogadro's Number, by D.L. Anderson; 34 (1966) 2.
OEPM-1 on Ordinary Electrical Porperties of Metals, by D.N. Langenburg; 36 (1968) 777.
ColR-1 on Collateral Reading in Physics, by A.M. Bork and A.B. Arons; 35 (1967) 71.
IQM-1 on Interpretation of Quantum Mechanics, by B.S. DeWitt and R.N. Graham; 39 (1971) 724.
EMAA-1 on Educational Materials in Astronomy and Astrophysics, by R. Berendzen and D. DeVorkin; 41 (1973) 783.
PE-1 on Physics and the Environment, by J.I. Shonle; 42 (1974) 267.
MPF-1 on Mechanical Properties of Fluids, by R.M. Stanley; 42 (1974) 440.

Each is a systematic and detailed resource bibliography on its subject. Other aids are provided by the Film Guide and Classroom Demonstrations that appear elsewhere in this Guide.

## 1. Reference Works

a. Besancon, R.M., ed., Encyclopedia of Physics (Reinhold Publishing Co., New York, 1966). Short articles on a wide variety of subjects within physics.

b. Condon, E.U., and H. Odishaw, Handbook of Physics (McGraw-Hill, New York, 2nd edition 1967). Fewer, longer articles on broader subjects than in Besancon. "What every physicist should know about physics."

c. Gray, D.H., ed., The American Institute of Physics Handbook (McGraw-Hill, New York, 2nd edition 1963). All areas of physics, mostly numbers, tables, and data.

d. Handbook of Chemistry and Physics (The Chemical Rubber Company, Cleveland, Ohio), revised and reissued annually.

e. Robson, J., Basic Tables in Physics (McGraw-Hill, New York, 1967).

f. Newman, J.R., ed., The Harper Encyclopedia of Science (Harper & Row, New York, 1967). Covers all fields of science; articles are shorter, more numerous, on a much less technical level than, say, Besancon.

g. Van Nostrand's Science Encyclopedia (Van Nostrand, Princeton, N.J., 3rd edition 1958).

## 2. Problems and Demonstrations

Collections of problems suitable (mostly) for introductory physics are:

a. Fried, R. Introductory Physics: Problems and Solutions in Mechanics (Allyn and Bacon, Boston, Mass., 1966).

b. MacDonald, S.G.G., Problems and Solutions in General Physics

(Addison-Wesley, Reading, Mass., 1967).

c. Pilling, H.V., *Examples and Exercises in A-Level Physics* (The English Universities Press, London, 1968).

d. Pincherle, L., *Worked Problems in Heat, Thermodynamics, and Kinetic Theory for Physics Students* (Oxford University Press, London, 1966).

e. Various in the *Schaum's Outlines* series (McGraw-Hill, New York).

f. Strelkov, S.P., and I.A. Yakovlev, *Problems in Undergraduate Physics* (Pergamon Press, New York, 1965), 4 vols.

In addition to the list to be found elsewhere in this Guide, the following contain suggested demonstration experiments:

g. Meiners, H.F., ed., *Physics Demonstration Experiments* (The Ronald Press, New York, 1970), 2 vols.

h. Sutton, R.M., *Demonstration Experiments in Physics* (McGraw-Hill, New York, 1938).

## 3. Mathematical

The following typify the various kinds of mathematical references of which many are available:

a. Schwartz, C.E., *Used Math* (Prentice-Hall, Englewood Cliffs, N.J., 1972). A very clear, very practical handling of the math needed for the first two years of physics. I wish I'd thought of the title.

b. Hay, G.E., *Vector and Tensor Analysis* (Dover, New York, 1953).

c. Dwight, H.B., *Tables of Integrals and Other Mathematical Data* (Macmillan, New York, 4th edition 1967).

d. Kruglak, H., and J.T. Moore, *Basic Mathematics for the Physical Sciences* (McGraw-Hill, New York, 1963). A fine review/summary of the math needed for first-year physics.

e. Margenau, H., and G.M.Murphy, *The Mathematics of Physics and Chemistry* (Van Nostrand, Princeton, N.J., 1956, 1964), 2 vols.

## 4. Bibliography

a. Deason, H.J., ed., *A Guide to Science Reading* (Signet Science Library, New York, 1962). Listing of paperbacks suitable for general reading, in all areas of science, but note date.

b. Whitford, R.H., *Physics Literature, a Reference Manual* (The Scarecrow Press, Metuchen, N.J., 2nd edition 1968). By no means exhaustive, but handy and thorough.

## 5. Miscellaneous Articles

a. International Union of Pure and Applied Physics "Symbols, Units, and Nomenclature in Physics" *Phys. Today* *15* (June 1962), p. 20.

b. *Phys. Today* *21* (May 1968) is a special issue devoted to "The Undergraduate Curriculum."

c. Roll, P.G., "Introductory Physics Textbooks" *Phys. Today* *21* (Jan. 1968), p. 34.

d. Haber-Schaim, U., "Teaching Relativity in the Senior High School" Phys. Teacher 9 (Feb. 1971), p. 75.

e. Schwartz, G., O.M. Kromhaut, and S. Edwards, "Computers in Physics Instruction" Phys. Today 22 (Sept. 1969), p. 40.

f. Sci. Am. 211 (Sept. 1964) is a special issue devoted to "Mathematics."

g. Socolow, R.H., "Teaching and the Environmental Challenge" Phys. Today 24 (Dec. 1971), p. 32.

h. Taylor, B.N., D.N. Langenberg, and W.H. Parker, "The Fundamental Physical Constants" Sci. Am. 223 (Oct. 1970), p. 62.